The Conquest of the Air

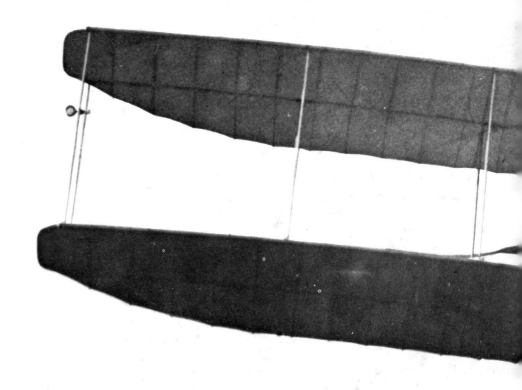

Frank Howard and Bill Gunston

Random House New York

THE CONQUEST OF THE AIR

Title page Orville Wright in
the 1908 *Wright A*

Acknowledgements

The publishers would like to express their gratitude to
Oliver Stewart, without whose invaluable help this
book would not have been possible; to Gordon
Swanborough for his kind assistance with captions;
to Miss Ann Tilbury, of *Flight International*
Photographic Library, for her unfailing patience and
efficiency in researching and supplying photographs;
and to individuals, particularly those in a number of
archives, museums, journals, libraries, manufacturers,
airlines and armed forces all over the world who have
given their generous help in the preparation of this
book. Detailed acknowledgements for the use of
copyright illustrative material will be found in the
List of plates.

First American Edition

Designed by Harold and Alan Bartram
and produced by Paul Elek Ltd.

© 1972 by Paul Elek Ltd.

Originally published in Great Britain by Paul Elek Ltd.,
London

ISBN 394 47474 0

Library of Congress Catalog Card Number: 72-3818

Filmset in England by Photocomp Ltd., Birmingham

Printed in Italy by Amilcare Pizzi SpA

Contents

Preface

With the coming of the supersonic passenger airliner, aviation completes what may fairly be looked upon as its life span. In the allotted three score years and ten, the winged flying machine has emerged, developed with unimaginable swiftness and reached almost the limits set by its atmospheric environment.

Nothing else in the whole realm of practical technology has rivalled the flourish, the resourcefulness, the speed and the scientific skill which aeronautical engineers have displayed during the whole of this period of growth. Nothing has outshone the adventurous feats of a long line of fearless pilots. From the hesitant hops of about 1900 to the confident supersonic voyages of the 1970s is a prodigious trajectory.

Supersonic flight lies on the border line between the province of winged lift and that of centrifugal lift. Consequently the introduction of the space vehicle marks, in this sense, the conclusion of the radical development of the winged flying machine.

Winged flight will make further progress; but as the spearhead of invention and mechanical discovery it has fulfilled its destiny. It must surely be restricted in the future to predictable, routine progress. There is not likely to be any giant stride comparable with the advance from balloon to powered winged machine, from piston engine to jet. The aircraft is settling down to a strictly utilitarian future, like the ship or the railway train. Now that much of the experimentation and adventurousness has been handed on to the workers who devote themselves to reaction-propelled, wingless vehicles, the tapestry of aviation is detached and goes on independent exhibition for the first time. It becomes possible to stand back to look at it in perspective and to wonder at its richness and variety.

In order to frame the major achievements, a glance must be cast at the pre-flight period of myths and legends. It is necessary also to discuss the means first successfully employed by man to raise himself from the Earth and to travel through the air, that is the balloon; but thereafter heavier-than-air craft in their innumerable forms (with large rigid airships only occasionally intervening) must dominate the story as they have dominated flight itself. And at the end, to close the frame, some speculation must be permitted about the future.

Part One

The Individual

Frank Howard

1 Myths and visions

About 2200 BC the Chinese Emperor Shun, by leaping from the top of a tower and descending safely with the aid of two large reed hats, set the pace for a long line of enthusiastic and courageous aeronautical experimenters. They strapped artificial wings to their bodies and, agitating them as rapidly as their strength would permit, hurled themselves from high places in desperate attempts to fly.

Some met the same fate as Bladud, the flying King of Britain who, as Hodgson relates in *The History of Aeronautics in Great Britain*, in 852 BC 'fell and brake his neck'. Others, like John Dante, who flung himself from the top of a tower in Perugia, survived with broken limbs. Yet others, like the English monk Oliver Elmerus, who, with wings fitted to hands and feet, was said to have flown a furlong, claimed a measure of success. But he, too, broke his legs.

In the seventeenth century John Wilkins, Bishop of Chester, studying these tests concluded that there were four different ways of flying. They were: '1: by spirits and angels, 2: by the help of fowls, 3: by wings fastened immediately to the body, and, 4: by a flying chariot'.

A Persian legend combined the second and fourth of these methods and spoke of a chariot with eagles harnessed to it providing it with lift and propulsion. Other experimenters, probably finding the help of spirits and angels not readily available and the results of wings fastened immediately to the body disappointing if not disastrous, turned to flying chariots.

Imaginative satisfactions were promised by flying chariots; wonderful constructions by skilled artificers, splendidly coloured and cunningly shaped, in which the supreme and intrepid Air-Man, grandly dressed, would sit and move swiftly and gracefully through the skies. They would represent a triumphant collaboration between Daedalus, the great architect, and Icarus, the brave pilot of Greek mythology.

Because bird flight – or aviation – was the prime inspiration of the inventors, the chariots were almost always supposed to be winged. They were thought of as machines, resembling full scale reproductions of the wooden pigeon of Archytas or the artificial eagles of an earlier legend. But in 1670 came a rude interruption to this aviation, or bird flight, train of thought. It was the famous aerial chariot of the Jesuit priest Francesco de Lana. He describes it in his treatise *Prodromo*.

On the face of it slightly crazy this was, in truth, a beginning of the scientific approach. For de Lana had a reasoned and reasonable basis for claiming that his method of flying was in accordance with the laws of nature. Nor were the fallacies immediately apparent.

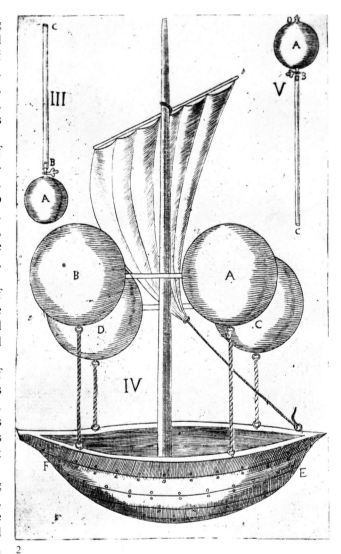

2

For de Lana said – and none would deny it – that a given vessel filled with air would weigh more than the same vessel when empty. An empty vessel, then, released into the atmosphere would be buoyant and would rise as an air-filled vessel rises in water. So de Lana proposed the blindingly obvious method of attaching four large vacuum globes to a chariot or boat. They were to be made of copper and, being exhausted of all air, would float the whole contraption upwards. The chariot was to have a sail to enable it to be directed from place to place.

Although the de Lana design, in spite of its ingenuous appearance of sweet reasonableness, was no more practical than any other early designs, it did do one remarkable thing. It suggested a way of obtaining lift for a full scale man-carrying machine completely different from the flapping wings or the fixed wings of a bird in

1 Legend of King Kai Kawus, *c.* 1500BC; seventeenth-century Persian manuscript illumination showing the king on his throne about to be carried through the air by eagles

2 Francesco de Lana's proposed aerial chariot, 1670

3 Leonardo da Vinci's
design for a fixed-wing
aircraft with ornithopter
extension

powered or in gliding flight. And this way of obtaining lift, by what might be called buoyancy instead of aerodynamics, was to be – as will be related – the method used in prototype levitational devices.

The de Lana air boat was poised at the interface between myth and vision; between the romantic dreams of uninstructed but adventurous people and the cold arguments of mathematicians and engineers. It was, as will be seen when the first aerial voyages are described, an indication of the ideological basis of lighter-than-air flight by balloon and airship.

It would be a mistake to dismiss the myths and legends as no more than comic enterprises or as the wild imaginings of disordered minds. However ludicrous they may seem in the light of later knowledge, they were expressions of the widespread, almost universal, human longing to fly; to rise into the 'universal navigable ocean that comes to the threshold of every man's door' as Sir George Cayley put it and there to move with the freedom, directness and speed of the birds.

Moreover the heroisms of the pioneers, however misplaced, however absurd, were a powerful stimulus to thought and study. They helped to interest men of intellectual ability and so to assist in the transition from myth to vision; from legendary lunacies to design actualities. But while the myths and legends were still circulating, there arrived upon the scene a genius who came close to foreseeing the scientific basis of winged flight and to depicting some of the devices that would be used for it, Leonardo da Vinci.

Just as it is necessary, if aviation is to be correctly

4

appreciated, not to underrate the actions of the first headstrong experimenters, so it is necessary not to overrate the actions of the better instructed visionaries who were their successors. Because of his outstanding genius as a painter and as an engineer, da Vinci has on occasion been described as the 'inventor' of aeronautical devices on which he merely made general proposals and suggestive drawings. Nonetheless the aviation works of da Vinci are so astonishingly prescient that he must be rated even by the most critical as a giant among all who strove to turn the dream of flying into reality.

3

4 'The flight of Daedalus
and the fall of Icarus';
woodcut from Riederer,
*Spiegel der Wahren
Rhetorik*, 1493

5 Leonardo da Vinci's
design for a spring-operated
flying machine

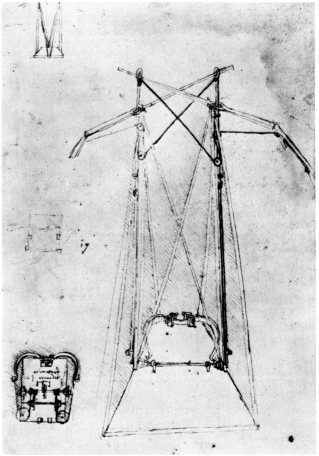

5

This great scientist finds widespread affection for the paradoxical reason that he was *not* a scientist; that is, he was not an officially approved or academically endorsed specialist in any established scientific discipline. He had no familial springboard for his career. Indeed his mother, who may have had a larger influence upon his life and work than most of his biographers seem ready to admit, was a retiring, humble and essentially simple woman, quite unimpressed by honours and distinctions, whose aim was that the young Leonardo should have a happy life with or without public acclaim.

Whatever the childhood influences, Leonardo, with no formal schooling and no university training, with nothing more than an apprenticeship to the goldsmith Verrocchio at the age of fourteen, made his mark in aviation and in mechanical engineering. And it was by the power of his original studies. His dissertations upon bird flight are classics as are his designs for mechanisms which would enable man to imitate bird flight and for dozens of other things. His inventive suggestions, notably for parachutes and for helicopters, if partially forestalled by the Chinese, were examples of forward vision and his work on basic mechanical engineering was hundreds of years ahead of its time.

There is irony, by the way, in the form taken by the strong adverse criticism which in more recent years was directed against da Vinci's aviation proposals by qualified engineers. This criticism was to the effect that Leonardo had failed to see that his man-powered flight proposals were absurd because he miscalculated the muscular energy of which a human being was capable.

It was a pity, said these technical experts, that Leonardo spent time on man-powered flight designs when calculation showed that man-powered flight—because of the inferior power/weight ratio of the human machine—was, is and always would be impossible. Da Vinci was, they asserted, making the same mistake Roger Bacon had made in the thirteenth century when he wrote: 'There may be some flying instruments, so that a man sitting in the middle of the instrument and turning some mechanism, may put in motion some artificial wings which may beat the air like a bird flying.'

There is irony in this, the most widespread criticism of Leonardo's work, because in May 1962 the de Havilland Puffin, man-powered aircraft took off and flew 994 yards. It had previously made separate flights of 547 and 656 yards and had made turns through 70° and 80°. Before this, in November 1961, Southampton University's man-powered aircraft had also flown, making an unassisted take off and acquiring the distinction of being the first man-powered aircraft to make a flight in the United Kingdom. Several other man-powered aircraft in Europe and at least one in Japan had also flown distances in the order of 450 and 550 yards. So the man 'sitting in the middle of the instrument and turning some mechanism' could really fly.

Leonardo had no steam, oil or any prime movers available. But he was right in thinking that the muscular power of a man could, in suitable circumstances and with suitable equipment, encompass flight. He was right, too, in indicating that pedalling was a practical way of obtaining the propulsive power, for both the South-

6 Model of Leonardo da Vinci's idea for a man-powered ornithopter

ampton and the Puffin were pedal driven. But there was one radical discrepancy between the manner in which Leonardo thought man-powered flight might be achieved and the manner in which it was achieved, or, at any rate, was first achieved.

The Southampton aircraft, the Puffin and the other successful machines were of the fixed wing type. Leonardo, however, had suggested – as Roger Bacon had also suggested – the flapping wing type. The Puffin was a delicate, elegant-looking, big span machine built to the

7

conventional fixed wing formula. Its wing span, in the form in which it first flew, was no less than 83 ft 9 in. And it was so lightly constructed that it weighed, together with the pedalling mechanism, only 110 lb, which was less than its own pilot. With the pilot scaling 140 lb the all-up weight was 250 lb.

Even here, however, it would be rash to state that the characteristics of the man-powered aircraft were conclusively established by the Puffin, by the Southampton or by any other of these fixed wing machines. The man-power flight money prizes first offered by Mr Henry Kremer in November 1959 and later doubled by him may have stimulated more daring experiments. Among them the flapping wing machine as favoured in principle by da Vinci might well be seen at last in practical form. There is nothing impossible about it.

Alexander Lippisch, whose work on the delta planform for high speed jet aircraft had world wide influence, designed and made flapping wing models which were so successful as to suggest that the fixed wing for man-powered flight may not be the last word.

Leonardo was right then about one of the major components of man-powered flight – the adequacy of the muscular power available. He may in the end also prove to have been right about another major component – the combination of lift and propulsion in the flapping wing formula. At the moment we may note that man-powered flight has been achieved, though in restricted form and only with fixed wing aircraft.

Leonardo da Vinci, if he was not the first was certainly the greatest of those who took aviation away from the myth-makers and romancers, the sorcerers and the wild adventurers, and gave it to the thinkers and scientists and engineers.

And here is the extraordinary thing. Although da Vinci died in 1519, his note books were not published until 1797.

7 On 19 March 1969 RAF Fl. Lieut. Potter flew this man-powered aircraft over 1,650 ft and up to a maximum height of 25 ft

8 Sir George Cayley (1773-1857)

They were then given their first full public description. This was 278 years after his death; it was thirteen years after man had made the first aerial voyage and, more important in our present context, it was twenty-four years after the birth of a Yorkshireman called George Cayley.

Paintings and photographs show Sir George Cayley to have been of a portly physique and of a bucolic rather than a scientific appearance. He looks like a rider to hounds, an expert at prodding pigs and looking into horses' mouths. Yet he was a master of mechanical engineering and, after Leonardo, one of the greatest creative thinkers in the history of aeronautics. The originality of his mind and the way in which he related the boldest and most forward-looking visions to the practical problems of realizing them were almost unique. In these respects, indeed, Dr F. W. Lanchester, to whose work we shall be referring shortly, seems the only man to come near to Cayley's attainments.

Orville Wright said that Cayley 'knew more of the principles of aeronautics than any of his predecessors' whilst Alphonse Pénaud, the French pioneer, and Octave Chanute, the gliding experimenter. both paid high tributes to his understanding of the basis of mechanical flight.

Here is Cayley's concise definition of the subject with which we shall be concerned throughout this book, and it is the beginning and end of all definitions of the term aerodynamics.

'The whole problem,' wrote Cayley, 'is to make a surface support a given weight by the application of power to the resistance of air.'

And here is what he said about the scope of aviation. 'A new era in society will commence from the moment that aerial navigation is familiarly realized.'

Cayley stood at the crossroads between that dream of aerial navigation and its realization and he did more than most to bring the realization about.

Like Leonardo da Vinci, Cayley was an uneducated man in the formal sense. He was born in Scarborough on 27 December 1773. Captain Laurence Pritchard, in a paper given to the Royal Aeronautical Society in November 1954, states that Cayley was the first—

8

9

1. To clarify the confusion of ideas about mechanical flight, and to lay down the principles of heavier-than-air flight.
2. To carry out experiments in aerodynamic research, for flying purposes, on the pressure on surfaces at various angles of incidence.
3. To use models for flying research.
4. To draw attention to the importance of streamlining and to outline the body of least resistance.
5. To show and discuss the movement of the centre of pressure of a surface in an air stream.
6. To discuss the problem of stability of an aeroplane, and to indicate methods to obtain stability.
7. To draw attention to the effects of the dihedral angle for wings, and of a movable tail plane and rudder.
8. To draw attention to the great importance of weight control.
9. To design a light aeroplane wheel.
10. To build a man-carrying glider.
11. To point out that curved surfaces had a better lift than plane surfaces, and that there existed a region of 'vacuity' on the top surface.
12. To suggest the 'internal explosion' [i.e. combustion] engine for aircraft.
13. To suggest jet reaction for propelling and steering air vessels.
14. To suggest the convertiplane, i.e. the combination of the fixed wing surface and vertical lift surface.
15. To suggest water recovery for airships.
16. To draw attention to the importance of the power/ weight ratio, and of finding a light prime mover.
17. To invent the expansion air engine.
18. To invent the caterpillar tractor.

Some might question Pritchard's statement that Cayley was the first to use models for flying research (item 3) because model hot air balloons were the stepping stone to the first full scale, man-carrying air vehicles, and curved surfaces for providing lift (item 11) were the subject of comment in da Vinci's notebooks. Nevertheless it is an impressive and, when the qualifying remarks are noted, a fair inventory.

There has been a great deal of argument about jet propulsion. Its demonstration in the early Hero of Alexandria experiment is usually accepted as the first indication that the principle was known to antiquity. Hero, who lived in the first century AD, describes his jet engine in his *Pneumatica*. A replica was made by Mr J. G. Landels and demonstrated at a meeting of the Classical Association in England in 1959. It consisted in a rotary steam boiler and, as the model made by Mr Landels showed, steam jets disposed around the boiler could cause it to rotate, proof that Hero had discovered a practical means of applying the principles of jet propulsion.

But Pritchard expressly says that Cayley's achievement was to suggest jet reaction 'for propelling and steering air vessels.' His contention presumably rests upon Cayley's remarks in his 1837 paper in *Mechanics Magazine*.

9 Engraving of one of Cayley's improved designs for a dirigible balloon, 1816: *left,* head on with screw propulsion; *right,* side view with flapping wings

13

Here Cayley speaks of 'communicating centrifugal force to air by means of a hollow drum' and describes it as a 'means of getting a propelling power conveniently applicable in every direction; for by having a movable mouthpiece from which the air escapes, the reaction will be in the opposite direction'.

This is a clear and theoretically and practically correct description of a centrifugal flow, jet engine like the early Whittle engines. Upon it Pritchard was justified in making his claim number 13 for Cayley died in 1857.

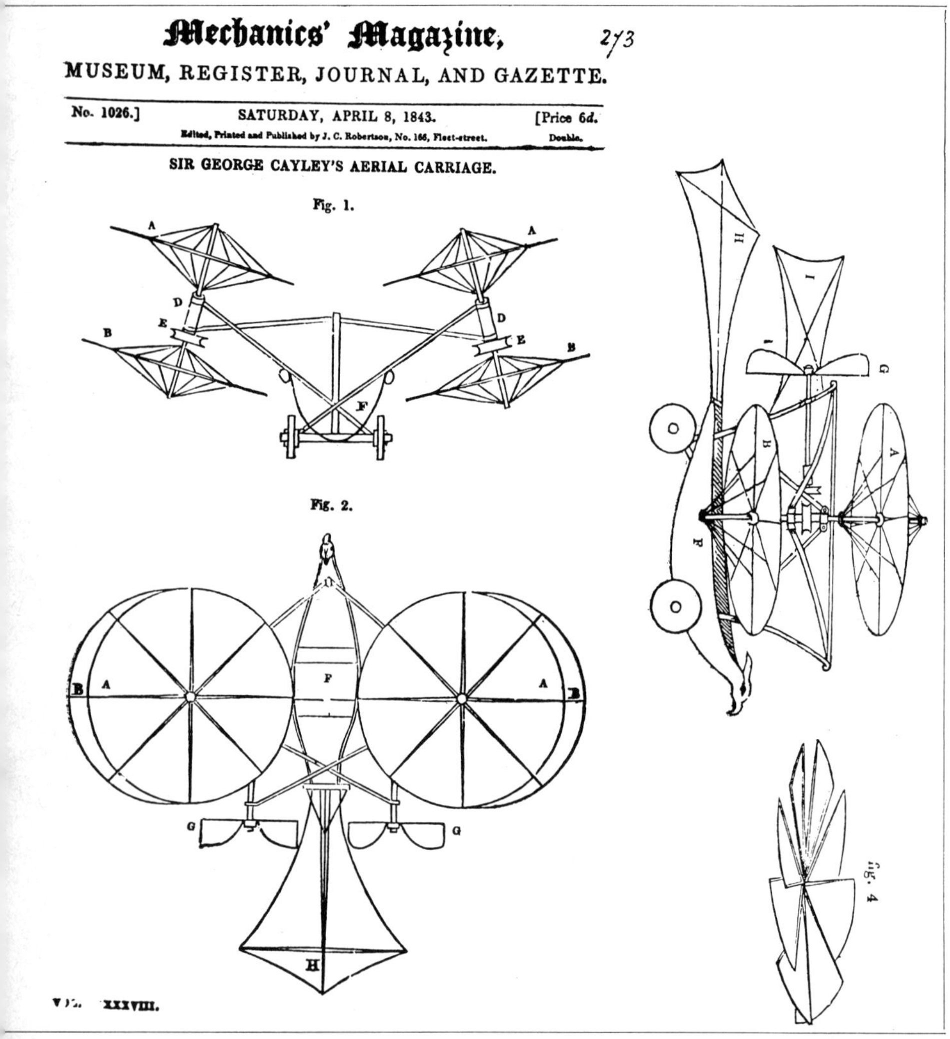

Mechanics' Magazine, 273

MUSEUM, REGISTER, JOURNAL, AND GAZETTE.

No. 1026.] SATURDAY, APRIL 8, 1843. [Price 6d.

Edited, Printed and Published by J. C. Robertson, No. 166, Fleet-street. Double.

SIR GEORGE CAYLEY'S AERIAL CARRIAGE.

Fig. 1.

Fig. 2.

VOL. XXXVIII.

10

10 Engraving of Cayley's design for a vertical take-off and landing aircraft, from *Mechanics Magazine*, 8 April 1843

eighty years before the aircraft jet engine began to move towards practical realization and fifty years before Sir Frank Whittle was born.

Cayley's vertical take off aircraft design may be said to derive from the Chinese top as did his separate helicopter suggestions. Da Vinci's helicopter suggestion might also be traced back to the Chinese top. But both da Vinci and, to a larger extent, Cayley looked upon the helix as a lifting device for vehicular flight rather than as an amusing toy. So their inventiveness took them beyond the Chinese top.

The drawings done by Cayley had none of the artistic elegance of da Vinci's drawings. They were closer to the style of engineering drawings. Some appear to be rough and to fail in giving detailed information. The general message, however, is not often left in doubt.

Cayley's view on man-powered flight differed from,

and, as we have seen, was less accurate than da Vinci's. 'Man,' Cayley said, 'will never be able to fly under his own power.' This did not prevent him from designing a man-power ornithopter.

The impact of the brilliant inventiveness and wide mechanical understanding of da Vinci and of Cayley was exerted at about the same time, for it has been pointed out that da Vinci's notebooks did not come to public knowledge until Cayley was twenty-four years old. The two bodies of work, therefore, arrived upon the public scene together. And they were strong influences in carrying aviation out of the region of myths and legends and into or at least towards the region of practical realization.

Before we turn to that period of realization, however, one other great engineer, inventor and visionary must be mentioned, Dr F. W. Lanchester. His published works appeared after powered flight had actually been achieved; but he was working upon them before that date. Thus Lanchester's book *Aerodynamics* was first published in 1907 and his book *Aerodonetics* in 1908, that is after the Wright brothers and Santos-Dumont had flown.

In 1894 when he was designing and building his own motor car, Lanchester lectured on sustentation in flight and propounded his vortex or circulation theory on which Ludwig Prandtl of Göttingen University based his further work. It was largely in the understanding of how the air behaves close to a wing, and how lift is generated, and of the effects of skin-friction and air turbulence, that he made a permanent place for himself in the annals of aviation progress. But his central achievements were surrounded by hosts of other achievements.

Lanchester's book *Aerodynamics* seems as fresh today as when it was written. He is bursting with invention and originality, but he is always guided by the scientific criterion of experiment. If he was at a loss for a word, he invented one. He invented the word aerofoil, for example, which he says is from the Greek ἀέρος and φύλλον (literally an *air-leaf*). In the Preface he records his conviction that 'the time is near when the study of Aerial Flight will take its place as one of the foremost of the applied sciences, one of which the underlying principles furnish some of the most beautiful and fascinating problems in the whole domain of practical dynamics'.

He employs the term 'peripteral motion' to denote the type of fluid motion generated in the vicinity of a bird's wing. He looks at, illustrates, measures and discusses what the air is doing when it is being used as a supporting medium. He lays down the principles on which all the vast amount of subsequent work on the boundary layer – the thin layer of air close to the outer surfaces of a wing – and on which boundary layer control was founded.

Lanchester was born at Lewisham, near London, on 23 October 1868. Motorists are familiar with his inventions even if they are unaware of his name. Epicyclic gearing, low tension magneto ignition, cantilever springing, live axles, overhead valves and high pressure lubrication were all Lanchester inventions.

As a man he was impatient of all forms of wilful obscurity especially when they appeared under the name

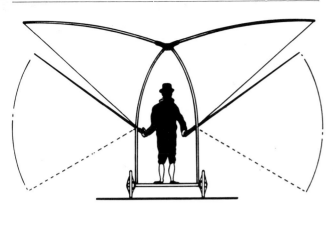

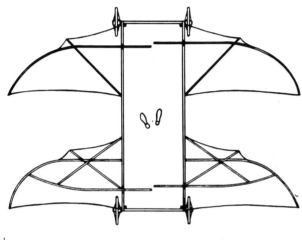

11

dream and reality; the Italian da Vinci and the Englishmen Cayley and Lanchester. There were others, notably Ludwig Prandtl of Germany who, as has been mentioned, carried on the Lanchester vortex theory of lift, and Professor S. P. Langley of the United States. But Professor Langley would seem to be more aptly placed in the category of the practical experimenters, with men like Clément Ader, Hiram Maxim and W. Kress of Austria, rather than with the theorists.

Langley not only made calculations and prepared

12

of science or technology and he was no less impatient with those who failed to take sufficient trouble to ascertain facts. 'To judge from the books written by ornithologists,' he wrote as a footnote to one of his lectures, 'it might be imagined that the writers were unaware that *birds fly*. No mention is made of the data relating to the function of flight. The weight of the adult bird is rarely given, almost by accident if at all. The normal flight velocity, if stated (which is rare), is usually wrong and often absurd. The sail plan is never given, for that one has to go to Mouillard [the French pioneer]. No observations are forthcoming on the important subject of gliding angle, and so on, the list is by no means exhausted. But the pretty colours of the plumage are described in detail and the descriptions are written in an imitation of literary style, the writers studiously avoiding anything in the way of tabular form or logical order.'

Lanchester, it can be seen, could be fiercely critical when he thought that those who ought to have been supplying the facts on which to build aeronautical progress were skimping their work. But he was much liked and admired by his contemporaries, one of whom recorded the fact that Lanchester frequently took him as passenger in one of his cars and whirled him at high speed round the English country lanes, apparently to test not only the excellence of the car, with its tiller steering and centrally mounted engine, but also the stoutness of the passenger's nerves.

We have named three men as representing the bridge makers who enabled aviation to close the gap between

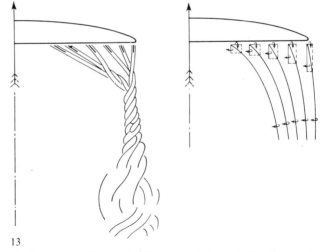

13

designs, but also made flying models and, finally, made a powered, man-carrying machine which he called the 'Aerodrome'. This failed to work although the model experiments had been promising.

There is one curious thing to be noticed when we move forward from theory to action. It is the manner in which lighter-than-air machines overlapped the designs and the plans for heavier-than-air machines. As we shall see as we enter the exciting period of practical, rationally based, full scale experiment, the first aerial voyage made by a human being took place in a balloon more than one hundred years before the first flight by a heavier-than-air machine.

When da Vinci's works received their first public

11 Cayley's proposed flapping-wing glider

12 Cayley's sketch of a man-powered ornithopter

13 Two drawings by F. W. Lanchester illustrating his vortex theory (*Aerodynamics*, 1907) showing airflow and streamlines at wing tips

14

attention and when Cayley was beginning his studies on bird flight, aircraft propulsion, helicopters and man-carrying gliders, aerial voyages had already been made. And it seems especially curious that aerial journeys were first accomplished by the type of craft that later dropped to the rear and thereafter remained in the background of aeronautical progress.

We have considered the myth-makers and the legendary pilots and flying men of the time when flight was no more than an aspiration. We have seen how the movement towards practical achievement was begun by a number of thinkers and inventors and designers. But they went little further than drawings and dissertations. Or if they did go further, to the actual construction of air machines, these were scarcely more successful in sustaining men in the air than the wildly flapping man-handled wings of the early and often suicidal experimenters.

But now we turn from theory to genuine action. We turn from speculation to practical achievement. To do this we must bring on to the stage one of the most splendid and most extravagantly baroque of all air vehicles, the Hot Air Balloon.

2 Into action with the soft machines

One hundred and twenty-four years before Louis Blériot travelled by air across the English Channel, Jean Pierre Blanchard, a Frenchman, and Dr J. Jeffries, an American, had done just that. It is another reminder of the size of the gap between the first aerial journeys and the first *winged* journeys; between the introduction of aerostatic machines and of aerodynamic machines, or balloons and aeroplanes.

To some extent balloons failed in the attempt to realize the dream of flight whereas winged aircraft succeeded. Balloons evolved into non-rigid dirigibles and rigid airships and both of these types of aircraft had their successes and played parts in the overall aerial achievement, but neither could be said to have set in train a continuing line of progress. Neither enabled aerial navigation to be, in Cayley's words, 'familiarly realized'. Cayley paid rather scant attention to them and da Vinci, although said by Hart to have known 'the principle of the fire balloon', showed almost no interest. Aerostation, to resurrect the eighteenth-century term, has proved less

useful, less susceptible to advance, less capable of offering economic or social advantages, less able to contribute to transport improvements, than aviation or flight in the manner of the birds.

Where aerostation did make a mark in history was as an entertaining and mainly enjoyable full scale overture to the greater, more complicated, more dangerous but often less picturesque feats of the power-flight people. Aerostation was a great public show. People dressed up and gathered in big crowds to wonder and applaud. The aeronauts were admired and frantically cheered or sometimes saluted by the discharge of cannon as they stood in their balloon baskets or galleries and waved flags or doffed hats to the multitude. Going to see one of Mr Montgolfier's experiments was like going to the opera with the added advantage that the experiments took place in the open air.

In many of the inventions which have contributed to aviation, there is no one view on the identity of the true pioneers, no universal agreement on the first men to

15 Ascent, in the presence of the French royal family, of an unmanned Montgolfier balloon, 19 September 1783

15

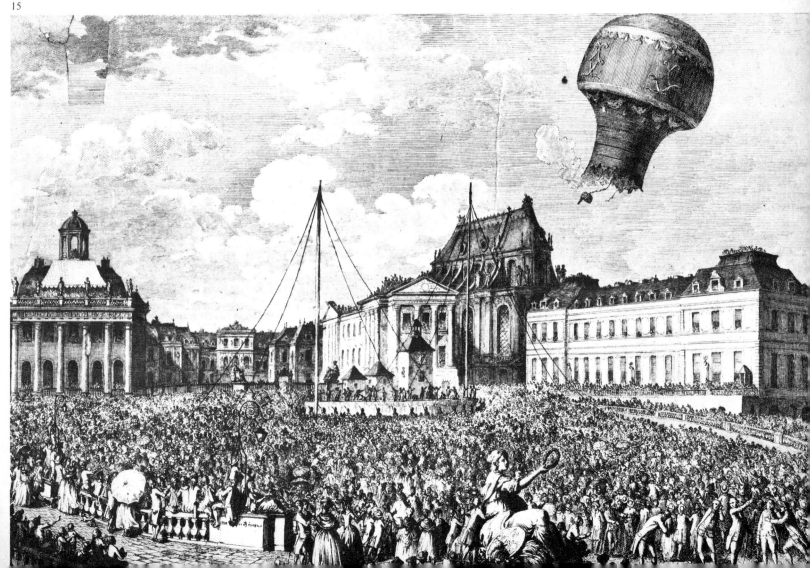

establish or to demonstrate this or that form of progress. The Montgolfier brothers are to large numbers of historians the men who first made aerial voyages by human beings possible. But they do not have that distinction for all historians. The Brazilian historian Alfonso de Taunay for instance has other views.

His claim is that one Bartolomeo Laurenço, later known as de Gusmão, who was born in 1685, invented the hot air balloon in 1709 which is some time before the start of the better known experiments of the Montgolfiers.

16

16 Handkerchief bearing a representation of the balloon of MM Charles and Robert, 1783

Taunay also gives a high priority to the dirigible of Júlio César giving it a status among the early French dirigibles which some historians would not allow. It is proper that no doubt should be left in the reader's mind that nearly all claims for inventions and innovations are challenged. There is no one account which will be received by all people in all countries, as absolute truth.

The time, place and personalities of the first balloon flight, glider flight, dirigible flight, helicopter flight and even aeroplane flight are the subject of prolonged and often heated arguments between the eminent chroniclers of different countries. The best that can be said of any one account is that it gives an accurate record of what is believed by many in the particular part of the world where the account is prepared. The reported incidents of flying history are often little more than majority findings by national groups.

In pursuing the progress of the Soft Machines, that is

the balloons, parachutes and non-rigid dirigibles of the aerostatic era, L. T. C. Rolt has done much to sort out the claims from many different sources. His history of ballooning from 1783 to 1903, *The Aeronauts*, is a comprehensive and careful survey of the western world's lighter-than-air saga. And it depicts – quite rightly – Paris as the centre of gravity of aerostatic experiment. France in the late eighteenth century was rich soil for innovators and inventors. The atmosphere in France was sympathetic to the burgeoning of ideas. There was less inclination among the French populace to direct ridicule and incredulity at mechanical novelties and their sponsors. Paris was the generator of progress; the mother of invention.

As will be seen later this same sympathetic, liberal French attitude was to prevail during the earliest days of the powered, man-carrying winged machine. To France and Paris of those periods, the art of aerial navigation owes much – indeed more than to any other place on the face of the globe. For no matter whether a new device was started in France or not, it would invariably – and here for once there can hardly be national differences of opinion – find there the best welcome and the most favourable conditions for further growth. So it was with the balloon.

At Annonay, 35 kilometres from Tournon, in the Ardèche, a centre for silk and paper manufactures, Joseph and Etienne Montgolfier went into the family business at the paper mills. The evidence is that they were thinking about flight in 1782. Rolt offers one or two amusing speculations on what might have played for them the legendary part, he says, of Watt's steam kettle and Newton's apple. Some asserted that Madame Montgolfier's chemise, when placed before the fire to air, took off and flew while others said that Joseph's shirt was levitated in this way, thus revealing the principle of the hot air balloon. But the original urge to experiment arose, Rolt says, from Joseph's reading of Priestley's *Experiments and Observations on Different Kinds of Air* in a French translation. On the strictly scientific side Henry Cavendish's work on hydrogen was relevant because there was for some time a kind of neck and neck race between the hot air balloon and the hydrogen balloon, culminating, as will be described later, in the first air disaster and the death of the world's first aeronaut.

Among the most trustworthy guides to the pioneer work on lighter-than-air craft is Tiberius Cavallo's *The History and Practice of Aerostation*, written at the time the experiments were being conducted, in the 1780s, when Cavallo was himself experimenting.

Cavallo became a Fellow of the Royal Society. His writing, though it often strikes what appears today to be a rather flamboyant note, is packed with factual information and constitutes not only a trustworthy record of events, but also a vivid picture of them. His book was published in 1785. Cavallo is sometimes careless – he insists upon calling Joseph Montgolfier John for instance – but his carelessness does not invade the technical and historical sides of his treatise.

After asserting that to 'fly by mechanical means was next to impossible' Cavallo goes on to say that the 'art of navigating through the air has functioned on two principles; to wit, on the specific gravity of inflammable air, which is much lighter than common atmospheric air of the same temperature; and on the specific gravity of heated air, which is lighter than air of the same sort when colder.' He pays a tribute to Cavendish and to Dr Joseph Black for their work on hydrogen, which he always calls 'inflammable air', and for establishing that it was 'seven times lighter than common air'.

He then tells of some of his own experiments in 1782. 'The possibility of constructing a vessel, which, when filled with inflammable air, would ascend into the atmosphere, had occurred to me when I first began to study the subject of air and other permanently elastic fluids which was about eight years ago. Early in the year 1782 I actually attempted to perform this experiment: and the only success I had, was to let soap-balls, filled with inflammable air, ascend by themselves rapidly into the atmosphere, which was perhaps the first sort of inflammable-air balloons ever made . . . I contented myself with giving an account of what I had done to the

17 The first free-flight aerial voyage by Pilâtre de Rozier and the Marquis d'Arlandes in a Montgolfier balloon, 21 November 1783

18

Royal Society.'

Etienne Montgolfier, the elder of the two brothers, made the first aerostatic experiment with hot air at Avignon, towards the middle of November 1782. Cavallo writes: 'The machine consisted of a bag of fine silk, in the shape of a parallelopipedon, the capacity of which was equal to about 40 cubic feet. Burning paper applied to its aperture served to rarefy the air, or to form the cloud; and when this was sufficiently expanded, the machine ascended rapidly to the ceiling. Thus the discovery was made.'

Cavallo gives an account of the unmanned ascent of 19 September 1783 before Louis XVI and his court. The notable thing about this ascent was the use of experimental animals, a procedure which was to continue in aviation up to the age of space vehicles. Montgolfier attached a wicker basket to his balloon and put in it a sheep, a cock and a duck. The balloon travelled about two kilometres and the creatures were unharmed.

Work on hydrogen balloons was proceeding alongside this work on hot air balloons. It was more formal and academic. The J. A. C. Charles hydrogen balloon was made of a kind of silk varnished with a 'dissolved elastic gum' which was presumably some kind of rubber solution. The brothers Robert made it and helped in the ascents. The 'inflammable air' was made from a 'mixture of iron filings and diluted vitriolic acid' and there was a good deal of trouble in devising satisfactory means of filling the balloon and preventing leaks. But it made successful ascents.

Now we come to a great date in aeronautical history, 15 October 1783. This was the time of the first ascent by a human being, J. F. Pilâtre de Rozier.

'The aerostat was completed,' says Cavallo and we retain his spelling, 'in a garden in the Fauxbourg

18 The second aerial voyage of MM Charles and Robert, 1 December 1783, and their reception by Parisians

19 Eighteenth-century fantasy. 'Aérostat de Poste' due to leave 10 March 2440 for China and neighbouring countries, carrying mail for Japan and Formosa

20 Triumphant night return of the balloon of MM Charles and Robert. They left the Tuileries on 1 December 1783

21 Vincent Lunardi's balloon on exhibition in the Pantheon, London, 1784

St. Antoine. It had an oval shape, its diameter being about 48 feet and its height about 74. The outside was elegantly painted and decorated with the signs of the zodiac, with cyphers of the king's name, fleurs-de-lys, etc. The aperture or lower part of the machine had a wicker gallery about three feet broad with a balustrade both within and without, about three feet high. The inner diameter of this gallery, and of the aperture of the machine, the neck of which passed through it, was near 16 feet. In the middle of this aperture an iron grate, or brazier, was supported by chains, which came down from the sides of the machine. In this construction, when the machine was up in the air, with a fire lighted in the grate, it was easy for a person who stood in the gallery, and had fuel with him, to keep up the fire in the mouth of the machine, by throwing the fuel on the grate through port-holes made in the neck of the machine. By this means it was expected, as indeed it was found agreeable to experience, that the machine might have been kept up as long as the person in its gallery thought proper, or whilst he had fuel to supply the fire with. The weight of this aerostat was upwards of 1,600 pounds.'

That is a fair description of the form and working of the hot air balloons that enabled men to make their first journeys through the air, for we may now pass from the first tethered ascent by Pilâtre de Rozier to a still more significant event, the first aerial voyage. This started from the grounds of La Muette in the Bois de Boulogne and de Rozier was accompanied by the Marquis d'Arlandes, a cavalry officer. At first, Cavallo tells us, the aerostat was kept confined by ropes and the wind agitated it so violently that it was forced to the ground and damaged. But by extraordinary exertions workmen repaired the aerostat and replaced it on the kind of platform that was used for these launchings. The all-up weight was between 1,600 and 1,700 lb.

The date was 21 November 1783, the time 54 minutes past one o'clock. The aerostat with de Rozier and d'Arlandes on board, on opposite sides of the gallery – again we quote Cavallo – 'passed safely over some high trees, and ascended calmly and majestically into the atmosphere. The aeronauts having reached the altitude of about 280 feet, took off their hats and saluted the surprised multitude. They then rose too high to be distinguished, so that the machine itself was scarce perceivable. When they rose, the wind was very nearly north-west, and it is said that the machine, in rising, made a half a turn round its own axis. The wind drove them horizontally over the river Seine, and over Paris. They passed between the *Hôtel des Invalides* and the *École Militaire*, and approached *Saint-Sulpice*; but as they were rather low, the fire was increased in order to clear the houses, and in rising higher they met with a current of air which carried them southward. They passed the *Boulevard*; and at last, seeing that the object of the experiment was fully answered, the fire was no longer supplied with fuel and the machine descended very gently in a field beyond the new *Boulevard*, about 9,000 yards distant from the palace *de la Muette*, which distance they ran in between 20 and 25 minutes' time. The Marquis d'Arlandes stepped out of the gallery the moment it touched the ground; but the machine collapsing im-

PRO BONO PUBLICO

AEROSTATE DE POSTE.

Qui partira le 1.ome. Mars de l'année 2440 pour la Chine et les pays circonvoisins. L'on prie d'affranchir les lettres et paquets pour le Japon et pour la petite partie qui reste de l'île Formosa. Le prix du trajet est 30 louis,
et 30 pour ceux qui auront la table du Capitaine, les paquets et groupes doivent être embarqués le premier du mois au plus tard. Pour l'amusement des voyageurs, il y aura des musiciens aériens, qui seront em-
ployés pour les bals et concerts qu'on donnera sur ce ballon. Les villes respectives qui voudront être régalées d'une Sérénade de la grande orgue du ballon, enverront au bureau 25 louis, et seront d'abord inscrites.

Explication des Signes.

AAA. Le globe. B. Statue pédestre, dans la tête de laquelle se trouve l'observatoire. C. Le fanal. D. La galerie. E. Tuyaux, pour laisser exhaler l'air inflammable. F. Officiers aériens. G. Le navire, nommé la grande Bretagne.
H. Le gouvernail. I. Logemens du garde-gouvernail. K. L'église et l'hôpital. L. Apartement du Capitaine. M. Grand tuyau aérostatique. NN. Voiles. OO. Echelles de corde, auxquelles en même temps le vaisseau est attaché.
P. Logemens des voyageurs. Q. Grand magasin des matières combustible. R. Filles de bonne volonté, avec l'escalier qui aboutit à leur cage. S. Demeure du chirurgien. TT. Ailerons pour ornemens. U. Cabinet d'aisance. X. Traiteurs
et cafés. Musiciens du bal sur l'air balcon. Z. Petit ballon de 30 pieds en quue de chaloupe. 2. Grand Téléscope public. 3. Grande orgue, pour donner des Sérénades. 4. Canon pour éveiller les habitans des villes qui auront souscrit pour entendre les Sérénades. 5. Tente dans la quel-
le doit rester nuit et jour l'inspecteur des cordages. 6. Casernes des matelots aériens et des pompiers.

Echelle de Trente pieds de Rome.

20

21

22

23

L'IGNORANCE PROUVÉE

Ou les Evénements de la Journée du 11 Juillet 1784 au Luxembourg.

Ce Globe qui s'enflame est d'un minet,
Meritant qu'on l'etrille ainsi que l'Asinet.

1 Le Balon commençant a s'embraser.

2 L'Asinet seringue a toute force pour l'eteindre.

3 La Phisique lui fait sentir la temerité de son entreprise.

4 Le Satyre lui fait connoitre quil devoit se borner a graver ses planches.

5 L'Abbé Minet entrainé par les Suisses se retire de l'embaras par une des porte de derriere.

6 Un Naigre sortant de dessous le Balon tombe evanouy, un jeune Magnatisme sans rience employe envain son savoir pour le rappeller a la vie.

7 D'un autre coté au meme moment un particulier s'etant trouvé mal, un inconnu plus experime l'ayant fait revenir par la vertu d'une eau quil lui soufle sur le visage, est appellé au du Naigre auquel il rend la vie par le meme moyen.

8 Autour du cercle grand nombre de mecontents.

24

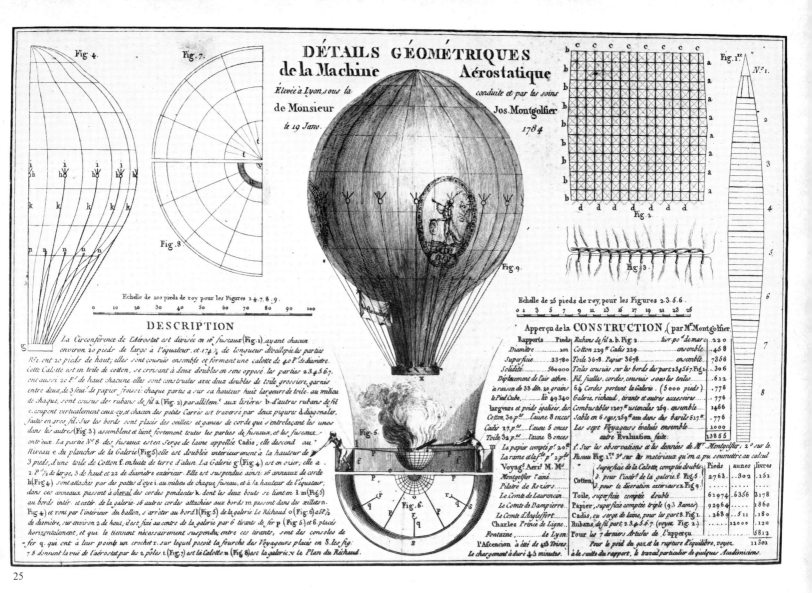

mediately after, Mr de Rozier, who stood on the side opposite to the wind, was covered by the canvas, from which dangerous situation however he soon extricated himself. Otherwise they had suffered no inconvenience whatever.'

About two thirds of the fuel still remained. The fuel used by the Montgolfiers was nearly always straw and chopped wool. They were under the belief that this fuel contributed to the lift in a special manner not solely connecting with the heating. In fact at one stage in their experiments they suggested that the smoke and heat formed a kind of gas with special lifting powers which, for a time, was called Montgolfier's gas.

That, then, was the first aerial voyage, the first time that human beings had been raised into the air and been held aloft and carried from the starting point at one place to the finish at another place at about the same level.

Possibly the leaps into space of the early experimenters as discussed in the previous chapter might, by a sufficient torturing of the English language, be called 'flights', but so might the manoeuvre of falling downstairs. There must be in the true and meaningful description of a flight the element of ascent, so that the take-off and the landing are made from approximately the same level. This distinguishes a glide (or a fall) from a flight.

Study of the early history repeatedly brings into focus the need for clear definitions. The man-powered flights of the Southampton and the Puffin aircraft already mentioned would not have had their historical importance had they not been done from level ground. So the evidence that the journey by Pilâtre de Rozier and the Marquis d'Arlandes of 21 November 1783 was indeed a 'flight' and the first one ever to be made is convincing. The Montgolfier hot air balloon was in this strict sense the first man-carrying air vehicle.

Balloon voyages increased in number and the hydrogen balloon, with modifications introduced by the ingenious Charles – gas valving devices for instance – overtook the hot air or Montgolfier balloon in performance. It lifted more and carried it higher. But hot air balloons of larger sizes were built. There was the burlesque-like incident of the *Flesselle*, a balloon of over 700,000 cubic feet. Pilâtre de Rozier, Joseph Montgolfier and four French noblemen were just about to go up in it when a row broke out about the excessive load and the noblemen drew their swords to defend their right to remain in the balloon gallery for the ascent and to exclude other passengers.

As the balloon was about to be released, however, de Rozier and Montgolfier, daring the noblemen's sword-play, leaped aboard and so did an unknown youth whose presence had not been previously in the calculations.

22 Place de la Concorde at Napoleon's coronation, 3 December 1804. Four temporary halls for dancing and a central pedestal were specially erected. The beginning of the festivities was announced by the release of five balloons carrying musicians

23 St James's Park, London, decorated for the grand jubilee of 1 August 1814

24 Sad end of a balloon on fire, 11 July 1784

25 Details of Montgolfier's 1784 balloon, *La Flesselle*

26

In spite of this overload of heterogeneous humanity the balloon did make an ascent.

Besides these experiments in size, there was a spread throughout the world of ballooning enterprises of various kinds. The first manned ascent in Italy was made by Paul Andreani with the Gerli brothers. An ascent was made in America. And Madame Thibble became the first woman aeronaut when on 4 June 1784 she ascended to a height of 8,500 ft from a site in Lyons. On 27 August in the same year an ascent was made by James Tytler in Scotland using a hot air balloon.

Structurally–after a few wild aberrations–balloons settled down to the spherical shape introduced by Charles while the suggestion of a Paris artist that gold-beater skin should be used in place of the oiled silk, linen, varnished paper and other fabrics that had been favoured by the pioneer makers received general acceptance. Rigging modifications were made to suspend the car more safely. Flights of ever greater distances were undertaken. The crossing of the English Channel by Jean-Pierre Blanchard and Dr Jeffries, a Boston doctor, was outstanding among these. It was made on 7 January 1785.

Their adventure was in part an indication of how greatly balloonists relied upon improvisation. The balloon was of about 27 ft in diameter and had a boat shaped car.

The flight affected the course of aeronautical history because Blanchard used it to test some of his ideas about balloon control. He had been interested in mechanical, heavier-than-air flight before he took to ballooning and when he made the change he insisted that it would be possible to control a balloon in flight. To do so he fitted wings or oars and a rudder. The idea was that one balloonist would bend energetically over the oars while the other could steer in any desired direction.

Blanchard was not the only one who believed that balloon crews would be able to sail and steer much as a ship may be sailed and steered. It may be recalled that

26 Departure of Blanchard and Jeffries from Dover Castle, 7 January 1785

the originator of the idea of the buoyancy form of flight, Francesco de Lana, visualized the use of a sail in his vacuum globe flying chariot. All this was the outcome of a popular misconception about flight; a misconception that lasted for a long time and even led distinguished aviation historians in quite recent years into making impossible and sometimes ludicrous statements about flying events.

It was not clear to some of the less thoughtful of the experimenters that, when *in* the air, an aircraft was *of* the air. A balloon might float in the air without relative movement between itself and the surrounding air so that the occupants felt no wind. But the mass of air in which it was suspended could be moving and, when winds were blowing, would be moving. So relative to the ground the balloon would move with the air mass. And that was the total measure of the manoeuvrability of the balloon. It was, therefore, fallacious to think that a rudder would be effective for directional control. Nor could a sail develop thrust. The balloon lacked any equivalent to the ship's keel which makes good the relativity of the motion between wind and water and enables the sail to process wind power into thrust.

Nevertheless the attempts of Blanchard and a few others to introduce controlling devices did, in the end, lead by devious routes to practical forms of propulsion and control. Thus Blanchard's 'oars' eventually became the blades of airscrews. There was even an attempt by two Frenchmen, Miolan and Janinet, to use a kind of jet propulsion for a balloon, tapping the hot air from the canopy and releasing it in what they thought would be propulsive jets. In short Blanchard's oars and rudders could be looked upon as a small step towards the *dirigible balloon*, forerunner of the airship. We turn now to Cavallo's vivid account of the cross-Channel journey of January 1785. It was written in that year.

On Friday January the 7th, being a fine clear morning, after a very frosty night, and the wind about N.N.W. but hardly perceptible, Mr Blanchard accompanied by Dr Jeffries, departed in the old balloon from Dover-Castle, directing their course for the French coast. The balloon was begun to be filled at about 10 o'clock; and whilst the operation was going on, two small balloons were launched, in order to explore the direction of the wind. The apparatus was placed at about 14 feet distance from the perpendicular cliff; and at three quarters after 12 o'clock, the boat being attached to the net which went over the balloon, several necessaries, and some bags of sand for ballast were put in it. The balloon and boat, with the two adventurers, now stood within two feet of the brink of the cliff, that identical precipice so finely described by Shakespeare, in his King Lear. At one o'clock, the intrepid Blanchard desired the boat to be pushed off; but the weight being too great for the power of the balloon, they were obliged to throw out a considerable quantity of ballast, in consequence of which they at last rose gently and majestically, though making very little way, with only three sacks of ballast, of ten pounds each. At a quarter after one o'clock the barometer, which on the cliff stood at 29·7, was fallen to 27·3, and the weather proved fine and warm. Dr Jeffries, in a letter to Sir Joseph Banks, Bart, P.R.S., described with rapture the prospect which at this time was before their eyes. The country to the back of Dover, interspersed with towns and villages, of which they could count 37, made a beautiful appearance. On the other side, the breakers on the Goodwin Sands appeared formidable. They passed over several vessels, and enjoyed a view perhaps more extended and diversified than any that was ever beheld by mortal eye. The balloon was much distended, and at 50 minutes past one o'clock it was descending, in consequence of which they were obliged to throw out one sack and a half of ballast, in order to rise again. They were now one third of the way from Dover, and had lost distinct sight of the castle. A short time after, seeing that the balloon was descending very fast, all the ballast was thrown out, but that not being sufficient to lighten the boat, a parcel of books was next thrown overboard, when they rose again, being at about midway between the English and French coasts. At a quarter past two o'clock, the rising of the mercury in the barometer shewed that the balloon was again descending, which obliged them to throw away the remaining books. At 25 minutes after two they were at about three fourths of the way, and an enchanting view of the French coast appeared before their eyes; but the lower pole of the balloon was collapsed, in consequence of the loss or condensation of the inflammable air, the machine was descending, and they, Tantalus like, were uncertain whether they should ever reach the beautiful land. Provisions for eating, the wings of the boat, and several other articles, were successively thrown into the sea. – 'We threw away,' says Dr Jeffries, 'our only bottle, which in its descent cast out a stream like smoke, with a rushing noise; and when it struck the water, we heard and felt the shock very perceptibly on our car and balloon.' Anchors, cords, etc., were thrown out next but, the balloon still approaching the sea, they began to strip, cast away their clothes, and fastened themselves to certain things, which proceeded from the hoop to which the boat was fastened, intending to cut the boat away for a last resource; but they had the satisfaction to find that they were rising; their distance from the French shore was about four miles, and they were approaching it very fast. Fear was now vanishing apace; the French land shewed itself every moment more beautiful, more extended, and more distinct; Calais, and above 20 other towns and villages, were clearly distinguished. Their actual situation, with the idea of their being the two first persons who crossed the channel in such an unusual vehicle, made them little sensible of the want of their clothes; and I doubt not but the sympathizing reader will feel an unusual sensation of admiration and joy in imagining their situation. Exactly at three o'clock they passed over the high grounds about midway between Cape Blanc and Calais, and it is remarkable that the balloon at this time rose very fast, so that it made a magnificent arch. The balloon rose higher than it had ever done in any other part of the voyage, and the wind increasing, varied a little its direction. The two adventurers now threw away their cork jackets, which they had taken for safety, and of which they were no longer in want. At last they descended as low as the tops of the trees in the forest of Guinness, and Dr Jeffries, laying hold of a branch of one of the trees, stopped their progress. The valve of the balloon was opened, in consequence of which the inflammable air got out with a loud rushing noise, and some minutes after they came safely to the ground, between some trees, which were just open enough to admit them; after having accomplished an enterprise, which will perhaps be recorded to the remotest posterity.

This crossing of the Channel took place the year after Vincent Lunardi had made the first ascent in England in a balloon made of oiled silk. And it is to be noted here

27

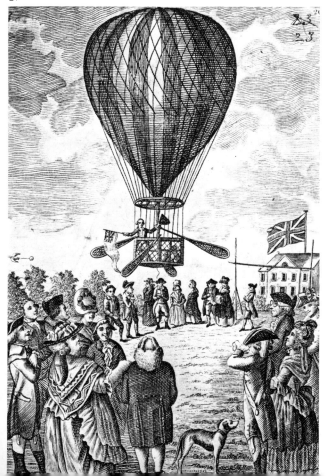

that Lunardi, like Blanchard, took up with him oars with the idea of propelling the balloon.

Later in the year of that triumphant first Channel crossing, there occurred the first fatal air accident. It happened to the composite balloon devised by Pilâtre de Rozier, the first of all the aeronauts, and M. Romaine. The idea was to combine the advantages of the hot air balloon and of the hydrogen balloon. Unfortunately it was not appreciated that the buckets of water and sponges carried in Montgolfier balloons for controlling the fire would be inadequate to prevent sparks from flying and igniting the hydrogen. And that is what happened. The balloon burst into flames and de Rozier and Romaine were killed.

Aerostation and aerodynamic flight were fated to exact a large toll in human lives. Moreover the fatal accidents often took on a horribly dramatic aspect, unlike accidents in other fields of endeavour. The flames which engulfed the first aeronaut were to be re-kindled countless times to shock the world in the following years. And there were to be many fearful misjudgments and miscalculations which sent brave men hurtling to their deaths.

Indeed there is a kind of parallel between that early accident and the accidents which befell the Comet airliners, the first of the jet airliners. But out of the balloon accident and out of the Comet accidents, as will be seen when they are examined in detail later in this book, there was extracted information which helped to make further progress possible.

An odd fact about any comparison between lighter-

28

27 Lunardi's ascent from the Artillery Ground, London, 15 September 1784

28 Blanchard's twenty-eighth ascent at Nuremberg, 12 November 1787

than-air flying machines and heavier-than-air, is that for over half a century the former proved capable of ascending to much greater heights than the latter, so that the world altitude record remained in the keeping of balloonists long after winged machines had reached an advanced state of development and when many looked upon balloons as old-fashioned and out of date.

On 5 September 1862 an ascent was made from Wolverhampton which was to rank as a world altitude record for something in the region of sixty years. There

29

have been doubts about the height attained by Henry Coxwell and James Glaisher on this occasion and it has been said that they carried no instruments capable of giving precise readings. It is also said that, without oxygen, the two men could not have survived at the height they claimed of 37,000 ft. Some cautious observers write down their actual height; but even so most are agreed that they must have exceeded 30,000 ft. It was not until 1920 – fifty-eight years later – that a winged machine flew higher than this.

James Glaisher was a Fellow of the Royal Society and, although a novice in ballooning, he brought to it a scientific approach and a considered programme of high altitude flights. In his account of this flight he described how he had to fight against dizziness, loss of muscular power and asphyxia. Coxwell was also nearly overcome

29 Another design by Leonardo of a man-powered flying machine

30 Poster advertising Cocking's parachute descent, Vauxhall Gardens, London, 24 July 1837

and was able to pull the valve cord when they had decided that they could go no higher, only by seizing it in his teeth.

Although, then, the balloon has faded from the scene as a practical transport vehicle, it had its special performance qualities which helped the scientists of the time to make observations of the upper atmosphere. It also contributed to the introduction of developments which, in the end, were to serve all forms of aviation. Besides the already mentioned airscrew, which was at first called in to make balloons dirigible, there was the parachute.

Da Vinci made drawings for a parachute – a 'tent of caulked linen' he called it – and is usually described as the inventor of the parachute. And if we exclude those 'large reed hats' of the Chinese Emperor Shun as well as umbrellas, skirts, monk's clothing and assorted lamp shades and awnings, da Vinci's design does seem to come closest to the thing itself. We shall be looking at parachute developments as they occurred during aviation's progress, but here mention has to be made of André Garnerin's descent in Paris on 22 October 1797, and of another in England in September 1802 and of the ill-fated Cocking, whose disastrous experiment is invariably mentioned in works upon ballooning. On 24 July 1837 Robert Cocking, at the age of 61, was taken up by the most distinguished and reliable of all British aeronauts, Charles Green, who had acquired a unique reputation as a skilled balloonist. Cocking and his parachute were suspended below Green's giant balloon.

Cocking, a painter in water colours, who had scientific aspirations, had designed a weird parachute in which the

30

ROYAL GARDENS, VAUXHALL.

GRAND DAY FÊTE,

On MONDAY, the 24th of JULY, 1837.

Extraordinary Novelty and Combined Attraction!

ASCENT IN THE ROYAL NASSAU BALLOON

BY MR. GREEN,

AND DESCENT IN A NEWLY-INVENTED

PARACHUTE,

BY MR. COCKING.

The Proprietors of Vauxhall have the satisfaction to announce that they are enabled to present to the Public another grand improvement connected with the Science of Aerostation; viz. a PARACHUTE of an entirely Novel Construction, by which a perfectly safe and easy descent may be made from any height in the Atmosphere attainable by a Balloon.

Mr. COCKING, a gentleman of great scientific acquirements, having, many years since, witnessed the descent of M. Garnerin, (the only one ever made in England,) was forcibly struck with the danger to which that gentleman was exposed on account of some error in the construction of his machine; and, after several years spent in numerous experiments, has succeeded in discovering the faults in M. Garnerin's instrument, and also in producing

AN ENTIRELY NEW PARACHUTE,

which is allowed by all who have seen it, to be constructed on unerring principles. The form is that of,

An Inverted Cone 107 Feet in Circumference!

which, during the Descent, is quite free from oscillation; and as it will be in its proper form previous to the Ascent, it is not liable to the objection of falling several hundred feet without expanding, which was the case with the Parachute of the old form.

MR. COCKING WILL MAKE HIS FIRST DESCENT ON MONDAY NEXT, JULY 24.

The great power of the Royal Nassau Balloon has afforded the means of making an experiment with the above-named Machine, which, from its great weight, would be impossible with any other Balloon hitherto constructed.

The plan adopted by M. Garnerin was to ascend alone and detach the Parachute from the Balloon, which having no person to conduct it fell in some very distant part, and was either lost or destroyed; but Mr. GREEN has undertaken to ascend in the Nassau Balloon, and to liberate the Parachute himself, a feat never before attempted by any Aeronaut.

THE PARACHUTE WILL BE EXHIBITED PREVIOUS TO ITS ASCENT.

In order to render this Fête more than usually attractive, the Proprietors intend giving a variety of Amusements during the Afternoon, the principal of which are—

A CONCERT in the Open Orchestra
A DRAMATIC PIECE in the Theatre, which will be lighted as at Night
The Extraordinary Performance of M. LATOUR, M. DE LA VIGNE, & their Sons
THE YEOMANRY AND QUADRILLE BANDS, &c. &c. &c.
AND A VARIETY OF OTHER ENTERTAINMENTS.

Doors will be opened at One; & the Ascent at Five.

The Descent will be made as nearly over the Gardens as possible.—ADMISSION, 2s. 6d.

VISITORS ARE REQUESTED TO COME EARLY.

The Admission to the Evening Entertainments will be as usual.——Parties can Dine in the Gardens

normal shape was inverted, like an upside-down umbrella. It was in the form of a downward pointing cone. The idea was to prevent the oscillations which Garnerin had encountered. It seems extraordinary that, at a time when balloons had reached a practical stage, a device of this kind should have been looked upon as feasible although it must be admitted that a Cayley drawing might be thought to justify it. But no sort of trials were made before the unfortunate Cocking hurtled to his death. Perhaps the accident is so well remembered partly on account of a horrific contemporary engraving of the parachutist during his fall. This sticks in the mind.

Possibly the first use of a parachute to make a successful escape was by the Polish aeronaut Jordaki Kuparente in 1808. John Hampton was the first English parachutist. He made a drop in October 1838.

By the early 1800s ballooning had reached a plateau in its history. Hydrogen balloons and, occasionally, balloons inflated with coal gas were well understood and progress tended to focus on size. There were occasional

31 Garnerin's balloon (and parachute) by which he ascended from Grosvenor Square, London, 21 September 1802

31

32

record flights, occasional scientific investigations but most of all there were the public spectacles. At the centres of outdoor entertainment, Vauxhall Gardens in London, for instance, balloon ascents were organized as displays intended to thrill the multitude. The balloons were fantastically decorated.

The publicity for the aeronauts had its period charm and the great figures–many with familial associations with circus artists–were known to the public and seen

33

as heroes of unusual courage and skill.

Sometimes they deliberately took fearful risks, but always with gay panache. As they made their ascents they waved flags or released streamers or even, like Madame Blanchard, let off fireworks. It was indeed the desire to surprise and to delight the large crowds of watchers that led to Madame Blanchard's death.

32 Three aerial travellers: Lunardi, George Biggin and Mrs Sage, 1785

33 Battle of Fleurus won by the French Army on 26 June 1794

30

The tragedy occurred at the Tivoli Gardens in July 1819 and Rolt has a compelling description. The setting he describes is typical of the pleasures of Tivoli, Vauxhall and Cremorne. 'In the lantern-lit, shadowy walks the crowd waited expectantly for the maroon that would signal the ascent. The moment it crashed out, all the trees in their heavy leaf were suddenly lit by the smoky glare of Bengal lights as, to the accompaniment of a triumphant fanfare from an unseen orchestra, Madame Blanchard soared into the air, trailing beneath her car a great star of silver fire. Tremendous applause. Now brightness falls from the air. Madame has lit bombs of gold and silver rain, sending them floating earthwards on miniature parachutes. Renewed applause, presently re-doubled as a great jet of flame shoots out of the balloon. Alas, this was no part of the performance, as was soon apparent. The port-fire Madame was using to ignite the fireworks had set light to the gas issuing from the neck of the ascending balloon. For a few moments the unhappy woman tried, with great presence of mind, to extinguish the flames. Then finding herself falling rapidly, she threw out all her ballast. The rush of the descent drove the flames back into the balloon and, according to some eye-witnesses, extinguished them. Had the balloon fallen into the gardens all might still have been well, but instead it landed upon the roof of a nearby house, the car colliding with a chimney stack and overturning. With a despairing cry of: *A moi, à moi!* Madame Blanchard slid helplessly down the steeply pitched roof and plunged to her death upon the pavement below.'

It must be admitted that bad accidents always had a kind of attraction for the spectators. The potential horrors when things went wrong were, to some, a sharp seasoning to the glamour and brilliance of the spectacle. But we need not believe those who assert that the public is attracted to air displays, whether those of the early days or those of the great display period of the 1950s, by the thought that there will be an accident. They go to witness a highly coloured, novel, technically flavoured spectacle.

Spectacle, then, was the key note of ballooning after the bulk of the pioneer work was over. The record breaking and scientific tests gradually became secondary to it. All the time, however, there was that insistent dream of flight; the background thought that somehow balloons ought to be but were not a means of travelling great distances, of making voyages of discovery and of voyaging across frontiers and between cities.

This thought was inevitably frustrated by the inherent quality of the balloon in that it is suspended in the air and that it has to go where the air takes it. It cannot be *directed*. Although meteorological observation and fore-casting helped the aeronauts to determine before take-off the direction and the distance a balloon would travel and although its size and the amount of ballast carried could sometimes modify both direction and distance when there were skilful balloonists aboard to adjust the buoyancy, the fundamental disability remained, that a balloon was in the grasp of the wind. It could not, like a sailing ship, tack and work to windward.

Ballooning went on and still goes on. There are experienced balloonists making flights today. The great

Charles Dollfus made balloon ascents at Royal Aeronautical Society garden parties in the 1950s, and a few balloon races are still held. But the major technical development may be said to have been completed by the early nineteenth century.

So after taking a glance at the manner in which balloons were impressed into the service of war, we shall be able to move on to the critical events in the transition between wind-determined flight and man-directed flight. Prime movers and the means of directing the courses of air vehicles form the next stepping stones.

Observation was the military requirement which the balloon seemed capable of fulfilling and observation was in fact the function which carried air vehicles – aeroplanes as well as balloons – into war. Some say that aviation's association with war has helped it to advance; but there are other views, notably that of the aircraft constructor Sir Richard Fairey, who was responsible for the production of many military aircraft of different types. Fairey argued, in a cogent paper read before the Royal Aeronautical Society, that war did not accelerate aviation progress, but actually retarded it.

Whatever its effects were, war certainly altered the course of aviation progress and altered it for the worse. In fact war has been the curse of aviation. Neither the intensification of flying nor the creation of huge aircraft industries paid back for the damage done to the peaceable possibilities of aeronautical travel and entertainment.

The siege of Paris in the Franco-Prussian war is usually quoted as the beginning of the practical use of balloons for military purposes. Just as the Wright brothers later

always diverts the course of progress, usually to its detriment.

The special feature of the use of balloons during the Paris siege was that they were employed on transport duties rather than on observation or offence. Balloons, indeed, because of their dependency upon wind force and direction, never acquired much military value as instruments of attack. A bomb load could, by a wind shift, so readily turn from a destructive blow at the enemy to a self-inflicted wound for the other side.

34

36

proposed the use of the new aircraft for war, so many aeronauts had canvassed the idea of using balloons in this way with the representatives of governments, thus showing that not the most dedicated pioneer can altogether forget how easy living can become when a government purse is opened and development is supported by subsidy out of public monies. But subsidy

In a restricted sense – and it must be emphasized that it is restricted – the Paris balloon operations in 1870 were no more and no less than an early air mail system. Messages were taken out of the capital by balloon and replies were brought back by carrier pigeons, also taken out by balloon. The pioneer in this work was the aeronaut Jules Duruof. Many balloons were made and used,

34 *Intrepid*, Professor T. Lowe's balloon, near James Hill, Virginia, sent up to reconnoitre in the Battle of Fair Oaks, 1862, during the American Civil War

35 Letter sent by balloon from Paris, during the siege of 1870

36 Sketch of Virginia made from Professor Lowe's balloon, 8 December 1862

31

Paris railway stations being turned into factories.

Less often mentioned has been the use of balloons in the civil war in America. Again the prime objective was observation. But this time tethered balloons were favoured as a means of reconnoitring enemy positions. And this was to be the form in which balloons returned to war much later.

Lighter-than-air machines have now reached a point of rest in this narrative. They are waiting for power. And while they are waiting the other form of aerial vehicle, the heavier-than-air machine, comes upon the scene. This is the period of glider development. And it is noticeable that balloons and gliders, although basically dissimilar, advanced along parallel lines sometimes overlapping. And both of them reached that same point of rest, when they were waiting for power.

We can clearly distinguish this historical pause in aeronautical progress. It was a pause while an engine, a lightweight prime mover was being invented; a pause between the achievement of man-carrying flight of one kind or another, and the achievement of man-*directed* flight. Balloons, like gliders, were held in leash by natural forces. Their users, the aeronauts and the pilots, were sharply restricted in the amount of control they could exercise.

Neither the balloon nor the glider could be directed by its occupants. They had to go where the winds and gravity took them. But just as the balloon made the necessary preparations for the appearance of the dirigible balloon and then the airship, so the glider made the necessary preparation for the powered machine.

37

38

37 Ascent of the *City of York* Balloon

38 Aerial travellers about to make a balloon ascent in Monmouth. Charles Stewart Rolls is immediately left of the balloon

39 Balloon at St Charles, Missouri, 1880

3 Winged aircraft show the way

That curious and unexpected overture of lighter-than-air lift was ended and man returned to his obsession of winged, heavier-than-air lift. He did so in two stages: kites and gliders.

Having flown kites in remote antiquity, the Chinese had established the principle of deriving lift from inclined surfaces in an airstream. The principle had therefore been known for centuries before the arrival of the man-carrying glider. What may not have been fully appreciated was the complex role in the derivation of lift played by the string to which the kite was attached. The centuries were spanned by that string.

For the kite is an aeroplane maintained in flight by being held against the natural wind by a string. It is a matter of relativity. Relative motion between air and kite is obtained by holding the kite so that lift is derived from the wind moving past it. There is nothing more wonderful about wind tunnels than about kites. Cut the string and the kite falls. The string, in short, has an affinity to the engine in a modern aeroplane or to the model's attachment in a wind tunnel. Or one could say that a kite is a glider using a natural airstream instead of an airstream engendered by gravity.

There is an association between balloons and kites and gliders, but it is extremely tenuous. They are all dependent upon natural phenomena to which they are absolutely linked. Without natural wind the kite will not fly; without natural wind the balloon will not travel; without gravity the glider will not glide.

Although the kite had been flying since the remotest antiquity it was not until Lawrence Hargrave did his work in the last quarter of the nineteenth century that the principle of how it sustained itself in the air was understood.

Hargrave was a born research worker. The question of whether he 'invented' the box-kite or cellular kite is unimportant. Working in Australia, he discovered much about the stability of kites and he showed that the multiplane, with adequate gap between upper and lower planes, could produce a good return in lift. He tried

40 Engraving of the Aeronautical Society's first exhibition in London, 1868

41 Lawrence Hargrave flying a box-kite, 1894 (original photograph lettered to indicate different designs)

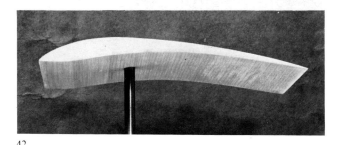

42

is given in the table below. The main lines of American practice are similar though the National Advisory Committee for Aeronautics, since the early days, has tended to extend the scope of its definitions. American documents on nomenclature, for instance, list thirteen types of 'airplane', including biplane, triplane and quadruplane, sub-classifications which were especially useful during the 1914-18 period.

43

cambered surfaces, thus moving on the same lines as Horatio Phillips in England. Phillips, a contemporary of Hargrave, patented the Phillips entry which was a form of wing camber, similar to that of a bird's wing, rather thick near the leading edge, then tapering away towards the trailing edge. This patent was more important than the unsuccessful 'venetian blind' multiplane with which Phillips is more popularly associated.

There is little indication that Hargrave in Australia and Phillips in England were fully informed of each other's work. Both men followed a rather similar pattern of activity for both concerned themselves with possible means of providing power for aircraft. Both, in fact, seem to have been concentrating on the evolution of a prime mover for a manned machine. They seemed almost to take it for granted that the kite-type flying complex would work as a free moving machine if only they could fit it with a lightweight engine. But in the end the Hargrave kite experiments were more influential than his work on power units. They were reported in papers to the learned societies in Australia and were a firm foundation for the full scale biplane.

We have now reached a point where it may be useful to clarify aircraft nomenclature. We have spoken of the aerostats or balloons, one of the types of lighter-than-air craft. Now we move into the story of the heavier-than-air craft. They have the generic title, aerodynes. From that title they branch into many different forms. Admittedly no nomenclature can be said to have greater authority than any other; but the practice advocated in British Standard 185 Part I has a good deal to recommend it. The Standard classification of main types of aircraft

42 Model of Phillips's aerofoil, 1893

43 Le Bris' second glider of 1868, mounted on wheels

```
                              Aircraft
              ┌──────────────────┴──────────────────┐
    Heavier-than-air aircraft          Lighter-than-air aircraft
          (Aerodynes)                        (Aerostats)
        ┌───────┴────────┐                        │
   Non-power driven   Power driven                │
      ┌────┴────┐                                 │
   Glider     Kite                                │
        ┌─────────┼──────────────┐                │
  Aeroplane/Airplane  Rotorcraft  Ornithopter     │
        │        ┌───────┼───────┐                │
        │   Cyclogyro Gyroplane Helicopter        │
   ┌────┼────────┐                                 │
Landplane Seaplane Amphibian                       │
     ┌────┴────┐   ┌────┴────┐                      │
   Float   Flying  Float    Boat                    │
  seaplane  boat  amphibian amphibian                │
              ┌──────┴──────┐              ┌─────────┴─────────┐
           Balloon                      Airship
        ┌────┴────┐              ┌────────┼────────┐
      Free      Captive       Rigid  Semi-rigid  Non-rigid
     balloon    balloon
```

The table omits the sailplane, a form of glider specifically designed for soaring flight, and the Autogiro, a form of rotorcraft invented and named by Señor Don Juan de la Cierva. Although Autogiro is a proprietory word, it should really be contained in any comprehensive classification of aircraft. The name has a precise and useful meaning as will become apparent when the Autogiro principle is described.

The word aerodyne has never become popular, yet it has a useful service to perform, for it is less clumsy than the more widely used term, heavier-than-air aircraft. The term aerostat, or lighter-than-air aircraft, as mentioned in the previous chapter, was current during the development period but later fell from favour. Perhaps both these terms deserve now to be more widely used.

Few will doubt that the dream of flying as it has been known through the centuries is primarily concerned with bird flight. The introduction of aerostation and all the enterprises that went with it, including the triumphs of the hot air balloons of the Montgolfier brothers, were a curious interruption or interlude or *overture* in the attempts to realize the dream. For flight by buoyancy was never in the minds of the main body of the early visionaries. They did not think of man as living at the bottom of a deep ocean of air. In fact outside de Lana's vacuum globe idea it is difficult to find anyone who predicted artificial lighter-than-air flight. All were thinking of wings and most often of flapping wings.

If, then, the table of nomenclature is consulted, it will be seen that the dream of flying was realized through those machines having the generic title of *aerodynes*. And they started with the non-power-driven machines, kites and gliders. Note that the ornithopter, or flapping wing machine, comes in the category of power-driven aerodynes. And so does the helicopter which evoked the inventive suggestions of da Vinci and of Cayley.

Mechanical power, indeed, is the factor separating those aerodynes which were mainly subject to natural forces and were only partly controllable by man from those aerodynes which were largely controllable by man and only partly constrained by natural forces. And there was here a rather vague parallel with the aerostats. The balloons which we have discussed were divided from the airships, which will be referred to later, by the power factor—by the absence or presence of a suitable prime mover.

That is why the invention of the lightweight prime mover will be given separate treatment. It was a critical factor in all forms of air travel. It was the bridge between the *aerostat* and the *airship* and between *kites and gliders* and *aeroplanes*.

It was possible to find out a great deal about powered flight through the agency of motorless flight, just as it would be possible to find out a great deal about motoring through the agency of motorless cars. After all a motorless car, moving down a hill, could provide information about control, stability, road holding, suspension and braking. And in the same manner a glider, gliding from the top of a hill, can provide information about control, stability, lift and drag. Putting a prime mover in either vehicle can transform it from something wholly under the influence of natural forces, to something partly controllable by driver or pilot. Hargrave and Phillips were clear about this.

So from the kite, particularly the Hargrave type of kite, to the glider was not on the face of it a large step; but it entailed a shift in outlook. This shift took place between about 1850 and about 1900. These fifty years were the critical period of gliding as a form of transition from kite flying to powered flying.

First there were the men who studied bird flight, mostly at sea, and particularly bird gliding and soaring. Captain Jean-Marie Le Bris, who was born in 1808, became especially interested in the lessons taught by the albatross, which he observed during his sea voyages. He considered carefully the project of making an apparatus which might glide in the effortless manner of the albatross. His practical labours to implement this idea have been the subject of comment which is sometimes conflicting. But it is clear that he constructed a glider and took out a French patent in 1857. What is not clear is whether this was successful in flight. One report states that it made towed flights, but exactly how it was towed and the other circumstances of the experiment are left in doubt.

The Le Bris glider is said to have had a wing span of 49 ft and a wing area of 215 sq. ft. The weight is said to

have been about 90 lb. Whatever the achievement of the Le Bris glider may have been, there is no doubt that Le Bris's observations were influential in advancing the concept of gliding flight.

Louis Mouillard, another Frenchman, born in Lyons in 1834, was especially clear thinking about the practice of gliding flight. This clarity was not universal. Indeed there are signs that many of the early workers in this field became confused by what seemed to be two different means of flying used by birds, first flapping wing

44

flight or ornithopter flight, and, second, gliding and soaring flight when the bird was poised in the air without visible wing movement.

Early gliders were mostly planned to have flapping wings whereas practical gliding was achieved with fixed wings. It was the bird in the *second* mode of bird flight that gave the clue to man-carrying flight. But here once more a note of caution may be desirable. Although the flapping wing glider failed completely during this early period of experiment, it could well appear upon the scene again. A comparatively recent experiment in Soviet Russia, not much noticed in the western world, was with a glider, the Kashuk, which had articulated wings capable of a limited flapping movement.

The Russian scheme, reported in *Aeronautics* in November 1954, was not to energize the wing flapping, but to use the articulation as a means of accommodating changes in the speed of the natural wind and of deriving lift from air currents. The work does not seem to have been followed up; but at least it is a warning not to accept the fixed wing glider any more than the fixed wing powered machine as the absolute finality in man-carrying flight.

A remarkable model made by Théodore Landes, an experienced glider pilot of more recent times, offers a mechanism for producing wing flapping movements, bird-like and multi-articulated, without making extravagant power demands, an invention which recalls da Vinci's scheme.

Mouillard, like Octave Chanute, was a thinker and publicist rather more than a constructor. He wrote a stimulating book, *L'Empire de l'Air* which was published in 1881, sixteen years before his death in Cairo. This book brought together much information on gliding, on what had been done, and established Mouillard as one of the great French aeronautical thinkers. It con-

44 Drawing of *Vautour Oricon* from Mouillard, *L'Empire de l'Air*, 1881

centrated upon gliding flight *'sans battements'* – with fixed wings – and it impressed the Wright brothers and must have exerted an influence upon the first and greatest of the successful gliding pioneers, Otto Lilienthal.

Before turning to the practical work of Lilienthal, we must take a little further note of the preparatory theoretical work. For this pregnant period from 1850 to 1900 saw a boiling up of theories and a great pullulation of designs and paper projects. A beginning was made in the assembly of research equipment and of means for measuring the loads and forces with which aerodyne designers would have to cope. It was, in short, a time of intense aerodynamical cerebration.

Probably the most notable manifestation of this outburst of theoretical study was the formation, in January 1866, of the first aeronautical society in the world. This was the Aeronautical Society of Great Britain, later called the Royal Aeronautical Society. Its first meeting, under the Duke of Argyll, was on 15 January and its declared aim was to work 'for the advancement of Aerial Navigation'.

F. H. Wenham, a great stimulator of design projects, was present at the first meeting. The Society flourished. Papers on all aeronautical subjects were read and discussed. Major B. Baden-Powell, brother of the founder of the Boy Scouts, was secretary and later president. Sir Hiram Maxim read a paper on 'Aerial navigation by bodies heavier than air'. Theoretical activity was intense and was mainly directed towards powered flight.

Stringfellow's objective, the 'lightest engine in proportion to its power', excited elaborate studies and

45 Stringfellow's steam engine, 1848; boiler above, engine below left

45

eloquent lectures. There was much model making. In short the British Society was always looking forward beyond gliders to powered man-carrying flight and was assembling facts and figures to that end.

In other countries, too, engineers, scientists and inventors were getting together to study the theory of flight. The noted Gustave Eiffel, of the Paris Eiffel Tower, who was born at Dijon in 1832, conducted tests to determine the forces acting upon a wing set in an airstream – the kite-wind tunnel concept again. Lanchester's work progressed and there were hosts of men, whose names are less well-known and sometimes forgotten, who observed, calculated, theorized and discussed the supreme project, a project which could now be seen to be coming closer every day.

Then, with the facts and figures, the theories and hypotheses all ready, it was the turn of the men of action. The most ingenious designs are as nothing until someone comes along and tries them. And that brings us back to Otto Lilienthal.

In Otto Lilienthal we find one of those men to whom progress in aviation has been beholden for its greatest advances; a man who combined technical knowledge with structural skill, inspiration and great physical courage. He not only thought and designed, not only studied the words of the theorists, he also built and tested. Aided by his brother Gustav, he must be ranked among the most influential pioneers in the critical period of winged flight, the period when man discovered how to sustain himself in the air with wings after severing all attachments to the ground.

Lilienthal's thoughts first turned to the very procedures which had attracted the attention of the earliest experimenters, that is wings strapped to the arms. But he was a trained engineer, having studied at the Berlin Technological Academy, and it was not long before he saw that the human arm is a totally different muscular and load bearing member from the bird's wing and that the approach must be made differently.

In 1891 his ideas consolidated and here there is a fruitful overlapping of work done in different countries. Phillips's work in England on cambered wings has been referred to. In England also there was a pioneer of almost the stature of Lilienthal in the gliding field, Percy S. Pilcher, also a combination of man of thought and man of action.

Starting with monoplane gliders, Lilienthal later made a biplane glider. He took the most direct route to flight in his designs, arranging a wing system around the pilot in such manner that the pilot's feet and the lower part of his trunk were suspended below the machine. His feet were, therefore, the *undercarriage* for take-off and landing. But in addition the arrangement of the pilot, in the centre of the wing lifting system, enabled him to exert a measure of control by movements of his body – or in other words by displacing the centre of gravity of the whole system.

It may be, as some aircraft designers have surmised, that it was the limitation of this method of control by head and body movement that led in the end to Lilienthal's death. The Wrights, however, believed that the tail control had proved ineffective. His accident occurred when his glider crashed in 1896 and he was fatally hurt. In the six years he had been actively interested, he had assembled a priceless store of information about the behaviour of aerodynes in free flight. It was a store which was to be commented upon and used by many of the great aircraft-makers. It was hard, practical information.

For Lilienthal did not make one or two hazardous runs; he made glides regularly and over distances of 100 yards and more. Mr J. B. Davy has stated that, in some of his experiments, he actually soared, that is rose above taking off level by use of upward air currents over the face of his gliding hill. Davy also states that at the Rhinower Hills near Stöllen he made glides of more than 750 ft. When his fatal accident happened he was trying a form of head control about the lateral axis, in pitch, which might have been inspired by the da Vinci system already mentioned.

Like Lilienthal, Pilcher had the technical background which enabled him to think rationally about the problem of a man-lifting glider. Born in 1866, he became a Lecturer at the University of Glasgow. He made a glider in 1895. Like Lawrence Hargrave he was obsessed with the idea of inventing a lightweight engine; but he also considered that a practical glider was of equal importance to the realization of flight. He saw, in other words, the simple link between the glider and the powered machine. He was killed in a crash during a towed flight in 1899.

At the same time, too, Octave Chanute was involved in bringing gliding flight to realization. He was born in Paris in 1852 but he did not become fully involved in the efforts to build a glider until much later in his life. As a boy he left France and went to live in the United States and it was there that he designed and built a glider having numerous advanced features, including warping surfaces on the tail for control and movable main lifting surfaces for stability. He was well past the age of sixty when his ideas took definitive shape. One of his gliders was a quadruplane, but he generally favoured the biplane. Chanute's chief contribution to gliding flight was his study of what had been done, his inferences from that

48

46

49

47

work, his suggestions for future work and, perhaps most of all, the encouragement he gave to the Wrights. He published his book *Progress in Flying Machines* in 1894.

Two other names must be mentioned, those of Professor John J. Montgomery in the United States and of José Weiss in England. Montgomery in 1883 was largely concerned with flapping wing flight, but he also produced a number of highly individual fixed-wing glider designs. Weiss, who lived in England, was much

46 Pilcher's first glider, the *Bat*, 1895

47 Weiss's flapping-wing glider, *c.* 1909

48 One of Otto Lilienthal's gliders, 1896

49 Pilcher's *Hawk*, in which in 1897 he set a gliding distance record of 750 ft, and in which he was later killed

concerned with inherent stability and built gliders with bird-shaped wings with the aim of achieving it. Gordon England acted as his pilot and later his ideas were to be developed and extended in various Handley Page designs – again with inherent stability in view.

We are now moving to the fringe of powered flight. But there continued the bizarre experiments of the flapping wing and helicopter brigade. Their suggestions seem now to have a fantastic quality. Yet when the history of flight is surveyed one must concede that ideas just as fantastic have now and again proved practicable and important.

In France ideas poured forth with a particular richness. In the Paucton 'Ptérophore', for instance, which was mooted in 1768, a manually driven horizontal rotor was proposed for lift and a separate rotor – a kind of air-screw – for propulsion. Then there was the better known and more practical Launoy and Bienvenu model heli-copter of 1784, a model machine in which birds' feathers were used to make the rotors. Power was derived from a bow and twisted cord.

There seems to be agreement among specialist researchers into this period that the Launoy and Bien-venu helicopter did fly. Consequently there is substance in the claim that it was the first powered aerodyne to fly. Unlike the Chinese top it carried its power plant in it. It was therefore a more radical solution to helicopter flight problems than Cayley's version of the Chinese flying top which was said to have 'risen' 88 ft into the air. In 1842 W. H. Phillips made a steam model helicopter

with steam fed along the rotor blades to the tips in the manner later extensively used in jet rotor helicopters. After these early rotorcraft attempts come the major steps towards the first man-carrying helicopter but these will be discussed in the chapter which traces rotorcraft progress.

In the meantime we can return to the final suspension-charged stages in the kite-glider-powered aerodyne transition. The kite, it has been emphasized, is a tethered aeroplane without an engine. The glider is a free aero-plane without an engine. Several of the men who devoted themselves to the study of kites and gliders were thinking all the time of the free-flight, powered aeroplane and some were experimenting with prime movers. From about 1850 to about 1900 this groping towards something that was tantalizingly near yet so difficult to realize reached its height.

Lifting surfaces, usually cambered – Horatio Phillips had developed the double curvature shape of wing leading edges – and having a form approaching as closely to the form of a bird's wing as structural methods and materials would allow, had been examined and their performance measured in different conditions. The multiplane con-struction had been shown to give useful lift. This had importance to the early constructors because the biplane was, in some respects, structurally simpler than the monoplane.

Stability had received attention and the dihedral angle had been tried as a means of providing a measure of inherent stability. A dihedral angle can be simply defined

50 Chanute's biplane hang-glider at Dure Park, Illinois, 1896

as the angle at which a wing of an aircraft is inclined to the horizontal. An aircraft with a marked dihedral is one in which, viewed from front or rear, the two wings appear to slope upwards from the body. It is possible to have negative dihedral, with the wings inclined downwards, but the form in which the gliding pioneers were interested was the positive, upward sloping dihedral because this tends to correct the tilting of the aircraft to one side or the other.

Control was less well understood and had been less thoroughly developed than lift or stability. The Lilienthal method, derived in some ways from the da Vinci proposals and used by Pilcher, had been shown in two accidents and in numerous trials to have defects. In fact it did not appear to be adequate to meet the continually changing conditions of free flight. This consideration of the requirements of *stability* and of *control* was the precursor of a controversy which sprang up during the war of 1914-18. For the two qualities are partly antagonistic. Among air pilots and aircraft designers opposing views were expressed; on the one side that aircraft should have a high degree of inherent stability, and, on the other, that they should be relatively unstable, but extremely responsive to control.

During the early gliding experiments, however, no such sophisticated division of opinion had appeared. The aim was to make an effective glider that could carry a man from a hill top to a landing place in the valley in safety. A measure of inherent stability was needed – hence the value placed on the dihedral angle for the wings – and a minimum measure of control so that the pilot could adjust the gliding angle, select the touch-down point and go through the usual aircraft landing process of flattening out, increasing drag and reducing speed, to bring about the characteristic tangential touch-down.

The state of the art of gliding had advanced far since the wild take-offs from towers with rudimentary wings strapped to arms and legs. Le Bris, Mouillard, Chanute, Lilienthal and Pilcher had carried forward, in technique if not always in time, the development of the man-carrying aerodyne. They had taken it from the kite to the free flight glider.

The next step – really a giant stride – was made by the men who later played a part in powered flight. Most of them began with some form of glider. All of them were looking for that elusive catalyst, the lightweight prime mover, and all of them eventually worked upon the physical realization of aerodynes with prime movers.

Of those who most clearly and explicitly bridged the gap between glider and powered machine, those who not only designed, but also built *and* flew gliders *and* aeroplanes, two names stand out, Voisin and Wright. The brothers Gabriel and Charles Voisin and the brothers Wilbur and Orville Wright contributed more than any others to the achievement of the critical transition from the practical motorless man-lifting aerodyne to the practical powered man-lifting aerodyne.

The word 'practical' is important. Clément Ader made the same transition, but his machine was not practical. The American Pierpont Langley almost succeeded with models but not in full scale. The Russian Mozhaiski's man-carrying aerodyne is dated 1884, earlier even than

51

52

53

51 Poster advertising a demonstration of a Montgomery glider, 1905

52 Model of Mozhaiski's flying machine, 1884

53 The Voisin brothers (Gabriel is on the left)

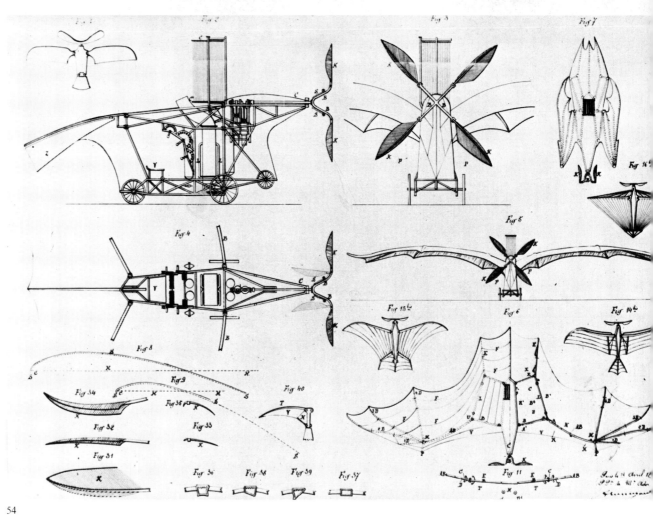

54

Ader's, but again it could not be held to be practical. Cody's work was practical but came too late to be classified among the originating achievements. So we return to the Voisins and the Wrights, the great creative geniuses of powered man-carrying flying machines.

Gabriel Voisin is one of those Frenchmen who rate Clément Ader as the most remarkable of all the pioneers. And, although English-speaking people may be inclined to underestimate Ader's studies and to think that his aircraft was unrealistic in terms of later designs, there does not seem to be doubt about his astonishing prescience. It is as if something of da Vinci's far-seeing genius were to be repeated in the field of practical work and trial.

The monoplane form with swept back wings, the wheeled undercarriage, the partly enclosed cabin, the variable wing sweep, the twin screws – these things were among the Ader characteristics which can fairly be said to have been prophetic. But how far Ader carried his far-sighted ideas towards hard, practical realization is something about which there have been many arguments.

Although Voisin was such an admirer of Ader, he did not, in his own designs, adopt the monoplane form. He preferred the biplane form or rather the form of biplane which Hargrave had tested in his kites, that is a biplane with vertical members joining the ends of the planes to make a box. This is the *box-kite* pattern developed most by Hargrave and it is the pattern of large numbers of the most successful early powered machines. Many were actually called 'box-kites'. Voisin named it

the cellular pattern.

Let it be remembered that the box-kite *is* the biplane. Aerodynamically the two are akin. There are two superimposed main planes, with a gap between them, to do the lifting. At one time the vertical surfaces joining the ends of the two main planes to form a box were the subject of minor misunderstandings. They were believed by many to give a degree of inherent stability. They were thought of as offering some of the advantages of a dihedral angle, preventing the aircraft from tipping to one side or the other, together with the advantages of preventing sideslip and yaw.

Yawing, that is slewing or skidding around the vertical axis – as distinct from turning, banked, and without slew or skid – is a breakdown of directional stability. If the arrow has no feathers, it is likely to yaw. If the glider or kite has no vertical tail surfaces it is likely to yaw. In the box-kites vertical surfaces were in some cases used not only on the main planes, but also on tail units. Thus box-kites often had one *box* for the main planes, and, at a slight distance behind it, mounted on booms, a second *box* for the tail unit.

The vertical surfaces – they were sometimes called 'curtains' – although they did not provide an effective substitute for dihedral angle, had their merits in preventing yaw, in giving directional stability and in checking side-slip which is a variant of yaw. These vertical surfaces cannot, therefore, be dismissed as a 'mistake' on the part of the early designers. And although they disappeared with the passage of time, so that the true box-

54 Original drawings of Ader's *Eole*

kite aircraft became obsolete, they were never an indication of an erroneous line of progress. Indeed there is some relationship between these vertical surfaces and the wing end-plates seen in some modern designs.

That disquisition on the 'curtains' of the box-kite formula has relevance to the early work of the Voisins as they moved from gliders to powered aircraft. They had done a great deal of keenly observed kite flying at Neuville-sur-Saône with Hargrave box-kites before Gabriel went for his *service militaire*. After it, in 1890, he received his inspiration to go forward from a meeting with Clément Ader.

From his talk with Ader and from his subsequent, almost reverent study of Ader's 1890 steam-powered aircraft, Gabriel got the message which fired his genius and sent him in quest of the powered, man-carrying flying machine. He was invaded by a divine obsession. His brother Charles shared it.

Apart from its inspirational aspect Gabriel's meeting with Ader prompted him and his brother to study and to grasp the difference—not then generally understood—between an aircraft in flight and a ship at sea. From the darkness of confused inferences, there emerged, for Gabriel and Charles, a true appreciation of the interplay of centres of pressure and centre of gravity in the complex of a lifting machine.

The brothers began to see the direction in which flight was running. They dedicated themselves to the realization of a practical, man-carrying flying machine to be developed from their successful gliders.

Gabriel was the more thoughtful, Charles the more daring. The combination worked well until Charles's death in an automobile accident. Gabriel had trained as an architect and this training helped him in making the drawings for his flying machines.

After their kite flying, which they took with scientific seriousness, the brothers turned to gliders as stepping stones to aeroplanes. Gabriel's 1900 design for a glider, having Lilienthal characteristics, was intended to be fitted with a power plant and a propulsion system based on Ader's work. He also used a forward control surface after Sir Hiram Maxim's scheme and, at the rear, a vertical surface to do the duty of a rudder.

The brothers did their preliminary gliding in memorable circumstances. They were always in love with 'their' river, the flower-decked Saône, with its leafy islands and silvery waters. Incidentally one of their first essays in design and construction was a small steam boat. They built it from scrap materials, fired the steam boiler with coal they had to purloin from the family cellars, and went cruising on their beloved river.

Gabriel absorbed the lessons of how a moving vehicle interacts with its surroundings, of how currents and winds must be taken into account if a journey is to be made in a predetermined direction and at a predetermined speed. These were the old facts of seamanship, but Voisin saw them afresh in relation to his persistent dream of flying. It may be one reason why he perceived, more clearly than some of the early balloonists, just how navigation through the air with a controllable aircraft must differ from floating in the air in a balloon and from sailing in a ship at sea.

Gabriel Voisin, there can be little doubt, always believed that France was the birthplace of rational aerodynamics just as he and many others believed it had been the birthplace of aerostatics. He gives a high place to Octave Chanute, emphasizing in particular his Parisian birth. And if later historians are inclined to underestimate the influence of Chanute and of Clément Ader it must be borne in mind that Gabriel Voisin knew both of them personally. His meeting with Ader has been mentioned. He met Chanute in Paris, with his niece,

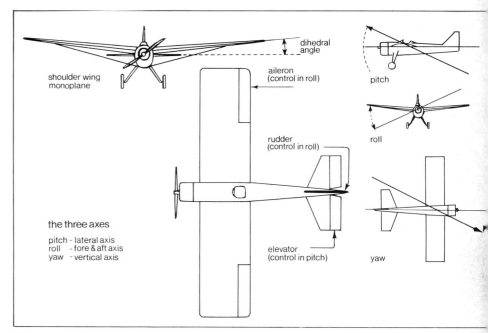

55

56

in 1908 when Chanute was on a visit to France after having gone to live in the United States. (He died in Chicago in 1910.)

In all these discussions of who did what and when, more weight should perhaps be given to the views of those who were alive and working at the time. Yet the shift in emphasis that has taken place in writings on aerial history over the years is often, strangely enough, in the opposite direction; that is away from the expressed views of the pioneers who lived and worked at the time, and towards the views of the literary researchers and diggers-up of ancient documents who came much later.

Gabriel Voisin is an example. His views on the work that led to the first powered, man-carrying flight are views he formed while he himself was making the transition from-kites-to-gliders-to-aeroplanes. He knew Ader.

55 The essentials of control and stability

56 The Voisin glider making the first manned flight from water, towed by a speed boat along the Seine, 6 June 1905

43

He knew Chanute. He knew Ferber, Santos-Dumont, Fabre, Levavasseur, Farman, Delagrange, Esnault-Pelterie, all of them. But now there are some who reject his views of Ader's achievements and of Chanute's and Hargrave's influence and who state that he is biased in his assessment of the work of the Wright brothers. Yet Voisin's glider work was indubitably a sound foundation for powered flight. He not only made glides from hill tops and from the sand dunes at Berck-sur-Mer some of them in 1904 with a biplane glider; but in June 1905 he also made his famous towed flights along the Seine in a hydroplane glider. The glider was towed by a racing motorboat. It had some success although it suffered a minor accident.

From every glide Voisin derived information, whether about the balance of the aircraft, the relationship between centre of pressure and centre of gravity, about drag and angle of incidence, or about the practice of piloting. The Voisins were original-minded, observant and devotees of the scientific method of experimental verification. So when, after all this, the prime mover arrived, they were ready for it with designs for practical airframes. And they were, it must be remembered, in the centre of the Parisian cauldron of boiling ideas and enthusiasms. They formed part of the aeronautical coterie. Gabriel knew Santos-Dumont well. In fact Santos asked for his daughter in marriage. As will be seen the Voisin glider was a progenitor of the historic Santos-Dumont 14-*bis*.

We come to the last of those bridging the gap between kites and powered aerodynes by designing, building and flying gliders; the Wright brothers, Orville and Wilbur. Out of the vast amount of comment and record on the Wrights' achievement, the letters in the Manuscript Division of the Library of Congress are revelatory not only of the aeronautical work they did but also of their characters and manner of life. Fred C. Kelly, the Wrights' authorized biographer, assembled a large amount of this correspondence in his book, *Miracle at Kitty Hawk*. The brothers had their own bicycle manufacturing business and lived at Dayton, Ohio.

Chanute's book was one of the starting points for the Wrights. It led to correspondence between them and Chanute. Wilbur's first letter to Chanute was dated 13 May 1900. It is a date of historic importance for it reveals the Wrights' realization that gliding was the road to power flying. It refers to the English pioneer Percy Pilcher. Chanute responded with generosity and helped to carry forward the Wrights' plans on a great wave of inspired speculation.

In September of the same year, 1900, Wilbur summed up his and Orville's attitude towards the art to which they were to devote their lives in a letter to their father: 'It is my belief that flight is possible and, while I am taking up the investigation for pleasure rather than profit, I think there is a slight possibility of achieving fame and fortune from it.'

The brothers' first glider they flew as a kite, thus going through the procedure which as we have seen was basic to the pattern of progress. It had a span of 17 ft and a wing area of 165 sq. ft. They flew it tethered in October 1900, and began to get together, from their observations

of its behaviour, the facts and figures they were to need as they turned to larger machines. They chose Kitty Hawk, on the sandy coast of North Carolina, for their experiments, because of its strong but regular winds.

The early kite had neither elevator, in the modern sense, nor rudder. The next kite was intended to double the duties of a veritable glider. The Wrights had not only had support and encouragement from Chanute but had also been in touch with Captain Louis Ferber to learn about his experiences with Lilienthal type gliders. Their new machine had a wing span of 22 ft, a wing area of 290 sq. ft and a weight of 98 lb. In the following year, 1902, they built and flew a third machine with span of 32 ft and wing area of 305 sq. ft, and with a single rear rudder in its improved version.

Opinions and ideas were exchanged with the European pioneers, including Mouillard and Pénaud. Design features were discussed with the eminent mathematician and astronomer Samuel Pierpont Langley, director of the Smithsonian Institution.

Langley had come early on the scene with a practical working model (1896) upon which he had then based his 'aerodrome' as he called it. This was a tandem wing monoplane, a seaplane fitted with five cylindrical metal floats attached to the underside of the main frame, a 'Pénaud tail' which had vertical and horizontal surfaces, and a five-cylinder radial engine designed and built by Langley's assistant Charles Manly. Launching was to be done by catapult from a houseboat on the Potomac River. But the aircraft failed to fly. It became the subject of later controversy over the Wrights' priority in powered flight. The Smithsonian Institution claimed that Langley's was 'the first man-carrying airplane in the history of the world capable of sustaining free flight', and it was not until some years later that this claim was withdrawn.

At the time of the Wrights' early achievements, international communications were rudimentary. There was nothing approaching today's flow of reports, newspaper accounts, papers, magazines and television and radio statements. Nevertheless the Wrights did contrive to keep themselves informed of work going on in France and France, on her side—and in contradiction to what so many who write about this period imagine—was kept

57

58

57 Orville Wright

58 Wilbur Wright

44

59

well informed about what the Wrights were doing.

The French magazine *l'Aérophile* was one of the earliest publications of its kind, a founder of the world's aviation press. In 1902 *l'Aérophile* published a description of the Wright glider. It may be said that if the earliest work of the Wrights was not, perhaps, given its due notice in America, it was given due notice in France.

The Wrights were meticulous with their measurements when they were making their gliding experiments. In October 1902 they recorded three glides of '506 ft, 504½ ft and 550 ft'. Later they recorded a glide of '622½ ft'.

Upon their theoretical knowledge of aerodynamics, the Wrights were building a practical result, that is a man-carrying, controllable glider. And here their letter to George A. Spratt dated 7 June 1903 is significant of all they were hoping and working for. They said that they had decided to put a 'motor with propellers' into their next machine.

And that word 'motor' brings us to the end of this period in the development of the aerodyne or heavier-than-air flying machine. There now intervenes a separate but crucial development, the development of a prime mover suitable for use in aircraft, the development, in other words, of a lightweight engine. The names of Wright and of Voisin come up again of course, but in order to preserve the logical sequence, the names of those who created the early lightweight prime movers must now be introduced and the remarkable work they did must be described.

59 Wilbur Wright on the second No. 3 glider, 10 October 1902

4 The prime movers move in

Gravity was the source of motive power for the gliding pioneers; but it was an awkward, unco-operative source of motive power. It worked in only one direction and it could not be turned on and off. A different, artificial source of motive power was needed before the glider could be turned into the free flying vehicle which was the real, zealously pursued objective of all who were engaged in the aviation effort. A prime mover was the indispensable partner to the aerodynamic cell. You could take an aerofoil to a level field, but you could not make it fly. A compact and, above all, a lightweight prime mover was needed. The future of free flight depended upon it.

It is paradoxical that, although a set of wings cannot achieve free flight without an engine, an engine can achieve free flight without a set of wings. The French Flying Atar was just such a device. This machine was shown to thousands in free flight at the Paris Salon de l'Aéronautique in the 1950s. It was no more and no less than a turbojet engine with small jets for control and with a pilot sitting on top of it and it took off, moved about freely in the air, then landed again at the place from which it had taken off. It was the strangest sight; a bit of tube, up-ended, with a man sitting on top. It was a freak, perhaps, but a reminder of the basic principles which are apposite to the form of engineering progress discussed in this chapter. For we are concerned with the application of power to move air masses.

Da Vinci, with more accurate foresight than is usually accorded him in this particular matter, thought of man himself as a prime mover, providing the power for free flight through a system of levers. Much later, as has been noted, man did indeed prove that he could provide the power needed for free flight and man-powered flight became practical, though in a restricted form. But prime movers much more powerful for their weight than man were needed.

Practical power processing devices were in use in the form of windmills and watermills when the search for an aeroplane prime mover began. The windmill, like the ship's sails, processed the natural winds and used them to produce rotary motion on the grinding floor. The watermill did likewise with the natural flow of water. But early balloonists trying to adapt this procedure allowed their reasoning to run away with them when they fitted balloons with sails. They omitted to take into account the effects upon a sailing vessel of the hull and keel in the water or upon a windmill of the land foundations of its mounting. Without that degree of restriction and the relativity that went with it the natural winds could not be turned into motive power. The sailing balloon was soon seen to be the outcome of fallacious

60

inference.

When it came to gliders the approach was more realistic and many of the pioneers saw that what was wanted was a portable device which would produce power from a natural source and do it without being too cumbersome or too heavy. Here there was a rapprochement between the aeronautical specialists and the working engineers. The great men of aviation turned to and were supported by the great men in mechanical engineering.

Inventors turned to hot air engines and gas engines. The gas engine concept is usually ascribed to Philippe

Lebon in 1799. And there were the engines of John Ericsson in Sweden in 1830, and of Dr Stirling in 1843. Stirling's engine was made in Dundee. Possibly the first use of a gas engine as the motive power for a transport vehicle was Samuel Brown's gas engined boat. This was tried on the Thames in 1835. The gas turbine patented by John Barber in 1791 was an example – like the Montgolfier hot air propulsion-lift idea – of the inventor thinking so far ahead of his time that his invention made almost no impact. It was accordingly

promise for the aircraft inventor, Richard Trevithick's locomotive of 1804. Here was a relatively compact engine, running on a fuel that could be carried without too much difficulty, and capable of driving a vehicle. George Stephenson's Rocket was running only twenty-four years later and establishing itself as a prime mover suited to land locomotion.

Those whose dream was of flying and not of railway locomotion saw in the locomotive steam engine a form of prime mover which, although in itself entirely

61

ignored.

Then aviation workers were given a fresh lead by Sir George Cayley. His hot air engine of 1807 was less important to the future of flight than his proposal for a form of explosion engine. Here he was on a promising track. He was not the only one, for the Abbé Jean de Hautfeuille had suggested an engine fuelled with gunpowder and the Danish inventor, Christiaan Huygens, had had a similar idea. But Cayley was thinking aeronautically. The explosion engine looked as if it might do what was wanted; that is be compact, light in weight for its power and capable of running upon a convenient fuel. But gunpowder was not generally looked upon as a fuel. It was not a convenient fuel – much less convenient than coal, for example. It was the time when coal appeared to be the fuel of choice and coal brings us to the prime mover which was first tried as a practical, full scale aero-engine; the steam engine.

After the steam engine of Denis Papin, in about 1700, there had been the practical, full scale engine of Thomas Newcomen in 1712. Then came something full of

inappropriate to their purposes, looked as if it might be developed and made suitable. And so a vast amount of design ingenuity, original thought and constructional craftsmanship went into the creation of a lightweight steam engine suitable for aircraft.

Although rival ideas for gas engines, explosion engines, hot air engines and the like were much discussed, the practical possibilities of the steam engine were a firm foundation for the early aeronautical engineer. And it turned out that Ader's powered, man-carrying flight was made with a steam engine.

On 24 September 1852, from Paris, Henri Giffard went up in his steam airship. It was, of course, a non-rigid airship, cigar shaped, and with the habitable gondola suspended beneath the envelope. The engine was rated at 3 horsepower but the detail design is not recorded although it is said that the installed weight was 352 lb. This would have made the specific weight 117 lb. per horsepower. Giffard is said to have claimed a speed capability of 10 ft per second for his vessel. This was with an airscrew of 11 ft diameter.

61 Giffard's airship, 1852

47

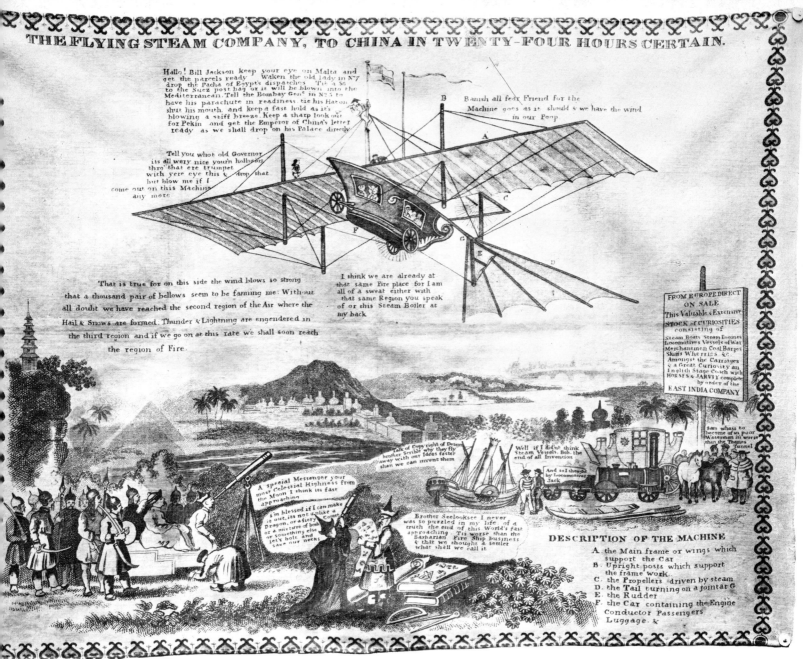

62

62 Handkerchief with a representation of Henson's Aerial Steam Carriage of 1843

Giffard is depicted in the prints of the period standing in the nacelle at the controls of his steam engine just behind the imposing boiler. His engine was fuelled by coal or coke and the distance covered by the airship during the flight was 17 miles. The steam engine, although it introduced fire hazards particularly in gas filled airships, seemed to be and was now shown to be the most promising aircraft prime mover of that period. Attention was re-focussed upon some of the more notable models. Fresh studies were undertaken of the Stringfellow model steam engines of 1844 and 1848. Henson's design also took on a new interest.

William Samuel Henson of Somerset is probably best remembered because of the admirable picture of his aerial 'steam carriage' (1843) which circulated widely and which fairly represented Henson's design. It was, moreover, a thoroughly practical-looking design: a monoplane, propeller driven with the wing bracing set up by king posts in the orthodox manner. It was supposed to have a span of 150 ft. Although it was never more than a picture, the steam carriage certainly showed a keen understanding of the kind of structure and the kind of engine-airframe-tail unit configuration which would prove practical.

Lawrence Hargrave who was, as has been said, an Australian citizen, although born in England (in 1850), used methylated spirit as the fuel for a small steam engine he built in 1892. He made a second model engine in 1893. In 1896 Langley fitted a small steam engine to his flying model. Charles Manly's engine of 1903 was a five-cylinder radial intended for Langley's machine. It had many points of resemblance to much later engines, being petrol fed and having a form of coil ignition. Crankcase and cylinders were of steel, the latter with cast iron liners. Manly himself was as skilful a craftsman as he was a designer and he undertook a good deal of the constructional work. He later worked on Curtiss aero-engines and in 1929 he was posthumously awarded the Langley Medal. His early radial engine never survived the crash of the Langley 'aerodrome' when it fell into the River Potomac on its first attempt to take off.

But before Hargrave had completed his engines and

before Manly had begun the construction of his, another inventor had launched into the design and construction of a full size steam engine intended from the start for use in a winged aircraft. This man was Clément Ader.

Engineers from many parts of the world have studied his remarkable steam engine in the Paris museum where it has been kept and they are at one in their admiration for the weight reductions which Ader achieved. In 1960, the Ingénieur Général R. Marchal, a director of the atomic division of SNECMA, the great French aero-engine complex, made a specialized study of Ader's work, examining his patents in detail. As a consequence he rated the Ader steam engine at 20 CV which is a little less than 20 in terms of brake horsepower. He gives the weight as 51 lb, which means a power to weight ratio (or specific weight) of about $2\frac{1}{2}$ lb per hp.

That would be a vast improvement upon Giffard's engine (about 120 lb/hp), but the difference is not in reality so great because the figures are not strictly comparable. This is one of the difficulties in discussing power units for aircraft. There are so many kinds of 'weight'; dry weight, net weight, gross weight and installed weight. And a painstaking examination of the details is needed before any guarantee can be given that the specific figures are truly comparable. This difficulty vitiates many statements about the performance of aero-engines; but in particular it vitiates comparisons between the performances of steam engines and of petrol or other kinds of engine.

In order to exclude the risk of misleading the reader, certain generalizations are now desirable. In the earliest days of aerodyne development, the weight of the power unit was critical. The wing cells were not as efficient as were later wing cells and the methods of construction were not so thoroughly developed. So the wings weighed more for their strength and it followed that the prime mover that was to propel them into the air had to come within rigid weight limits.

But what should be included in prime mover weight? Should the fuel – coal, coke, naphtha, methylated spirit, petrol, paraffin or whatever it might be? If so there would need to be an additional figure taking into account specific consumption and adjusting the power plant weight to time in the air. Steam engines demand water. How much water should be included in the weight? Petrol engines may require a coolant, water or some other liquid. How is the quantity of coolant which should be included in the weight to be determined?

In the end the term 'installed weight' seems to carry the meaning in the right direction. The installed weight of an aero-engine is its weight with all accessories and components related to the running of the engine, including any cooling liquid or steam raising water, lubricants and fittings and controls, but not including fuel. If installed weight were the universal, standardized basis of comparison, the figures would be truly comparable. It is not, however, so simple as that. Hosts of minor variables come in to confuse things. Nevertheless broad conclusions can be drawn from specific engine weights based on the installed weight concept.

Let us then note immediately certain relevant figures for the pioneer steam aero-engines. Their significance in the continuum of flight development will become more marked as we turn to other kinds of engine and particularly to the petrol or oil fuelled internal combustion engine.

Thus the Giffard airship engine was, as already pointed out, 120 lb/hp in specific weight. The steam engine envisaged for the Henson and Stringfellow aerial carriage of 1843 was rated at 30 horsepower with a weight, including boiler and water, of 600 lb. This, according to Davy (*Henson and Stringfellow*) was Henson's 'final calculation'. This specific weight – 20 lb/hp – is an enormous improvement upon the Giffard engine; but it was not a practical working engine, only a design for one. Stringfellow's model engines achieved remarkable results in actual practice under proper testing conditions; but they were still models.

F. W. Brearey of the Aeronautical Society, writing in July 1868, speaks of Stringfellow's most famous model and rates it (but without water) at 16 lb per horsepower, a weight which, as Brearey noted, was 'probably the lightest steam engine that has ever been constructed'. But it must again be emphasized that this was without water and that the engine was a model. Ader's engine – on full scale – was $2\frac{1}{2}$ lb/hp and that was a more significant achievement than any model.

Sir Hiram Maxim, working in England, also spent time on designing and producing full scale steam engines for his flying machine. His design reached a power weight ratio of 1·55 lb/hp, which appears astonishing until it is appreciated – once again – that it excludes the boiler and the water. Maxim's steam engine was of relatively high

63 Stringfellow's model engine, *c.* 1850

64 Steam engine for Henson's model aircraft, 1843. In neither 63 nor 64 is the boiler present

63   64

power and was a splendid piece of design, but it is almost certain that it was much heavier than Ader's engine. For the steam engine the Russian Mozhaiski used in his aircraft of 1884–which was said to have made short flights in the hands of a pilot called Golubev–no comparable figures have been available since the Soviet Union decided not to press claims for Mozhaiski's priority. On the admittedly scrappy evidence, it would seem that of all full scale steam aero-engines, Ader's had the lowest installed weight for its power.

It would be a mistake to dismiss steam aero-engines as having been a hopeless project from the start. On the contrary there was nothing to prevent the development of a steam engine for use in aeroplanes. Gabriel Voisin emphasized its excellence. And in fact in the 1930s the Besler brothers in Oakland, California, did produce a steam aero-engine which was stated in a journal called *Steam Aviation* to have been successful.

It is indeed difficult to discover why steam aero-engines disappeared from the scene so early and after they had proved that they could reach the power to weight ratios needed for free flight. Steam engines had done well in cars, the Serpollet steam cars being notable during the early stages of development particularly for speed record breaking. Other makes took their places in automobile history with reputations as fast, trustworthy power units for road vehicles. Nevertheless the steam aero-engine was to suffer a total eclipse.

We may pass over the use of electric motors because these did not enter the aerodyne field. They did make a brief appearance in the aerostat field. The use of an

66

eight horsepower electric motor to power the airship *France* was the most notable feat. This vessel was by Charles Renard and Arthur Krebs and it flew successfully in August 1884. Renard had devised lightweight batteries and made a lightweight motor but the power to weight ratio still came to about 230 lb/hp, a great deal heavier than Giffard's steam engine.

This electric airship was probably inspired by the model which had been made three years earlier, in 1881, by the brothers Tissandier who were balloonists. The small Tissandier power plant had a higher specific weight than the Renard and Krebs power plant.

All these varied efforts to introduce a suitable prime mover into aircraft were signs of the great and increasing pressure that was being felt by inventors and particularly by those who were pioneering in aeronautics, to break away from the natural restrictions integral with the use of gravity as a motive force, and also with subjection to natural winds as dominant navigational factors. Men were desperately determined to fly freely. They were desperately determined to get up into the air, rising above level ground and then directing their vessel in any direction they desired. It was made abundantly clear, when the Giffard airship flew, that a suitable prime mover was the supreme and conclusive link in the chain of aeronautical progress.

Here Hargrave comes into our picture once again. His vigorous efforts to develop a prime mover for aircraft were complementary to his work upon kites, particularly box-kites, and upon lifting surfaces in tethered flight. He saw how close the kite was to the aeroplane. He equated the kite string to the prime mover. And, as has been said, his steam engines were promising, lightweight prime movers. He also studied engines which used 'petroleum spirit vapour' in 1888 and 1889. And he is claimed by technical bodies in Australia to have discovered the principle of the rotary engine. He made a small three-cylinder model. So just as Hargrave had fore-

65

shadowed the steps that had to be taken in order to produce a practical lifting wing system–the box-kite–he also foreshadowed the steps that had to be taken in order to produce a practical prime mover that would enable the wing system to be launched into free flight.

We now come to the definitive aero-engine; the petrol burning internal combustion engine. It is not necessary to rehearse the story of the internal combustion engine although it will be necessary to speak in some detail of the remarkable forms of internal combustion engine that were designed expressly for aircraft use. But the main course of the development is well known. The Sadi Carnot cycle for a heat engine of 1824 led to the Beau de Rochas or Otto cycle of 1862 and 1876. This, the four-stroke cycle, was the basic pattern of the IC aero-engine. The name of Gottlieb Daimler has prominence in aviation as in automobilism, his small high-speed engine burning petrol as fuel being dated only five years after Dr Otto's gas engine.

Basically the prime mover for winged machines was to be an engine with cylinders and pistons and valves. It was to employ the four-stroke cycle, that is an induction, a compression, a power or explosion and an exhaust strike. This was the skeleton upon which the flesh of practical power production was to be grown by inventors and engineers. And when the four-stroke, internal combustion engine had been refined it became a springboard for the whole of the accumulated aerodynamic knowledge of the years.

Steam had led the way, but for reasons which have never become plain, it did not carry flight forward. There were lightweight steam engines; but perhaps the formula of the steam power plant failed to match the aerodynamic cell. The compact, internal combustion engine, with no external flame, which processed a liquid fuel the whole way from tank to rotational power at the crankshaft, seemed made for the winged machine. It was a package that could be slipped in or clipped on whereever there was room for it.

Certain aero-engines of the earliest period of flight were and remain tributes to the creative thought of their engineers. Of these historic importance is most strongly attached to, and, indeed, is concentrated upon the Antoinette. The name is that of the daughter of a financier, Gastambide, who provided the money for a great deal of experimental work on both engines and aircraft. The designer was a stocky Frenchman with a luxuriant beard of quite remarkable expanse and richness, Léon Levavasseur.

Levavasseur, born in Cherbourg in 1863, is one of the supreme geniuses of the pioneer period of winged flight. He not only designed and produced a prime mover which, today, exhibits features of advanced modern form, he also designed fast motor boats and elegant aircraft. Levavasseur discovered and applied engineering devices which were painfully re-discovered and re-applied by much later engine makers.

Yet French works on aviation history ungenerously– or is it unknowingly?–pass over the achievements of Levavasseur. Many of the most respected do not even mention him. Yet the fact is he imposed upon the internal combustion engine a fresh, original and amazingly

prescient design pattern and he made and ran successfully engines weighing less for their power and more compact than anything previously made.

Winged flight would not have become a developed, understood, practical form of locomotion by 1910 or even later, had it not been for Léon Levavasseur. Santos-Dumont, Cody, A. V. Roe, Henry Farman and the Voisin brothers made flight history by permission of Léon Levavasseur, the man whom the French reference books forget.

67

68

Levavasseur made many Antoinette engines, of different powers. The 50 hp aviation engine was an eight cylinder V, turning at the relatively low speed of 1,100 revolutions per minute. It weighed approximately 110 lb according to Voisin. This would give a specific weight of 2·2 lb/hp. It was steam cooled or 'evaporative cooled', as later terminology put it, and it had direct fuel injection working with automatic inlet valves.

Many years were to pass before another aero-engine

67 Léon Levavasseur

68 50 hp Antoinette engine, 1905

was to appear (a Rolls-Royce) and to go into general use with evaporative cooling. Direct injection took even longer (over fifty years) to make its re-appearance upon the scene and to justify the thinking of the forgotten pioneer Léon Levavasseur. Voisin's weight figure has been queried on the grounds that it did not include the water for the evaporative cooling. But the engine would still weigh less than 3 lb/hp; indeed a 'safe' figure of $2\frac{1}{2}$ lb/hp could be put on it.

The year of the design of the first Antoinette engine is difficult to determine. It may have been 1901. Antoinette engines were fitted to racing motorboats in 1904 when Levavasseur was 39. This was after his fateful meeting with Gastambide and his daughter, Antoinette. The 24 horsepower model came first. The 50 horsepower model was the more influential, but it was not an entirely reliable engine. It was hardly to be expected that a unit which broke away from all previous practice and attained a lightness superior–on the basis of installed weight–to anything that had been known, would also have the trustworthiness of the comparatively heavy, bulky, lumbering engines that were in use on the ground. But it did enable aviators to get into the air.

Levavasseur's imprint on aviation history was deepened by his airframe designs, one of which, selected by Hubert Latham for his early flight attempts, achieved renown as being the handsomest monoplane ever to fly. It had a slender, V-section fuselage and a big wing span, of high aspect ratio. A dihedral angle and a rather stalky undercarriage with front skid completed the picture. In the air it produced a wonderful effect of grace and delicacy. And, although the control system, which included a large wheel mounted on a horizontal axis, was criticized, the aircraft performed well on many occasions particularly in rather fresh winds.

Many of the early aircraft makers also tried to rival Levavasseur in the making of aero-engines. Esnault-Pelterie achieved success with the REP engine which was used by J. W. Dunne for the experiments he was making in Scotland, largely in secret, with a machine with sharply swept back wings. Lancelot Gibbs was his pilot. Captain Geoffrey de Havilland was another designer-maker-pilot who built his own engine.

The de Havilland engine, which appeared in 1908, was the outcome of much thought. It was a flat four giving between 40 and 50 horsepower and it was used to drive an adjustable pitch propeller–not a variable pitch propeller in the modern idiom, but a propeller the blades of which could be set at different pitch angles according to the flight requirements. This engine had a power to weight ratio of 5·4 lb/hp.

The Wright brothers' engine, as used for their 1903 experiments, was not a great achievement of original design thinking. It was far outdistanced in originality by the Antoinette, the Manly, the REP and a few others. But because of the eminent place held by the Wrights in aviation history the design of their first engine is important.

It was a four-cylinder, water-cooled engine, the cylinders laid on their side. There was nothing to mark it out particularly from automobile engines of the time. Like the Antoinette it had spring-loaded automatic inlet valves. And like the Antoinette it did without a carburetter; but instead of using direct fuel injection, it used a vaporizing device consisting of a small, heated metal container, into which the fuel flowed by gravity. The heat vaporized the fuel to provide the combustible mixture for the engine.

The power of the early Wright engine has been variously given, but Air Commodore Banks, lecturing at a Royal Aeronautical Society meeting at Brough in November 1961, said it was 'about 13 brake horsepower'. He gave the specific weight as $11\frac{1}{4}$ lb/hp. A later engine built by the Wrights, with cylinders vertical, was credited with developing 30 brake horsepower and with having a specific weight of 7 lb/hp.

Meantime a stroke of engineering genius not so remarkable as that which produced the Antoinette, but still outstanding, produced another series of aero-engines, different from the Antoinette, the Wright and all the others, yet offering a useful power to weight ratio. These were the rotary engines, beginning with the Gnome.

Two brothers, Laurent and Louis Séguin were the originators of this extraordinary engine, an engine which gave the biggest impetus to powered man-carrying aviation since the first hesitant hops of the pioneers, an engine which turned flying from an uncertain experiment into a trustworthy procedure.

Hargrave, it has already been said, is credited with discovering the rotary engine principle. In the ordinary stationary engine the cylinders are fixed, the pistons reciprocate and the cranks convert the reciprocating motion to rotary motion at the crankshaft. Airscrews,

71

therefore, are attached to the end of the crankshaft or to a gear train meshed with the end of the crankshaft.

In the rotary engine the process is reversed. The crankshaft is held fixed while the crank converts rotary to reciprocating motion at the pistons and the pistons convert it back again into rotary motion at the cylinders and crank chamber. It sounds crazy; but it works.

69 An Antoinette piloted by Latham

70 The *Antoinette* at the Paris Air Exhibition, 1909

71 The first Wright aero-engine, 1903

53

72

73

Where light weight is a prime consideration it works well. In fact in the early 1900s it worked better than anything else.

But obviously the difficulties of feeding combustible mixture into cylinders which are whirling around are many. The difficulties of exhausting gases after combustion are many. The difficulties of lubricating are many. And, above all, the difficulties of cooling the cylinders are many. The Antoinette engine, we have seen, was evaporative-cooled, using water as the medium. The Wright engine was water-cooled on the lines of automobile engines. But neither water nor steam appeared to the brothers Séguin to be convenient or even feasible for their rotaries. So they chose air cooling, giving the cylinders finned surfaces so that, as they turned, the fins, taking up heat from the combustion heads, could dissipate it to the air.

A wealth of ingenuity went into the Gnome engines. Alimentation was a kind of reversed system compared with that in ordinary engines, much as the form of motion was reversed. The centre of the hollow crankshaft became the channel whereby combustible mixture could be fed into the cylinders through automatic valves in–of all places–the piston heads. Getting rid of the exhaust was a simpler process. Valves in the cylinder heads were opened by way of rockers and push rods riding on a cam ring and the exhaust gases simply burst out through them.

This was the basis of a line of successful rotary engines. They started with five-cylinder units, went on to seven

72 100 hp Monosoupape Gnome engine, 1914

73 50 hp Gnome engine, 1908

74 90 hp RAF engine, 1915

75 80 hp Renault engine, 1913

and nine and eventually to two-bank engines of higher numbers of cylinders. One fundamental development was in the induction. The inlet valves in the pistons sometimes caused trouble. They were accused of causing breakdowns and of introducing fire risks.

So the brothers Séguin, employing the inescapable but complicated logic which led them to their earliest engines, decided to do away with inlet valves altogether. And in the Monosoupape (one valve) series of rotary engines they actually did that. They fed the mixture to the cylinder combustion chambers through ports in the lower or inner parts of the cylinders. These ports were uncovered by every piston down stroke. The whole engine was whirling round at speed so that fuel mixture in the crankcase was thrown outwards and went through the ports into the cylinders the moment the ports opened.

It sounds crude. It was crude. But it was also a pinnacle of ingenuity. And the Monosoupape engines proved trustworthy and powerful for their weight. They were used in large numbers of French, British and other aircraft.

Air cooling which, to some extent, was imposed upon the designers of rotary engines was also used in early stationary engines, one example being the Renault. This was a V engine with finned cylinders. It was used in many of the aircraft employed for training and for military machines just prior to and during the first world war. It had, as a rival, the successful RAF engines, the letters in this instance not being related to the Air Force but to Farnborough, then called the Royal

Aircraft Factory. The RAF engines were of 8 and 12 cylinder varieties, in V form and air-cooled. They were said to be 'imitations' of the Renault and were not so highly regarded by the pilots of the period.

Another form of air-cooled engine which set the stage for massive later developments was the radial. There were liquid-cooled radials, the Salmson Canton Unné for instance, but most of the radials were air-cooled.

One of the objects of arranging the cylinders radially from a central crankcase was improved cooling. The fins of air-cooled cylinders arranged in a straight line or in a V received the cooling air stream unequally, the front cylinders tending to be better cooled than those at the rear. The radial arrangement gave even cooling all round. There was also the contention that the fuselage of most aircraft being of circular or near circular cross section, the radial arrangement of the cylinders fitted more conveniently and could be more neatly mounted. With speed increases, however, this argument tended to give way to the one which called for low frontal area. Stationary in-line and V engines were able to provide a lower frontal area for a given power than either rotaries or radials.

Among the early air-cooled power units were Anzani radials. Unknown to those who made and used them in the early days, these were to become the starting point for the war against the rotaries which finally led to the disappearance of the rotary form of aero-engine.

Rotary engines did more for the pioneers than radials. They had their particular appeal at this early stage in flying. And their advantage was based upon the same advantage as the Antoinette, their excellent power to weight ratio. This varied between the Gnomes, the Monosoupapes and the Le Rhônes, the Monosoupapes having a slightly lower specific weight than the others, but being heavier on fuel and oil.

But the stationary engine supporters were always ready to point to superior fuel consumption, lower demands for lubricating oils and greater (they claimed) reliability in order to justify their belief in air-cooled and liquid-cooled radial, in-line and V engines, that is to say in stationary engines. The streamlining element also came in but later.

And among the stationary engines were many of outstanding merit. There were, for instance, the in-line, 6 cylinder Mercedes and the Austro-Daimler 6 cylinder. The early models of the Mercedes were rated at 100 hp and those of the Austro-Daimler at 160 hp. The latter was taken up by Beardmore in England. The most successful British engine in this category was the Green of 1909, a water-cooled, vertical in-line engine with fine looking sheet copper water jackets. Another engine of British design which helped some of the pioneers was the ENV, but this was built in France. It gained its name from the fact that the cylinders were arranged 'en V'.

Let us seek to organize the primary engine information of the period when the *achievement* of free flight and then the *preliminary development* of free flight depended upon the power unit more than upon anything else. We find that the engines fall into two main categories: stationary and rotary. We then find that the cylinders could be arranged vertically in line, on their sides in line, in a

74

75

76

V radially or—as in the de Havilland—horizontally opposed or 'flat'. After that there is cooling. Stationary engines could be liquid-cooled—water, or water mixed with chemical ingredients—evaporative-cooled or air-cooled. Steam engines and electric motors had come upon the scene, made brief experiments in full scale flight and then disappeared. Henceforward the world of flight was the world of the internal combustion engine.

A prodigious struggle ensued between air-cooled radial engines and liquid-cooled, in-line engines. It intensified through the years, was stimulated by two world wars and was then resolved by the appearance of the gas turbine. Attention will be devoted to the gas turbine, the turboprop and the turbojet later on, when something must also be said about rocket propulsion; but, for the time being, the argument about prime movers for aircraft can rest upon the conventional petrol burning internal combustion engine. And this examination of the types of engine that were invented and built with the purpose of enabling the pioneers to drive their doubtful aircraft into the air will be invested with significance by

assembling in order the specific weights of the engines that have been discussed.

Power to weight ratio or specific weight is, always has been and is likely always to remain the critical factor in prime movers for aircraft. If an engine is too heavy, no amount of airframe design ingenuity will allow it to get into the air. There is, however, a fringe region in which a good airframe, in easy conditions, might get into the air with a power unit so heavy that it would not be able to give a less good airframe the ability to take off.

Let us now list the engines and give specific weights alongside them.

	Specific weight in lb/hp
Steam engines	
Giffard airship	120
Ader	2.5
(Maxim. No boilers	1.55)
(Henson. Design	20)
Electric motors	
Renard and Krebs airship	230

Internal combustion engines. Stationary	lb/hp
Antoinette. Evaporative cooled. V8	2.5
Wright. Liquid cooled. In-line	11.5
Wright. French built. In-line	7
Green. Liquid cooled. In-line	4
De Havilland. Liquid cooled. Flat 4	5.4
Renault. Air cooled. V8	6
Rotaries	
Gnome. Air cooled	2.8
Monosoupape. Air cooled	2.75
Radials	
Anzani. Air cooled	5.4
Salmson Canton Unné. Water cooled	5

We must once again lay stress upon the risks of making direct comparisons between these figures. There are almost no sufficiently detailed and comprehensive figures about the early engines to enable the interpretation of installed weight or even of power output to be precisely known. There are questions not only about cooling components, but also about fuel lines, electrical wiring and control runs. And the area of uncertainty is greater for engines outside the standard internal combustion pattern–steam engines for instance. There are some interesting pioneer engines missing from the above table such as those used by Félix du Temple de la Croix when he attempted to fly in 1874 and by Mozhaiski in 1884 but specific weights are not available nor the details from which approximate performance figures might be worked out. Much the same is true of the 'carbonic acid gas' engine used by the Romanian Trajan Vuia in his early and very promising experiments with monoplanes and motorized Lilienthal gliders in France. These carbonic acid gas engines were by Serpollet and it is the greatest pity that neither their specific weights nor facts about the manner of their use are available.

Despite these shortcomings, the list would appear to be fairly representative. Ader's steam engine has evoked the praise of many competent engineers for its exceptional lightness. And even if it is thought that the installed weight, in the sense we are using the term here, would have been greater than the figure of $2\frac{1}{2}$ lb/hp would indicate, it must still be conceded that the Ader engine was so light in specific weight that it would have been able to induce an airframe of even low aerodynamic efficiency to rise from level ground. The Maxim aircraft did rise from the ground, using a good deal more steam power than Ader's but under the control of a rail system. Steam engines, it is shown, can realize the low specific weights necessary for heavier-than-air flight.

Another point brought out by the list is that the Wrights' engine of the 1903 experiments was extremely heavy. It was more than double the weight of any other prime mover used in successful aeroplane flights. It was not until they came to France and had engines made by Bariquand et Marre and by Léon Bollée that the Wrights were able to fit their excellent biplane wing system with engines of sufficiently low specific weight to enable the potentialities of the airframe to be realized, particularly during such critical manoeuvres as take-off and climb. Before then the difficulties of

taking off unassisted and from strictly level ground were so great that the Wrights sometimes employed trolleys, rails and forms of catapult.

Two distinct lines of progress now converge to meet in the free flying, man-carrying, powered aerodyne: one is the aerodynamic line and the other is the power plant line. Kites and gliders had opened the way of satisfactory wing systems. Small scale models, stationary and locomotive steam engines and hot air and gas engines had opened the way to prime movers suitable for installing in the wing systems.

The remaining link or fastener between power plant and wing system was the airscrew. This had been studied and made in different forms long before man had first succeeded in raising himself from the earth by hot air balloon. And once again Leonardo da Vinci appears as one of the earliest people to see that the screw could be applied to the propulsion of aircraft. But the origins of the screw go back to far beyond the era of recorded history. The probability seems to be that screws were in use in China long before da Vinci, and that helical 'lifts' were in use in Egypt from the times of the Pharaohs.

The use of screws for propelling vehicles was established early in the eighteenth century by Jean Pierre Paucton. James Watt had visualized a kind of rotating 'oar' which was none other than a screw propeller. In the United States screws for propelling boats were in use at the start of the nineteenth century.

By the time the prime mover was ready to take its place in aircraft, then, the means of converting rotary motion into linear thrust was well understood. No new dis-

78 80 hp Le Rhône engine.
1913

79 60 hp ENV engine, 1910

78

79

coveries were needed when the earliest designs were prepared for power driven aircraft. The engine could be represented as driving–either directly through its crankshaft, or indirectly through belts or chains–one or more airscrews or propellers. And that was how the first successful aeroplanes converted the power from their prime movers into aerodynamic thrust.

The blades of an airscrew are no more and no less than aerofoils with almost identical characteristics to the main aerofoils which form the main planes in an aeroplane. But in order to obtain the best results from airscrews, a vast amount of research and development was undertaken. It proceeded as the development of the airframe and the engines proceeded. Suffice it to say that at the time we are now concerned with, the airscrew was a familiar device.

We arrive now with our three major components all ready; the wing cell, the prime mover and the propeller. Next comes the critical act of bringing them together in a practical aircraft. This was the supreme act of creation in the story of flying. It was the act that set off the whole heroic effort of the pioneers. To this effort we now turn our attention.

5 First flights

The theory of winged flight had been studied. Everything was ready for the moment of truth. Everything was ready for the magic touch of the man of action.

Given that a machine was believed to be capable of flight, the 'intrepid aviator', for that was how he was usually known, would be called upon to justify the belief. He had to install himself in the rudimentary cockpit, to manipulate the levers, wheels and switches and to cause the whole contraption to accelerate over the ground until it reached take-off speed. At that moment he found himself in a new element, without knowledge or experience of its effects upon the lifting surfaces or of the manner in which his machine would respond to its pressures on the controls.

Man had to fly without ever learning how to fly. Man had to do again what the original experimenters had done, and to throw himself simultaneously both into the air and into the lap of providence.

In many instances the intrepid aviator was also the ingenious designer and the painstaking constructor. He stood to gain or lose by success or failure. And perhaps the designing and the building helped to give him confidence and to make that hazardous take-off into an undiscovered country less extraordinary and less alarming.

It has been the prerogative of inventors through the ages to make large claims for their inventions. The numbers of men who have invented perpetual motion machines is almost infinite. None of them has been too modest in his claims. Aviation inventors were no more pessimistic about their achievements than other inventors.

At the early aero shows remarkable drawings and models were shown together with even more remarkable claims by their originators as to what the machines they represented could do. It was not until 1905 that the Fédération Aéronautique Internationale was formed in Paris, with agent organizations in other countries such as the Royal Aero Club in Britain and the Aero Club of America, and that any claim for an air performance had to be endorsed if it was to gain credence.

These then are the two aspects of the earliest flights by man-carrying powered machines that are always in evidence and that have led to differences of opinion: first the definition of *a flight* and, next, the testimony of *a performance*.

No one has any divine right to lay down what constitutes a 'flight' by a man-carrying, powered, winged aircraft. But some argued, with what appears to be a good deal of justification, that true powered flight involved an unaided take-off from level ground, a climb, a descent and a landing. They insisted that in order to qualify as having 'flown', the aircraft should take off and climb without the employment of any auxiliary devices not carried in it. Some suggested that a distance of at least one hundred metres should be covered in level or climbing flight. But they had no authority for this figure. Why not a hundred feet? or a hundred kilometres? or a hundred yards? or two hundred yards? or five hundred miles? Why not a circular flight? No reason could be adduced for saying that an aircraft that covered a certain distance in a straight line had flown whereas one which had covered a slightly shorter distance had not flown.

Let us take the practical view that a powered man-carrying flight requires that the aircraft should take off unassisted from level ground, should climb and then land again on level ground at the same altitude as the take-off. The point of this definition is that it excludes the glide and, more especially, the powered glide where an engine may be fitted, but where, although it may flatten the glide path, it is of insufficient power to maintain level flight. Armed with that definition we may look at some of the early experiments with a steady eye.

We have to consider Clément Ader, Jatho, Maxim, Wilhelm Kress, the Voisin brothers, the Wrights, Vuia, Ellehammer and Santos-Dumont. The Russian pioneer Mozhaiski, as has been said, is no longer held by the Soviet Union to have made what would meet our definition of a powered flight although his aircraft, which was steam powered, is held by some engineers who have studied the design to have incorporated qualities which might have allowed it to fly.

Clément Ader's *Eole*, however, *did* take off from level ground, climb and descend. It *was* unassisted in the take-off either by rails, catapults, trolleys or any other extraneous aids not carried in the machine. Moreover the October 1890 flight, usually given as 50 metres, was witnessed by ten people. Written testimony was given. Witnesses also testified before legal persons, *huissiers*.

The *Eole* was a monoplane with great bat-like wings of 49 ft span; the steam engine already described drove a single tractor propeller. But the first man-carrying aeroplane in history to raise itself unassisted from the ground could do no more than just that. It did not achieve anything like controlled or sustained flight, and rose only just above ground level. There was no elevator. The pilot's seat was at the rear behind the boiler, which gravely obstructed his field of view. Ader did not succeed in satisfactorily developing the *Eole* or its successor the *Avion II* and *Avion III*. The latter, a twin-engined, steam powered, twin-screw machine, crashed in the second of its official tests before military observers in October 1897.

Sir Hiram Maxim next approached the solution of the flight problem in the capacity of an engineer. He designed and built some lightweight steam engines, probably not so light in installed weight as Ader's, but still light enough to come within the bracket of power to weight ratios which were eventually shown to confer upon the right kind of airframe the power to fly. He also proceeded in a manner more typical of the professional engineer than most other inventors. He conducted a series of experiments, each one adding to the assembled

80

knowledge and leading towards his objective.

Perhaps Maxim's limited success was the outcome of this step by step procedure. For instead of launching himself off in his machine when he arrived at the stage when all seemed ready, he took the intermediate step of attempting a form of tethered flight. The aircraft was set on rails. Arranged above them on a series of cantilever supporting arms was another track, the idea being that the aircraft would run along the lower rails, lift and engage with the upper track so that the amount of the lift could be measured and knowledge of the performance of the lifting surfaces worked out.

A degree of experimental success attended this work. Sir Hiram himself wrote a book in which he detailed the advances he had made from the time he became involved in a study of helicopter flight in 1856 and, in 1889, in a study of fixed wing powered flight. The construction of his full scale machine was begun shortly after Ader's first flight of 1890. For inherent stability Maxim used a dihedral angle by extending the main plane on either side with auxiliary planes, sloping upwards. He fitted two steam engines driving two airscrews. In 1894 the aircraft was given test runs and on one of these it lifted from the lower rails and engaged with the upper, restraining track. A structural failure occurred, however, and the machine was smashed to pieces.

Maxim succeeded in measuring the lift of his aircraft and there was evidence that it took off within the limitations imposed by the upper and lower tracks. But this degree of success was inadequate to enable the Maxim

80 Clément Ader's tentative flight in *Eole* in the grounds of the Château d'Armainvilliers, 9 October 1890; watercolour by Brenet

experiments to be grouped with the generally accepted first flight attempts.

Kress's aircraft has been described as the world's first powered marine aircraft. It had two aluminium floats and was powered by a Daimler internal combustion engine. Kress, a Viennese, started work on aeronautics in 1877 and nearly got his machine into the air in 1901 but his attempt ended in an accident. The importance of the Wilhelm Kress seaplane is that it prompted Octave Chanute, in one of his many letters to the Wright brothers (this one to Wilbur), to report upon it, to tell them of its capsize, but to express nonetheless favourable opinions about its capabilities.

The Voisin brothers went through the classic sequence. They started with kites, came under the influence of Hargrave's work, improved their kites, turned them into gliders, made gliding experiments from hill tops and sand dunes, made further gliding experiments towed by racing motorboats, and finally designed and built man-carrying powered machines. Their aircraft had a close affinity to the Hargrave box-kites. More important in the context of aviation history, they were the machines used for the earliest officially observed performance records— that is to say for flights over required distances or including specified manoeuvres.

Karl Jatho, a Hanover civil servant, has a place in aviation history for his powered winged experiments of 1903. With his first leap into the air on 18 August, in a kite-like structure fitted with a 9 hp engine, he claimed to have covered 59 ft, and two months later, in a rudimentary biplane, 200 ft. Because of the probability of downhill take-off, however, and an obvious lack of control, these attempts, while being creditable feats, are not to be accounted true flights, nor is any such claim made for them in Germany.

Jacob Christian H. Ellehammer was a Dane who made an aircraft in 1904 and fitted it with an engine of 15-20 horsepower. The claim is that his first flight was made on 12 September 1906 on the island of Lindholm and that a distance of 42 metres or 138 feet was covered just clear of the ground. Ellehammer made other machines, a biplane and a triplane. His Lindholm flight was not officially observed; but there was a useful witness of it, a naval officer called Uelditz. Ellehammer's machine had features which later became general. It was a tractor machine with wheel undercarriage. But it is said to have lacked any form of practical control in yaw; that is it had no rudder in the ordinary sense as used in aircraft. There is also some question about the form of control about the transverse axis and here the hanging weight— the pilot himself—was brought in as a variant on the Lilienthal glider control system.

Horatio F. Phillips whose valuable investigations into wing shapes, particularly their camber, have been mentioned, was said to have made a flight in 1907 with his famous 'venetian blind' machine but once more independent evidence is lacking. Trajan Vuia, a Romanian living in France, used the Serpollet carbonic, acid-gas engine referred to in the last chapter. He designed and made attractive-looking aircraft and in the early spring of 1906 he is supposed to have flown near Montesson. But again there was no official observation, no recorded evidence, no consistency, even, in the claims that were made for what Vuia had done. We now turn to the work of the Wrights.

Through their gliding seasons of 1900, 1901 and 1902, the Wright brothers had become both experienced pilots and experts in theory. Chanute had encouraged them, at a moment when they were in despair over shortage of funds, with his opinion that they now knew more than anyone in the world what had to be done to achieve powered flight. They had absorbed all that could be learnt from Chanute and the work of Lilienthal. They had grown to mistrust the theory of others and built a wind tunnel in their workshop in which experiments enabled them to compile their own tables of air pressure on wing surfaces, and their calculations were proved in practice by the successful glider of 1902 in which nearly a thousand controlled glides were made.

They had perfected their technique of wing warping. Wing warping, a method of obtaining lateral control also used by other pioneer flyers, consisted in providing the pilot with the means of twisting the wings so as to increase or diminish the angle of incidence towards the wing tips. In this way the wing on one side could be twisted, or warped, so as to give a greater incidence and therefore more lift, while the wing on the other side could be warped so as to give a reduced incidence and therefore less lift. The aircraft would then roll about the fore and aft axis in accord with the lift differential. In the Wrights' improved mechanism of 1902 the warp-cradle was linked by cables to a single rear movable rudder; rudder and wing warp worked together to enable the glider to perform a smooth banked turn.

The engine and the propellers that the brothers proposed to put into their 1903 machine proved more difficult matters than they had first imagined. No automobile engine that they saw was light enough, so, helped by their skilled mechanic Charles Taylor, they designed and built their own: as already noted, it was about 12 hp, and it was still extremely heavy for its purpose, weighing 200 lb. They also built propellers on the basis of their own research.

The biplane thus equipped was similar to the 1902 glider except that the vertical rear rudder and front elevator were double instead of single structures. Wing span and wing area were increased to 40 ft 4 in and 510 sq. ft respectively; the two pusher propellers were driven by bicycle chains. The machine was supported on a pair of skids.

81

82

81 Ellehammer's tethered flight of 12 September 1906

82 Sir Hiram Maxim's biplane in position on the runway at Baldwyn's Park, Kent, 1894

Although constructed in the summer of 1903, it was not until December that the *Flyer* was ready for trial on the sand dunes of Kitty Hawk, by which time high winds and freezing temperatures made for difficult flying conditions. On 14 December, before witnesses summoned from the nearby life saving station, the machine was launched from a downward sloping rail. Wilbur, who had won the toss of a coin to decide who should fly first, made the error of climbing too steeply, and the *Flyer* stalled and crashed into the sand. Damage, however,

alongside holding the wings to maintain level balance. At a speed of 7–8 mph in the teeth of the wind, after a 40 ft run, the machine took the air to make an undulating flight lasting 12 seconds, ending with a sudden dart towards the ground after a distance of 120 ft had been covered. The miracle had occurred: man had achieved true flight, in Orville's words 'the first in the history of the world in which a machine carrying a man had raised itself by its own power into the air in full flight, had sailed forward without reduction of speed, and had finally

83

83 First flight by Orville Wright in *Flyer I*, 17 December 1903, at Kitty Hawk, North Carolina

was slight, and the machine was soon ready for another attempt.

But high winds made this impossible for the next three days. Orville has recorded the breathtaking details of what happened on the 17th. A wind of about 25 mph blew from the north, showing no sign of abating. Puddles from recent rains were now covered with ice. But at 10 a.m. the brothers decided to get their machine out. They summoned five witnesses and positioned a photographer to cover the end of the take-off rail, which this time was laid level. It was Orville's turn to take the pilot's prone position. The engine took the machine along the rail at an accelerating pace, with Wilbur running

landed at a point as high as that from which it started.'

Three more flights were made that morning; the second covered 175 ft, the third 200 ft, and the fourth, which lasted 59 seconds, 852 ft. When the elevator was damaged in landing after the last flight, the brothers decided to return home to Dayton, winter by now having well set in. They sent a telegram to their father telling him of their four flights and asking him to inform the press. But now was to be seen America's—and the world's—scepticism towards the Wrights, which was to last for five years. The *Dayton Journal* refused to print the story.

There were understandable reasons for this reaction.

Only ten days beforehand, Langley had disgusted the assembled press when his *Aerodrome* had totally failed to fly and had plunged into the Potomac for the second time. Many took this second fiasco involving a hitherto respected scientist as convincing proof that a heavier-than-air machine could never achieve powered flight.

The second reason for a sceptical reaction lay in the Wrights' own secrecy. They had a patent pending (they had applied for one in 1902), and until this was granted they were anxious that the details of what they were doing should not be revealed. At the time of their first powered flights they published nothing, they called upon no official observers; everything was done without public involvement. Wilbur, in fact, referred to the 'dangerous publicity' that threatened. Over the next two years the Wrights were to develop their *Flyer*, make amazingly advanced flights and evolve a completely practical machine. They then tried to interest the US and the British governments in turn in contracts, but achieved no success for several years as official quarters would not believe what they had not seen, and the Wrights would not reveal too much before commitment from the other side. So the world at large was to remain in ignorance of their achievement until the autumn of 1908, when Wilbur astounded the French with his first ever public flight at Le Mans, and Orville aroused equal excitement in America with his first demonstration flights before US Army personnel at Fort Myer, Virginia.

It is now time to turn our attention back to Europe. In France aviation was in the minds of many men. There were scores of aeronautical inventors there to lone inventors in other countries. In France, too, lightweight internal combustion engine development had proceeded at a greater pace than anywhere else even including Germany. The achievement of Levavasseur has been called the real key to powered winged flight in Europe. Lighter-than-air flight, as we saw in an earlier chapter, had made swift progress in France. Hot air balloons, gas balloons and dirigible airships had been produced and tried. 'Air-mindedness' was more widespread in France than elsewhere. There was the *expectation* of flight in France, particularly in Paris.

So the sudden statement that man-carrying powered winged flight had been achieved in the United States, where there was general scepticism about its possibility, seemed extraordinary. And when more news about the achievement was not forthcoming there ensued a period of uncertainty and then of disbelief. Octave Chanute and Wilbur Wright had corresponded since May 1900 and the letters were an avenue for information to pass between the two countries on what the Wrights were doing. But even that correspondence was inhibited by the Wrights' 'veil of secrecy'.

As early as 1898 the French Aéro Club had been formed. When Santos-Dumont turned from aerostats to aerodynes, prizes for officially observed flights were being offered particularly by Ernest Archdeacon, an enthusiastic amateur balloonist. Santos-Dumont's collaboration with Gabriel Voisin was fruitful. The two worked late into the night in the Santos design office at Neuilly and in the workshop of the brothers Voisin.

Gabriel Voisin, in his autobiography, relates the

manner in which they collaborated and tells of the strain involved. Santos-Dumont had a wealth of experience with balloons and with dirigible airships and had earned for himself an unrivalled position as a daring and highly skilled aeronaut. In addition he displayed remarkable originality in thought and in deed. It was a form of genius for aerial enterprises of all kinds. He was a great public figure, known to and admired by all.

Voisin was at this time engaged professionally on the making of aircraft and his relationship with Santos-

84

Dumont was in part that of a contractor engaged to construct a machine according to plans given him by his employer Voisin's accumulated knowledge and experience of heavier-than-air flight obtained with his kites and his gliders gave the collaboration especial promise. Both men were influenced by Hargrave's work on box-kites and the Santos-Dumont machine took the form of a box-kite, though in tail-first configuration.

Voisin arranged preliminary tests with the new machine suspended on a wire by means of a pulley. But there was no means of accelerating the machine sufficiently to enable the purpose of the trials to be fulfilled. To find out if the controls were effective, Santos-Dumont then thought of carrying his aircraft aloft below one of his airships–pre-dating by many years experiments of exactly this kind done in England by members of the Royal Air Force. But again the arrangement failed to work. He had fitted an Antoinette engine and all that could be done was to test the working of this engine, though without allowing the aircraft to be lifted off the ground by the airship.

A notorious editorial comment in the London *Times* at about this time discloses something of the state of public knowledge in Britain about the Ader and Wright experiments. In the *Times* engineering supplement of 24 January 1906 a letter from Alliott Verdon-Roe, to whose pioneering work we shall come later, stated his faith in the prospects of winged flight and in the work of the Wright brothers. In his appended comment, however, the Editor resoundingly declared his opinion that 'all attempts at artificial aviation on the basis he [Roe] describes, are not only dangerous to life, but foredoomed to failure from an engineering standpoint.' Lord Kelvin, too, at about the same time expressed lack of faith in aerial navigation other than by lighter-than-air vessels. Many famous people held the same opinion.

The aircraft which now comes on to the stage is the curiously named *14 bis*. Peter Wykeham in his biography

84 Santos-Dumont's *14-bis* (suspended from an overhead wire) being towed by a donkey at Neuilly in preparation for flight, 1906

of Santos-Dumont says that the *bis* was a reference to the first ascent, with airship aid, of Number 14. The *bis* also had the higher powered Antoinette engine. It was, as we have seen, a 'tail-first' aircraft which is to say that the main wing cell had a fuselage running forward with a secondary box cell, movable for control purposes, right out at the fore end. This was the type of aircraft later to be known as the 'canard' type. There was nothing fundamentally against this arrangement. But nor was there anything much in its favour relative to the seemingly more direct and simple configuration with fuselage or tail booms *behind* the main wing cell and the tail at the after end.

Early in the morning of 13 September 1906 at Bagatelle, in the Bois de Boulogne, Santos-Dumont made his first effort. There were many spectators. The excitement was intense. And the aircraft did rise from the ground, only to fall back again, perhaps following a stall as Wykeham suggests, perhaps simply because flying speed was not there in adequate quantity to cope with the higher wing incidence as Santos-Dumont wound up what would now be called his elevator control. The second attempt led to damage. The Voisin workshop facilities were called in to repair it.

Then, at 0800 hours on 23 October 1906, with official observers present, the preparations were made for another attempt. There were hesitant preliminary runs over the grass surface. Minor troubles occurred and were rectified. By 1600 hours all was ready. The Antoinette engine was called upon to prove in public that it could give more power for its weight than any other prime mover. Santos-Dumont–himself also a lightweight of only 108 lb, standing upright at the controls, opened the throttle. Sixty metres (197 ft) was the distance said to have been covered at a height of two to three metres. Santos-Dumont profited by what he had learnt in those few moments of flight and introduced ailerons in his machine in order to give lateral control. On 12 November

he made his definitive flight, as it might be called, of 220 metres (722 ft), again officially observed, again in full view of countless spectators.

Santos-Dumont had succeeded in demonstrating to the world at large the power to fly from level ground in a winged flying machine. His flights were the first officially accepted, fully and comprehensively witnessed, powered aeroplane flights. He had used an admittedly gawkish-looking aircraft in the design of which he had collaborated with Voisin. But in modifying this machine to his own requirements Santos-Dumont had, perhaps, departed from original and better concepts. The glider in which Gabriel Voisin made towed flights over the Seine, behind a racing motorboat, in the year before the Santos-Dumont flights, was closer to the kind of box-kite aircraft that proved to be successful in later years. It was a Hargrave-type machine, but not a canard. It had the conventional tail arrangement and in appearance resembled the box-kites that became so widely used for pilot training before the first world war.

The earliest flights were measured in a straight line. Santos-Dumont made his flights at Bagatelle on approximately a single heading and the distances were measured in a straight line. Some asked whether that was enough. A powered man-carrying aircraft, if it could be said to be capable of *flying*, should, they argued, show proof of controllability. The pilot should be able to direct it; to alter the heading at will. He should have control in azimuth as well as altitude. The pilot should not only be able to tilt the aircraft into a climbing attitude and to tilt it again into an attitude of descent, he should also be able to ensure that it did not topple over sideways. So there would have to be automatic stability about the fore and aft axis or else control about that axis, that is, lateral control.

There were conflicting ideas in Europe on how this lateral control could best be achieved. The dihedral angle was favoured by some, including Sir Hiram Maxim.

85 Santos-Dumont's definitive flight, 12 November 1906 in *14-bis*

85

Vertical surfaces, in the manner of the box-kite, were favoured by others. Santos-Dumont added small movable wings near the main wing tips, or 'ailerons'. Always confident in his own powers as a manipulator of difficult machinery, he wanted not only a measure of inherent stability, but also the power to over-ride that stability and to impose his will upon the machine.

It will be noted that nothing much was said or done about control in yaw, that is about the vertical axis. A ship is controllable in yaw by its rudder and its navigator can determine his heading in azimuth by using the rudder. But an aircraft does not turn one way and the other as a ship turns. The process of turning an aircraft is more complex for it incorporates both yaw and bank, a mixture of aileron or lateral control with control by rudder or in yaw. Rudder and ailerons need to be employed together in nicely judged proportions in order to make an aircraft do an accurate turn.

The whole gamut of requirements is incorporated in a flight made on a course which brings the aircraft back to the place from which it started and ends with a landing on that same taking off site. No minimum distances, heights or durations need to be set. If the aircraft takes off, climbs, turns, descends and lands on the site where it took off, the flight must have been a flight within the meaning of the term as it may reasonably be interpreted.

Thoughts running on these lines were in the minds of the officials of the Aéro Club de France when the conditions were established for the performance of a circular kilometre. They had already established the conditions

for the homologation (to use the slightly grotesque but official terminology) of a kilometre record in a straight line. They then introduced the circular kilometre as a step-up in difficulty.

It would seem that the Wrights had far more control over their first *Flyer* than Santos-Dumont had over his *14 bis*, and that only the Wrights' machine might have been sufficiently controllable to accomplish a circular flight. The Wrights did in fact achieve a circular flight on 20 September 1904 in their second *Flyer* at Huffman Prairie, near Dayton, and thereafter completely mastered the technique. But their flights of 1904 and 1905 will be discussed in the next chapter; for present purposes the Wrights are ahead of their time.

Santos-Dumont, after his achievement of November 1906, seemed to get bogged down and although he produced new designs, they proved unsuccessful. The Wrights, as has been noted, were involved in their period of self-imposed secrecy. Meanwhile the Voisins had been making publicly acknowledged progress. Here the testimony of the specialist aeronautical press begins to have importance. *L'Aérophile* had reported and illustrated the gliding flights at Berck-sur-Mer by Gabriel Voisin in 1904, and it described—what interests us now—the first *official* closed-circuit flight, the 'circular kilometre'.

It was done on 13 January 1908 by Henry Farman (he preferred the English spelling of his first name) in a Voisin biplane with a Levavasseur Antoinette engine. The place was Issy-les-Moulineaux, an aerodrome to

86 Henry Farman flying the first official circular kilometre in his modified Voisin at Issy-les-Moulineaux, 13 January 1908

87

which the French public later flocked in large numbers particularly at week-ends, to watch displays of flying. Ernest Archdeacon had offered a substantial prize.

Certain observations may be made about this record flight. It met a specified performance requirement and the rules proclaimed that the aircraft should be 'autonomous', meaning that it should be integral with all equipment, components, power plant and fittings. Once again the light weight of the Levavasseur engine was in evidence. Henry Farman was a friend and pupil of Gabriel Voisin and these two were responsible, with Levavasseur, for the achievement.

It is also to be noted that the Voisin aircraft used in this flight had a form of control that was to become common in the following years and to be used in all but a small number of aircraft. It consisted in a wheel mounted on a column, the column being hinged at the foot. Cables led from the foot of the column to the control surface king posts. Control was exercised by moving the whole wheel forward or backward, thus tilting the column forward or back, in order to obtain control in pitch, and by turning the wheel to left or to right to obtain control in roll.

The triumphs of the Wrights, Santos-Dumont and Farman had by 1908 proved that flying in a winged, powered, controllable machine was practical. We may now turn to aviation's most joyous, most dramatic and most entertaining period, the time of the practical pioneers.

87 Farman's Voisin
No 1-bis in 1908, with
Henry Farman inspecting
the forward control surfaces

6 Pageant of the pioneers

Aviation, still untainted by war, entered its most joyous and uninhibited period – perhaps its finest period. It became an inexhaustible source of interest and entertainment. It seized the attention of scientists and engineers, of sportsmen and rich dilettantes, of artists, aristocrats and inventors and, above all, of ambitious and daring adventurers and men of action.

There had never before been anything like it. A new world seemed to be opening, a world of wider horizons. And still France was the place where the dream of flying received its fullest realization. Paris, the world's artistic and intellectual centre, the city of light and luxury, welcomed flight and flyers. The heady thought of aeronautical freedom spread through the sizzling Parisian atmosphere. A spirit of exultation bubbled up. Where other big cities were moodily sceptical, as was New York, or gloomily uninterested, as was London, or indifferent. as was Berlin, Paris was welcoming and encouraging.

Prodigious schemes poured forth; there were plans for aeronautical advances of the most imaginative not to say fantastic kind. Here was probably the supreme celebration of a triumph of applied engineering. Not even space travel has matched it.

The name of Alberto Santos-Dumont was at this time more influential than the names of the other great pioneers. He represented a new kind of hero, a man who had a gift for exploring novel inventions, a man ceaselessly extending his scope as a master of machinery. Small, dapper, mercurial, he was all that the young man of the early 1900s longed to be. He was rich, he was brave, he was sought after.

His grandfather was a Parisian who had married a Bordeaux goldsmith's daughter and gone to Brazil as a merchant in precious stones. His grandson Alberto was born in the province of Minas Gerais at a small farm on 20 July 1873. His Brazilian-born father was an engineer who was educated in Paris. Alberto was his seventh son. He started his education in São Paulo and completed it in Paris. There he was fired by the prevalent enthusiasm for mechanical progress. It was everywhere, among the rich and the poor, in the theatres and music halls, at grand social functions and in the humblest cafés. It seemed to be part of the gaiety and the mechano-artistic character of Paris. Machines were being developed as curiosities or as playthings and aids to civilized living, not – at this time – as instruments of war. The sporting side was predominant and Santos-Dumont was deeply involved in it.

He took up motor car racing. He bought a Peugeot car and also a motor tricycle and a motorcycle. He took part in competitions. He saw the lightweight prime

88

mover as the powerhouse of future progress. But then his father's death suddenly checked his career and temporarily destroyed his hopes. It took him back to Brazil and it was not until 1897 that he returned to Paris. He decided to make it his home and to resume his studies in mechanical transport.

It has been said that Jules Verne influenced him, and that accounts of the unsuccessful Polar balloon voyage of Andrée in 1897 from Spitsbergen also impressed him. Directly he returned to Paris he ordered a balloon from the builders Lachambre and Machuron and obtained delivery of it for the modest sum of 250 francs. So began one of the most remarkable stories of pilot ability and adventurousness that aviation has produced.

Always well dressed, in a slightly foppish manner, often wearing a straw hat of the 'boater' pattern and extravagantly striped shirts, Alberto brought to danger a smiling effrontery which captivated Parisians. He was already a hero when he made his great contribution to winged flight at Bagatelle in October 1906. The touch of the elegant, fearless little man was magical and magistral. His name was on everyone's lips. Songs were composed about him. At Maxim's where he often took luncheon, he was a centre of attraction. At the Opera his presence had the flavour of royalty but with something added in the form of fearlessness and manipulative genius.

If Paris was aviation's capital city at this time while other world capitals were aeronautically uninterested, it was largely due to the sparkling personality of Santos-

88 Santos-Dumont's 19-bis *Demoiselle* with the 24 hp Antoinette engine mounted between the wheels and driving the propeller by a belt, November 1908

Dumont. He bridged the gap between the specialists—those like Levavasseur and the Voisin brothers who were directly involved in invention and development—and the larger non-specialist public. He *translated* the engineering and aerodynamic achievements into the common language of ordinary people. But although pre-eminent, Santos-Dumont was not alone. In France there were others who tried to do as he was doing, not on the same scale, but in something approaching the same way.

As adulation for Santos-Dumont mounted, recognition of the work of other great pioneers faded. Clément Ader had been partly forgotten. His work as an electrical engineer and inventor of the microphone and therefore, to some extent, of the Bell telephone, was still recognized but not his work as an aviation pioneer.

A new generation of practising airmen appeared contemporary with Santos-Dumont. The Voisins were collaborators with Alberto, for Gabriel helped him with his first aircraft. Moreover Santos-Dumont had watched Voisin's Seine experiments.

His 1907 box-kite, intended to carry the *14 bis* concept forward to a more practical stage, was totally unsuccessful. His *Demoiselle* closely approached the concept of a small aircraft which might be used for touring by private pilots. It failed in many respects, but it proclaimed the kind of ideals Santos-Dumont had in mind for the aircraft of the future.

He thought of aircraft as elegant carriages in which men and women would be able to pay visits, to tour the country, to go to the restaurant and the theatre, to engage in sport and entertainment of all kinds. He saw

Government representatives, however, were inclined to call for practical demonstrations before they would consider purchasing patents. The United States Board of Ordnance and Fortification insisted that the stage of practical operation must be demonstrated to their representatives before they would move. They said this at the beginning of 1905 and they repeated it in more detail in October of the same year when they indicated that they had no further interest in the invention 'until a machine is produced which by actual operation is shown to be able to produce horizontal flight.' The British government was also asking for demonstrations.

It was a sign of the success with which the Wrights had maintained their policy of secrecy for they reported, as became known later, that they had made 105 flights during 1904. Moreover towards the end of that year they spoke of flights of five minutes' duration and some in which they encircled the Huffman field on the property of Mr Torrence Huffman, a local banker, they were then using as their base. They had flown distances of three miles and at speeds of 35 miles per hour. They had flown in a straight line, in circles and over S-shaped courses. To cap it all they flew slightly over 24 miles on 5 October 1905.

The Wrights kept detailed information about these flights. They were made at heights of between 10 and 20 ft and in a single week in 1905 seven experiments were made, covering an estimated distance of 15 miles. The 1904 work had been done with a new machine having a total weight of 915 lb. This weight, however, included 70 lb of steel bars which were used as ballast.

89

aircraft, in fact, as instruments of peaceful amusement. Unlike the Wrights and other great constructors he did not, it seems, think of them as instruments of war.

During the years 1904 and 1905 the Wrights had made a number of attempts to sell their invention to the war departments of different countries, among them the United States, Great Britain and France. They were of the opinion that flying would be used in time of war particularly for reconnaissance and for communications and in the approach the brothers made to Congress early in 1905 they referred specifically to 'scouting and carrying messages in time of war.'

89 The original Santos-Dumont *Demoiselle*, with engine mounted above the wing, 19 November 1907

90 The Wrights' *Flyer III*, September 1905

90

Wilbur Wright estimated that the aircraft, with water and fuel for one hour's flight and with one man on board, would weigh 850 lb. Rail launching was used and the landing was done on skids.

It was in April of 1905 that Wilbur Wright began discussing the possibility of building a two-seater and of modifying some of the control details. All the signs were that the Wrights were confident that they had solved the major problems of flight. It is therefore the more remarkable, when the events are seen in the perspective of the years, that Wilbur himself, when he made contact with the French ambassador with the object of interesting the French war office as a possible purchaser of their patents, should refer frankly to the widespread in-incredulity about their achievements. 'It will seem incredible,' he wrote to the French ambassador in November 1905, 'not only that long flights have really been made with motor airplanes, but also that they have been made so quietly as to escape the attention of the newspapers.'

Nevertheless the Wrights had invited a number of witnesses to see their performances and in their copious correspondence with Chanute they had poured out the fullest information about what they were doing and how they were doing it.

It has been said that the early Wright aircraft took off from rails and landed on skids. Their controls showed steady development as they acquired the art of piloting. Thus the project of adding a front rudder for assisting control in yaw was brought forward when the 1905 machine was being designed. And there was the important decision, later, to divorce the lateral control from the directional. At first the Wrights introduced wing warping connected with the tail controls. It was in part this form of interconnected control that led later on to a number of unfortunate disputes, some leading to the courts of law, about priorities in the employment of warping wings.

Warping wings, as we have seen, are a crude means of applying control about the fore and aft axis or lateral control. But warping wings are essentially the *natural* form of control and in theory might well be shown to be the most efficient. For in wing warping the entire wing is deformed to produce an increase in lift on one side and a decrease on the other whereas when conventional ailerons are used only a small rectangular cutout is moved to produce the lift differential.

Wing warping was certainly the first idea for lateral control. It was used by Clément Ader in 1890. Professor R. Marchal, a scientist in the atomic division of the French SNECMA engine company, made a study of Ader's inventions in the 1960s and quoted Ader's claims in his application to the Bureau de la Propriété Industrielle in August 1890. These claims include a clear indication of wing warping 'à gaucher le bout de l'aile' and one can only assume that it was translator trouble that prevented this from being more widely known.

After Ader there was S. F. Cody who used wing warping for the control of his man-lifting kites. This is stated by his biographer G. A. Broomfield but the point has been disputed. In his book *Early Aviation at Farn-borough* (1971), however, Dr Percy B. Walker, a leading

Farnborough scientist, states categorically that Cody used wing warping in 1903 for control in pitch and that he may have used it also for control in roll, that is about the fore and aft axis. Walker mentions that although the Wright brothers contested infringements of their lateral control patents in France and America, they attempted no legal action when Cody used wing warping in his powered machines.

The Wrights' policy of working in secret which had done so much to encourage scepticism about their claims

91

92

in many parts of the world was abandoned in 1908. They had sent an aircraft to France and in the summer of that year they obtained the co-operation of the automobile pioneer Léon Bollée and were given permission to give demonstrations at a race course close to Le Mans, at Hunaudières. The promise that all the mystery which had surrounded the work of the Wrights was suddenly to be swept away had the well known stimulating effect upon the news media and great excitement prevailed among the French public. Would the claims be justified? How did the Wrights' way of flying differ from the ways that had been developed in France?

91 Wilbur Wright on *Flyer III* at Issy, 1908

92 The 1908 Wright *Flyer III* flown by Wilbur on 21 September 1908 at Auvours near Le Mans

69

Wilbur Wright gave them full satisfaction. His flights were short but he showed a degree of mastery over the behaviour of his aircraft in the air that astonished the French and revolutionized ideas. British observers at the scene were also greatly impressed and were almost unanimous in concluding that a major aeronautical breakthrough had occurred. And the fact that all the preliminary work had been done in an atmosphere of secrecy lent spice to the situation. Léon Delagrange spoke for many French flyers when he exclaimed: 'We are

With their new and larger aircraft the Wrights were able to lift greater loads so that they were able not only to step up the duration of their flights, but also to carry passengers. And this undoubtedly helped them greatly to win support. Big commercial organizations such as Michelin, the tyre makers, offered prizes for various feats of performance and several of these, in cash, were won by the Wrights. Most flights were of about five minutes' duration, but Wilbur increased the periods to over one hour and then to over two hours.

93

95

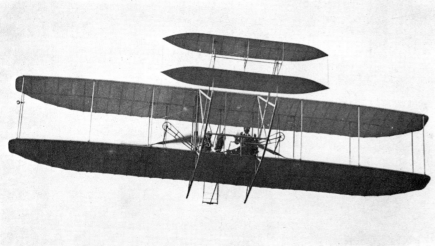

94

93 The Wrights at Fort Myer, Virginia, in 1909. Wilbur at the wing tip and Orville between the skids of their biplane during flight tests for the US Army

94 Orville Wright's 62½-minute flight at the 1908 military trials at Fort Myer on 9 September. A week later this aircraft crashed, Orville being severely injured and his passenger killed

95 Wilbur Wright flying near Pau, France, 1908

beaten! We do not exist'; and Blériot: 'A new era in mechanical flight has commenced . . . it is wonderful.'

One of the objects of the Le Mans demonstrations was to further the Wrights' aim to interest the French war office in their invention. And the French Army did in fact respond by entering into negotiations and then asking for further demonstrations at their gunnery range at Auvours. On the other side of the Atlantic the Wrights' aim to interest the United States military authorities also seemed to be prospering so that Orville in the United States and Wilbur in Europe became busy publicizing their achievements. There was a chance of military contracts.

The Wrights' invasion of France brought them into contact with the designers and makers of the lightweight French engines. They took full advantage of this and brought in the firm of Bariquand et Marre to build them engines with a better power to weight ratio than their own engines and with these they were able further to improve their aircraft performance capabilities.

In the United States the year 1908 also saw pioneering work by the Aerial Experiment Association, which was founded in October 1907 by the ageing inventor of the telephone, Alexander Graham Bell, in the belief that to build and fly powered winged machines was within the bounds of practical possibility for all. One of the members of Bell's group was a young man obsessed by speed, Glenn H. Curtiss.

Curtiss had won fame in New York as a racing cyclist, and with his prize money he had started a bicycle business, like the Wrights. He had then turned to building motor cycles and motor cycle engines at Hammondsport on Lake Keuka, New York with the intention of achieving ever higher speeds. At Ormond Beach, Florida in 1906 he had set a motor cycle record of 137 mph.

One of Curtiss's lightweight motor cycle engines had been admired by a pioneer American builder of airships, Captain T. A. Baldwin, who asked Curtiss to build a 20 hp engine for his Zeppelin type dirigible. It was after this that Bell met Curtiss and persuaded him to join his group with the idea of building a practical 'Aerodrome', thus carrying on the work of his ill-fated friend Dr Langley. Bell had been experimenting with large tetrahedral kites, and it was his desire to find an engine for one of these that led him to seek out Curtiss.

Shortly after its foundation the Association centred its activities on Curtiss's Hammondsport factory, and Curtiss, Lieutenant Tom Selfridge and two young Canadian engineers, F. W. Baldwin and J. A. D. McCurdy, began to build aircraft. In 1908 four biplanes were completed, each designed by a different member of the Association, and all incorporating features derived from Wright and European aircraft.

The two hops made by the first machine to be constructed, the *Red Wing*, designed by Selfridge and flown by Baldwin on 12 March, may be taken as the first powered heavier-than-air flight achieved in public in the United States. The aircraft had a wing span of 43 ft and was fitted with skis to take off from frozen Lake Keuka. It flew rather more than 300 ft at a height of 10 ft above the ice. The more successful second machine, the *White Wing*, designed by Baldwin, had wing tip ailerons, the first to be seen on an aircraft outside Europe. Curtiss

96

97

98

designed the third machine, the *June Bug*, which also had wing tip ailerons, and on 4 July, before a large crowd, he won the prize offered by the *Scientific American* for the first machine to fly a measured kilometre in the United States. These machines, with their slightly bowed wings, forward elevator, tailplane, vertical rudder and 30 hp Curtiss engine, were to be influential in the subsequent course of aircraft design in the United States.

When the Wrights heard of Curtiss's use of ailerons they sued him, claiming infringement of the patent they had been granted in 1906, which covered their wing warping technique. A protracted, bitter court battle was finally settled in favour of the Wrights.

In March 1909 the Aerial Experiment Association was dissolved and Curtiss took over many of its designs and patents. He now formed, with Augustus Herring, a company for the construction of engines, motor cycles and aeroplanes. The first aircraft built by the company was flown by Curtiss in July 1909 at Mineola, Long Island over a substantial distance, the flight winning the *Scientific American*'s prize a second time. This machine, which has often been referred to since as the *Gold Bug*, had tricycle landing gear, a Curtiss Vee engine and ailerons between the wings.

Glenn Curtiss was one of America's greatest aviation pioneers. His name stands second only to the Wrights. He was also to become one of the foremost aircraft manufacturers in the United States. He soon turned his attention to the development of flying-boats, and to his work in this field we shall return.

96 *Red Wing* on Lake Keuka, New York State, where it made the first public flight in the United States on 12 March 1908

97 *June Bug*, which won the Scientific American Trophy for a 1-km flight on 4 July 1908 with Glenn Curtiss as pilot

98 Curtiss flying Langley's 1903 'Aerodrome', rebuilt, at Hammondsport in 1914 in an unsuccessful effort to discredit Wright patents

99

In Europe a breed of pilots now appeared, pilots who were ready to try anything that had the slightest chance of being urged into the air, pilots who were the forebears of the test pilots of later periods. And from these men one again emerged who, although not of the stature of Santos-Dumont, was highly regarded among pilots themselves. He was Adolphe Pégoud, the pilot who, as one aircraft engineer put it, 'taught the world how to fly'.

Pégoud's fame was mingled with a form of development which must now be made clear. It concerned the primary type of wing cell used. The Hargrave box-kite had been the inspiration of much of the work done on the first man-carrying powered machines. The box-kite was a particular kind of *biplane*, differing basically from later biplanes only in having in its early forms vertical

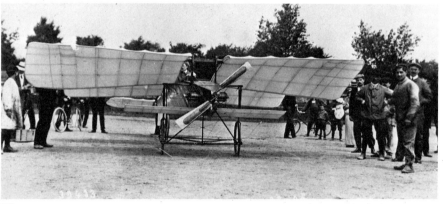

100

99 The first tractor biplane of Alfred de Pischof, tested (with little success) at Issy-les-Moulineaux, 1907

100 The German Koechlin-de Pischof tandem monoplane which made a flight in October 1908

panels or 'curtains'. In the United Kingdom the box-kite form was successful and was used by Bristol and Grahame-White in particular. The Wrights used the biplane form, but their machine was without vertical surfaces.

The biplane, then, was the popular type of early powered machine. But it is one of the curiosities and one of the interests of this early work that the monoplane was well known and, in glider form, well tried. Lilienthal, and Pilcher, as we have seen, used the monoplane for some of their most successful glides. And possibly because of the innate desire to imitate the birds, the monoplane was always in the minds of the pioneer pilots and constructors. In the end there arose a furious controversy between the advocates of the biplane and the advocates of the monoplane, each side claiming absolute rightness.

One other significant point arises: it had to do with lateral stability—that is with stability about the fore and aft axis of the aircraft or stability in *roll*. At first there was a mistaken idea that the vertical curtains of the Hargrave box-kite were agents of lateral stability and they were retained in some of the early powered machine designs under this impression. But Voisin did not use vertical surfaces between the main planes of his 1904 glider although he fitted them in his 1905 glider for the Seine towing experiments.

Santos-Dumont, for his 1906 flight, although he used the curtains, had the inspiration to see how lateral control—though not lateral stability—could be secured by the fitting of ailerons. Lateral stability could be secured in part by using a dihedral angle on the main planes. And in the Santos-Dumont *14 bis* there was, in addition to the curtains, a marked dihedral angle though there seems to be some doubt about whether its functions were understood.

An aircraft does not need to have inherent lateral stability provided it has full lateral control. The pilot can maintain the aircraft in level flight or can bank it to one side or the other by means of the aileron or wing warping controls. There must be adequate lateral *balance*, but there need not be *inherent lateral stability*. The Wrights did not have inherent lateral stability in their early aircraft. The wings were not given a dihedral angle. They had sufficient means of securing lateral control by pilot action.

When Léon Delagrange and Charles Voisin went to Issy-les-Moulineaux for the 300 metre flight of 5 November 1907, they used a Voisin box-kite without side curtains to the main planes and without dihedral angle. And in this form, with adequate aileron control, a long line of aircraft was to appear. Such machines were to be used in many parts of the world and to be a main training type for thousands of pilots.

Wing warping, we have noted, was visualized by Ader and mentioned in his patents as a means of lateral control and wing warping had its advocates against those who preferred ailerons. Wing warping, it was said, gave a more *natural* adjustment of the angles of incidence of the opposite wings. And wing warping worked well though in some machines it demanded a good deal of strength on the part of the pilot in order to operate it. Ailerons, which determine wing incidence in the same way though more coarsely, finally superseded wing warping partly because of their superior mechanical practicality. They could be made easily and they could be operated without undue force.

Fore and aft control, that is control in pitch or about the lateral axis, was as much a matter of divided opinions as control in roll. The Santos-Dumont canard configuration was belittled by the critics who failed to notice that it pioneered the forward elevator for control in pitch. Eventually the forward elevator was used in extremely large numbers of successful aircraft, the widely used Maurice Farman Longhorn among them. The Wrights also used a forward elevator. Santos-Dumont did not link up his forward elevator control—the tilting of the entire forward box—to any form of tail control whereas the Maurice Farman did. Eventually, in box-kite types, the elevator moved to the rear and altogether disappeared from the front.

Henry Farman, Delagrange, Charles Voisin, Ferber and, at first, Louis Blériot all used box-kite configurations – mostly with forward elevators – for their first experiences in piloting. And they all eventually came to working the control surfaces by means of a 'steering' wheel mounted on top of a tiltable column. The Wright vertical levers were given up as being a less 'natural' form of control.

great breed of pilot virtuosi employed for their displays, we have to remember that controversies about biplane and monoplane – as between air-cooled and liquid-cooled engines and between rotary and radial engines – were largely influenced by the technical knowledge and materials available. Thus the multiplane, whether biplane or triplane or quadruplane, had advantages over the monoplane in construction. The box girder could be the basis of the whole skeleton. Its torsional strength and other properties were known and understood by

101

103

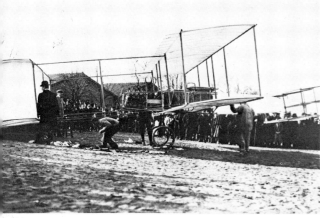

102

Blériot was now to produce a radical effect upon aircraft development. He had a vision of a highly manoeuvrable machine with a single pair of wings and a tail, in the form of a bird, and quite different from the Hargrave box-kite biplane and the Wright biplane. Louis Blériot, in fact, headed the contingent who declared that the future of aviation lay with the monoplane and that the biplane was obsolescent. And Pégoud gave force to this belief by his brilliant piloting of Blériot machines.

It did not at first work out that way. The biplane was destined for a long and satisfactory period of development. In fact the biplane form has not to this day been completely superseded. It must be emphasized that in that early time the biplane was seen not as an accompaniment to the monoplane, but as an alternative to it. One type was seen as 'right' and the other type as 'wrong'.

When glancing back to the aircraft which the first

engineers. To introduce the cantilever was not, at that time, easy.

Clément Ader's *Eole* and likewise his *Avion II* and his *Avion III* were unbraced monoplanes closer to modern aircraft in form and structure than the later biplanes. Although strongly influenced by the flight of bats and of insects, Ader in 1890 went the whole way towards bird flight in the arrangement of the wings of his machine, their variable camber and variable sweep. But his concept involved enormous structural difficulties. These he tackled by excessively delicate and unpractically high-grade workmanship.

The biplane, on the other hand, could be made strong and light in a practical manner by using wooden spars and struts, braced by means of wire. This was how the early machines came to be called 'birdcages', 'stringbags' and other slightly derogatory names. But external bracing wires, although they were known to encourage the aerodynamic enemy, drag, were convenient, safe and easily fitted devices for holding the structural shape.

A *box* of struts and wires was readily made and introduced no demands for especially high-grade workmanship. And the wings could be part of the box, their shape being determined by lightweight wooden former ribs with compression ribs disposed at intervals. The necessary camber could thus be provided within the limitations of the box-girder frame. And the covering could be fabric, stretched tight over the former ribs and made to retain its tightness by being lavishly brushed with 'dope', a liquid tautener which had much to do with giving the

101 Henry Farman No 1 at Issy, 1907

102 The second powered Voisin biplane flown by Delagrange in 1907

103 Blériot VIII monoplane at Issy, 1908

73

The Reims Meeting, 1909. Thirty-eight machines entered, twenty-three took part over the eight days in over 120 take-offs, and twenty-two pilots flew. The longest distance flown was 112 miles, by Farman. The highest altitude (over 508 ft) was attained by Latham's *Antoinette*, and the best speed was 48 mph by Blériot.

104 Breguet I biplane

105 Louis Paulhan in a Voisin

106 Santos-Dumont and other participants in the grandstand

107 The Italian Etienne Bunau-Varilla in a Voisin

108 Eugène Lefebvre, who about a week later became the first pilot to be killed, in a Wright Model A

109 The President of the French Republic, Armand Fallières, and Lloyd George

110 Latham piloting an Antoinette

104

107

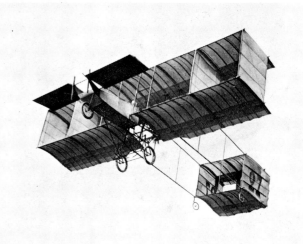

108

105

109

106

74

110

111

112

113

114

111 Henry Farman in his version of the Voisin biplane

112 Blériot XI

113 Blériot with his Type XIII monoplane which later crashed and caught fire

114 Curtiss in a *Golden Flier* type machine, in which he won the 30 km and 20 km speed contests

early machines their pale yellow colour and their drawn-in aspect, the ribs standing out along the wing surfaces.

In 1909 the Reims air meeting brought together the best aircraft of the time and the most successful pilots. It was, to some extent, a show-down for aircraft designers for it enabled the different kinds of machine–biplanes and monoplanes–to display their powers, and their limitations, before a large public.

The Reims meeting set the pace for thousands of air meetings. They were to continue after the first world war,

115

between that war and the second world war and again after the second war. Air meetings were public entertainments, but they were also demonstrations of technical achievement. It is possible to argue that aviation became so much a public interest because it was a technical activity which could be practically shown to large concourses of public spectators.

At the big air meetings the new breed of skilled pilots made their impact. At the first meeting at Reims Glenn Curtiss made his mark in a race using his own design of biplane. There were, too, competitive events in which the Wright biplane achieved success and proved its great superiority as an aerodynamic cell. The feats of the many pilots demonstrated clearly and to the larger public that the new machine was now a practical vehicle.

Santos-Dumont was there with his *Demoiselle*, a development of his small, 18 ft wing span monoplane of 1907. It was a high wing monoplane with tractor airscrew. Control was by a system similar to that of many early aircraft, the conventional elevator and rudder and warping wings for lateral control. The engine was the Antoinette. A version developed from this had a Bayard engine and was claimed to be faster.

Also there were Delagrange, Esnault-Pelterie, Louis Paulhan, Captain Ferber, Gabriel Voisin, Henry Farman and Louis Blériot. Voisin biplanes were there in large numbers. There were also Wright biplanes and Farman biplanes which Henry Farman had been developing from the Voisin machines he had used for the kilometre and closed circuit records. The only British competitor, G. B. Cockburn, flew one of the Farman biplanes.

The monoplanes were Blériots, REPs, the Santos-Dumont and the new Levavasseur Gastambide et Mengin Antoinette. One of these was piloted by Hubert Latham. Another name which was to take a high place among the pioneers was that of Louis Breguet. He entered his own biplane at this meeting but his fame as an inventor, as we shall see when we come to this form of flight, was initially founded upon rotorcraft.

So the Reims meeting was a conspectus of heavier-than-air flight. Large crowds assembled and there was tremendous excitement when the newly developed powers of the new craft were demonstrated.

Air meetings of the Reims type spread to England, first to Doncaster and Blackpool, and aviation interest spread with them. The year 1909 also saw a number of historic flights on the continent of Europe. The first German pilot, Hans Grade, flew a triplane derived from Ellehammer's machine at Magdeburg, and another aircraft resembling the *Demoiselle* at Borck. The Austrian Igo Etrich flew his *Taube* ('Dove') monoplane, bird-like with its swept-back wing tips, at Wiener-Neustadt. Van den Schkrouff flew a Voisin at Odessa. Powered flights took place for the first time in Sweden, the Netherlands, Portugal, Romania and Turkey.

French engines were establishing their world lead. The Antoinette now had many companions, all of light weight for their power. The Gnome rotaries, the air-cooled stationaries, in V and in-line, were proving themselves in service. The Buchet engine was not only in use in aircraft in France but it was also brought over to Britain for fitting in various machines including the Dunne swept-wing biplane.

Two designer-pilots of outstanding importance must now receive attention: Louis Blériot and Alliott Verdon-Roe, one in France, the other in England. Blériot, as has been said, had been concentrating his attention upon monoplanes. He had success with his early machines; but it is doubtful if his name would have attained prominence had it not been for his cross-Channel flight.

116

117

118

115 Esnault-Pelterie in his REP in 1908

116 Crashed Blériot XII, 1909

117 Hans Grade, the first German aeroplane pilot, 1909, with his second machine

118 Etrich Taube at Paris

76

Blériot made his crossing early on Sunday 25 July 1909. His monoplane had an Anzani air-cooled radial engine. The flight has been described on many occasions, best of all by Blériot himself in an interview he gave to the London *Daily Mail*. According to Harry Harper, the *Daily Mail* air correspondent, Blériot was by no means robust in health and he had suffered an accident shortly before so that he was hobbling with one foot causing pain. Nevertheless he decided to make the attempt after a brief test flight in the Calais region. At Les Baraques, after seating himself in his No. XI monoplane, he peered out over the mist-enshrouded Channel and asked rather plaintively: 'Where *is* England?' Then he took off with the destroyer *Escopette* accompanying him.

Hubert Latham, with his Antoinette monoplane, was Blériot's rival. In a later attempt to emulate Blériot he was forced down into the sea not far from Dover. Blériot suffered some moments of anxiety during his flight and one report – not confirmed by Blériot himself – had it that a shower of rain saved him by helping to keep the engine – which had been showing signs of overheating – cool. Blériot had no compass and he lost sight of the *Escopette* early in the flight. But he found St Margaret's Bay and then came in over the cliffs to make a slightly bumpy landing. Among the first people to meet him was a customs officer who wished not to congratulate him but to be absolutely sure that he had nothing to declare. A stone plaque let into the ground marks the spot where he landed.

Blériot learnt to fly the hard way and had several crashes. But his seventh monoplane was a success and earned him a French Aero Club medal. His Channel flight brought him much needed funds and the distinction of a Chevalier of the Legion of Honour. But his supreme achievement was twofold: to champion the monoplane against the biplane and to demonstrate to the world the impact of aviation upon geography and upon the freedom and independence of nations.

We now turn back one year to 1908 and look at the activities of a remarkable character who had been working on aircraft of his own design and construction at Brooklands motor racing track not far from London. He was Alliott Verdon-Roe. Small, humorous, tenacious, modest, with a low pitched voice, Roe or 'AV' as he came to be known, is often underestimated. He had been to sea and had studied bird flight. He had engineering training. He was fired with enthusiasm for flight. Through his models he acquired an understanding of the primary lift/drag problems, of the means of applying thrust to an airframe and, particularly, of some of the requirements for obtaining adequate stability in free flight.

His extraordinary vision sometimes seemed to have the quality of extrasensory perception. And there was also his own personal dexterity. He was a competent trick cyclist and it was partly his interest in cycling that led him to invent, build and prove a motorized two-wheel machine of the scooter type subsequently popular, with low slung frame, good weather protection and good stability. Research might give A. V. Roe priority as the inventor of the motor scooter.

In his autobiography *The World of Wings and Things*

119

Roe tells in detail of his days at Brooklands, of his troubles with the track authorities, of the subterfuges he adopted in order to be allowed to continue his work there and, finally, of his success with the biplane he had designed and built when on 8 June 1908 he first managed to take off and fly and thus to become the first Englishman to fly in England. He covered a distance of 151 ft and made a smooth landing. On 28 June he flew 180 ft,

120

the flight being observed among others by his brother Humphrey. He made seven flights in all during this month.

In these early attempts we have seen that when there is no official observation, the chances are that later commentators, relying upon indirect, generally hearsay evidence, may cast doubt upon the claims. Newspaper reports were scarce and some later critics, seeking to belittle Roe, said that there were none; but Roe's son after some painstaking research was able to discover 34 newspaper references to the achievement, beginning with a *Manchester Guardian* reference of 26 January 1909. They include references in the *Observer*, *Flight*, the *Aeroplane*, the *Motor*, *The Times* and the *Daily Express*. And there were five witnesses besides Roe's brother.

Most important, surely, was the fact that the biplane Roe used was based upon a successful model and that its engine, an Antoinette, had the necessary power for its weight to make the flight feasible. Roe had tried to fly

119 Blériot over the French coast at the start of the first Channel crossing, 25 July 1909

120 The end of Latham's first attempt to cross the Channel in an Antoinette IV, 19 July 1909

earlier with a 9 hp JAP but had failed. The Antoinette, however, developed adequate thrust.

When in 1956 Roe unveiled a plaque at Brooklands, he glossed over his first flights, referring to them as 'hops', but he had no sort of doubt that they were flights within the definition that has been suggested. The Brooklands Memorial Plaque says: 'From this area, on various dates in 1907-8, A. V. Roe made a series of towing flights and flight trials with an aircraft of his own design and construction, powered, in the later trials, by an 18/24 hp

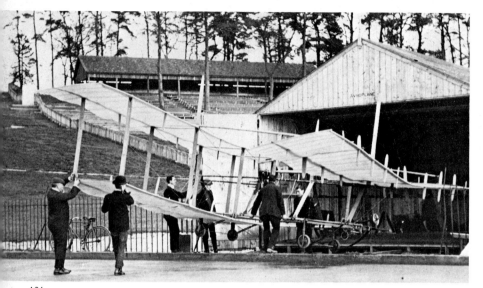

121

Antoinette engine.'

British aviation had a great leader in A. V. Roe. It is the more puzzling, then, that after a great many years had passed since his first flight at Brooklands in 1908, a movement should have got under way to filch from Roe some of the distinction that belonged to him. The point was whether he had been the first Englishman to fly in England or whether that distinction should go to Colonel J. T. C. Moore-Brabazon, later Lord Brabazon. Brabazon was a sportsman who took up any new activity with zest, becoming a first-class car driver and then a fine pilot. He had gone to France and flown Voisins a few months after Roe's first Brooklands flight.

The Royal Aero Club appointed a committee under Lord Gorell to investigate and to pronounce upon 'who was the British subject to make the first flight in a heavier-than-air aircraft in the British Isles, and the date of such flight', to quote the committee's terms of reference. The committee met on various dates in 1928 and 1929.

Roe produced evidence, written and other; but preference was given to Moore-Brabazon's claim. His flight had been during the week-end 30 April – 2 May 1909 at Eastchurch. Brabazon's first flight in a Voisin at Issy was dated the 'end of 1908' and the one at Chalons January 1909. Oswald Short gave evidence of the Eastchurch flight in 1909. So the first Briton to fly in the British Isles was officially named as Moore-Brabazon.

Roe's first triplane – a light spidery little thing of under 20 ft and weighing not quite 200 lb – was made after he had been forced to leave Brooklands and to transfer his 'works' to a railway arch at Lea Marshes. It had a 9 hp JAP engine of the kind he had originally fitted in his biplane; in later models 20 hp and 35 hp engines were

used. He later changed the JAP for an Antoinette. His triplane flight in July 1909 however was made with the JAP engine so that it became the first powered flight in Britain with an all-British machine. JAP engines were created for motorcycles. They were air-cooled, with finned cylinders, and they ranged from twins up to eights. Work was done on liquid-cooled models, but the types used in aircraft were air-cooled.

At the Olympia airshow of 1910, Roe presented a two-seat triplane with Green engine. The Green came closer to an automobile type engine, the early models having some general resemblance to the Wrights' first engine, water-cooled with four cylinders in line and between 30 and 40 hp. The specific weight of Green engines was higher than that of some contemporary air-cooled engines.

The triplane form reappeared at various stages in aviation history; but Roe was the earliest to develop it fully and practically. However it was the biplane form to which he returned for his most famous machine, an aircraft which has claims to have been *the* most famous of all, the Avro 504.

The 504 was fitted with many different engines, but it was at its best as A. V. Roe designed it, with a relatively low-powered rotary engine. It was a superlatively sensitive, graceful and obedient aircraft. It was impossible to fly it without thinking of the remarkable man who created it.

It had nothing redundant; it was simple and strong; it was light and well balanced. Piloting a 504 must remain for anyone who experienced it one of the outstanding pleasures of flight. The take-off run, with the rotary engine buzzing and the aerodrome grass moving along at an accelerating speed under the wheels, produced the overall impression of *flight*; of escape, that is, from a heavier, more lugubrious place into another, lighter, finer, brighter world. And the central control stick, uncluttered except for the ignition button on top, began

122

121 A. V. Roe's biplane being lifted out of its shed at Brooklands, June 1908

122 Cover of the first issue of the English journal *Flight*, published on 2 January 1909, showing Moore-Brabazon's flight at Issy on 3 December 1908 in a Voisin-Farman

123

to speak to the pilot as flying speed came. It touched his hand and pressed it this way or that to tell him what the air flow was doing to the wings, the ailerons and the elevator. And the rudder bar had its own interpolatory comments as it pushed at one foot or the other and made its suggestions and exclamations.

In the air the 504 was obedient but independent. The windscreen in the early models was small and the pilot felt the air passing the sides of his head. He acquired as he sat at the controls a compact of sensual impressions, to eye, to ear, to touch and even to smell for the castor oil used in the rotary engine had its own distinctive odour. The very delicacy of the aircraft discouraged rough treatment of the controls. The pilot felt he had to flatter, to hint, to suggest rather than to force.

Almost everything could be done in a 504. It could be looped, rolled and spun of course; but it could also be flown inverted and made to do a few more advanced manoeuvres. Of course it was not capable of more than a particle of the aerobatic repertoire within the reach of a modern aerobatic machine like a Zlin, but in response to the controls, in harmonious obedience to the pilot's movements, there has never been a better aircraft.

This is where a portentous figure, bravely mounted upon a white charger, with high plumed hat, flowing locks and magistral whiskers, appears upon the scene – Samuel F. Cody.

Cody was a remarkable man not only as a practical aeronautical engineer of outstanding merit, but also as an inventor and innovator in many different fields. His aviation work could be said to date from 1906 when he was appointed Chief Kiting Instructor to the British Army; but he was already famous as a crack rifle shot,

a splendid horseman, an expert with the lasso, a professional strong man, an actor and showman.

Cody reached competence as an aircraft builder and pilot through his man-lifting kites. The technique of these was as follows. A cable was first set up on an array of large kites and the man to be lifted travelled up this cable in another kite with a device for allowing it to slide up the cable.

Service interest in Cody's work began with the Royal Navy which collaborated with him in a series of man-lifting kite trials at sea. The object was improved reconnaissance. Cody himself went up in the kites and although there were some mishaps he showed that they were capable of holding an observer aloft in a fairly wide range of different weathers. The Army interest was linked with both kites and airships in the first instance but then rapidly reoriented itself in the direction of

124

123 The Avro 504 of 1912, prototype of a famous line

124 Cody, in the large hat, watching one of his man-carrying box-kites on Laffan's Plain, 1905

powered aircraft.

Cody faced the same problems as other experimenters in finding a prime mover light enough for its power to turn a glider into a powered machine and, like the others, he had to go to France to get it. He obtained a Panhard Levassor engine from the automobile pioneers and then an Antoinette, originally earmarked for the airship *Nulli Secundus*. He fitted this to his biplane and on 16 May 1908 made a short flight, thus becoming the first man to make a powered flight in England (he was actually still

125

a citizen of the United States). However, it is his later flight of 1,390 ft on 16 October 1908 at Farnborough that–notwithstanding Roe's June flights–is officially recognized as the first powered flight in Britain.

Like Roe, Cody has been the victim of extensive comment by people who never saw him at work and who had no direct touch with anything he did. Fortunately there were also first-hand witnesses, among them G. A. Broomfield, who wrote his biography. Broomfield, who was the station master at a nearby station and who had become an enthusiastic supporter of Cody and an industrious chronicler of his work, says that the press reported the first flight as a 'rolling' experiment but that senior officials of the Balloon Factory–the progenitor of the Royal Aircraft Establishment–and various residents including himself, witnessed the flights.

Cody had fitted a Buchet engine to his 1907 kite and this and his large glider, with a wing span of just over 50 ft and a wing area of about 750 sq ft, had given him a foretaste of and an impetus toward powered flight. In 1910 he flew his own machine, fitted with a Green engine, to qualify for his Aero Club aviator's certificate. His best machines were biplanes but among his six distinctive types was one striking monoplane with side-by-side seating for pilot and observer. A crash prevented it from demonstrating its many potentially important design features. One big Cody biplane was nicknamed the 'Cathedral', some thought because it was so huge and ornate that it looked like a cathedral, others because its wings were set at an anhedral (opposite to dihedral) angle.

The British War Office military aircraft trials at Larkhill, Salisbury Plain in 1912 were critical in bringing Cody's work to public notice and in establishing him as a serious and successful aircraft designer and pilot.

125 Cody's biplane at Laffan's Plain, 1911, similar to that used at the Larkhill Military Aircraft Trials in 1912

126 Avro triplane, 1909; replica

127 Blériot XI, 1909; restored

128 Curtiss Pusher, 1912; restored

129 Thomas Pusher II, built by the Thomas brothers of Bath, New York, 1912; restored

130 Vickers FB.5 Gunbus, 1914; replica

131 Avro 504K biplane, first built 1913; restored

132 SE.5a, 1917, flying over the Royal Aircraft Establishment at Farnborough known, when it was designed there, as the Royal Aircraft Factory

133 Sopwith Pup biplane, 1916; restored

134 Caudron G.III, 1915; restored

Before the trials there had been thoughts in the mind of the public that Cody was nothing more than a show-man without claim to the engineering capabilities which were seen to be necessary in anyone who aspired to a place among the aviation pioneers. Cody's flamboyance, his personal appearance and the stories that were told about him as a circus performer militated against his acceptance among the engineers. But in the end he proved himself to be the equal in enterprise and in serious design ability to other practical experimenters as well as to those who shut themselves away in cloistered seclusion and engaged in mathematical mysteries.

Colonel J. L. Capper, Superintendent of the Balloon Factory at Farnborough, believed that Cody's aircraft was superior to the Voisin machines as modified by Henry Farman and used in France for the flights that have already been mentioned. His view was endorsed by Colonel Mervyn O'Gorman, champion of Farnborough's own BE biplane. Cody's machine was a three-bay biplane with three sets of interplane struts on either side of the central nacelle and it had a front elevator, an empennage with tailplane and vertical rudder, a four-wheel main undercarriage with small wheels in front of and behind the pair of main wheels, as well as small wheels mounted at the wing tips. The Antoinette engine drove two airscrews by belt.

It seems extraordinary that a man so committed to show business, so much a part of it, so flamboyant, so spectacular in appearance, should have become one of the great aviation pioneers. Yet that is what happened. Cody won the 1912 British military trials and a prize of £4,000. A monoplane was second, a Deperdussin piloted by Prévost. Although the winner was a biplane, mono-planes attracted much attention, particularly the Blériot, Hanriot, Bristol and Martin-Handasyde types.

The end came in 1913, when Cody took up a passenger from Laffan's Plain, the scene of so many of his triumphs. The aircraft according to eye witnesses showed signs of control trouble and reared up suddenly. Passenger and pilot were hurled out of it and fell to their deaths.

No other aviation pioneer exceeded Cody in courage, skill and plain physical strength or in the spectacular manner of his achievements.

Lord Brabazon's early flights, which earned him the Royal Aero Club Aviator's Certificate Number 1, were made in a Voisin biplane he had brought over from France. He had a genius in the handling of motor cars and aircraft and he was often inspired by a desire to astonish the world by his novel and varied exploits. He had a mind which quickly absorbed the essence of new discoveries. He would espouse any new thing and was always ready to help in its development. It was in this capacity as a helper of those who were striving to introduce new things that Brabazon came into contact with Short Brothers, Britain's senior aircraft constructing company, whose activities will later be considered.

The priority of Short Brothers in Britain as aircraft constructors arises from their decision to start work in 1900. They began as balloon makers. And it was partly the influence of Lord Brabazon that re-directed their efforts from balloons to aeroplanes.

The year which saw the full explosion of public interest

126

127

128

129

130

132

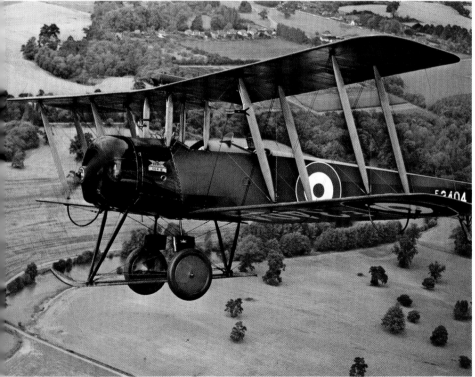

131

133

134

135

136

137

138

139

140

141

in aviation in the United States was undoubtedly 1910. A number of international air meetings were held, and there arose a characteristically American breed of pilots, tough, dedicated, dare-devil 'barnstormers' who lived – those who survived – on the proceeds of stunt flying and the hope of prize money. These flyers sold thrills rather than aviation, but it was through their appearances that many were introduced to aeroplanes.

America's first international air meeting was held in January 1910 at Dominguez Field, Los Angeles. Here the Frenchman Louis Paulhan set an altitude record of 4,165 ft, and Glenn Curtiss, who had already won the speed prize offered by James Gordon Bennett, publisher of the New York *Herald*, the previous year at Reims, set a new world speed record of 55 mph. A few weeks later Curtiss flew down the Hudson River from Albany to New York (stopping twice to refuel) to win another prize offered by the New York *World*.

Among those who witnessed Curtiss's arrival in New York after his 137 mile flight was a sixteen-year-old Wall Street runner who dreamed of aerial conquest – Harry Bruno, who was to become a prominent aviation publicist. In his book *Wings Over America* Bruno communicates something of the impression that this early flight of Curtiss's made on New Yorkers.

On a magic, electrified spring Sunday, an idle excursion I made to New York was interrupted by a copy boy I ran into on Park Row. 'Curtiss is on his way down from Albany by airplane!' he said. 'He's expected at Governor's Island within the hour.' At this I forgot about my job; forgot about everything. In a few minutes I was breathlessly boarding a Lackawanna ferry. Finding the upper deck deserted, I ran to the rail and searched the skies towards Yonkers. Back and forth the ferry plied. My neck ached, perspiration poured down my face, still I continued my vigil. But after the second trip I was not alone. Word had spread through the downtown area from Park Row – then the newspaper centre – that Glenn Curtiss had already reached New York, having made the flight from Albany to upper Manhattan at a speed of over fifty miles per hour. He was now supposed to be flying from Inwood to Governor's Island.

There were a hundred pairs of eyes on the deck of my ferry when we sighted the biplane. At first we saw merely a black speck off in the distance, and my heart pumped furiously – it was the first time I had ever seen a real airplane. As it approached, the biplane started to lose altitude. By now, all the men on the ferry were shouting and waving, and trying to set up an even greater din than the steam whistles shrieking up and down the river. Then, even over our own tumult, we could hear the rattling burr of the famous Curtiss engine.

The plane was now down to about three hundred feet, and approaching our ferry at a fast clip. We could all see Glen Curtiss, sitting in the open cockpit between the twin wings of his airplane. His outfit took my breath away: he looked like a conqueror of the air, sitting proudly in his long fisherman's boots, his brown leather jacket, his soft cap on backwards, his eyes protected by heavy motorcycle racer's goggles. As he drew nearer, I could even see – or fancy that I saw – his luxurious black mustache catching the breezes he had tamed.

And then, with a triumphant roar, he passed directly over our heads. We all cheered as he circled the Statue of Liberty three times and then landed gracefully on the parade grounds at Governor's Island.

At Boston Harbor in September the Englishman Claude Grahame-White won a race against American and British competitors and then flew his Farman to Washington where he created a sensation by landing and taking off in a street beside the White House. He also took part in the meeting at Belmont Park, New York, in October, which was attended by high society, and after a 33 mile race between the Park and the Statue of Liberty bitterly contested the decision with the swashbuckling adventurer John B. Moisant; however, he won the Gordon-Bennett prize in his Blériot over three miles with

135 Curtiss JN-4D trainer ('Jenny'), 1917; restored

136 Pfalz D.II, 1916; restored

137 Vickers Vimy transatlantic biplane, 1919; replica

138 The first aircraft, a biplane with floats, built at the new Seattle factory of William E. Boeing, 1919; replica

139 Bristol Fighter, two seater biplane, 1917; restored

140 Fokker E.III, 1916; replica

141 Ansaldo SVA-9, 1918; restored

142 Composite photograph of the meeting at Belmont Park, New York, October 1910. Among the aircraft are a Curtiss (*bottom left*), two Antoinettes (*centre*) and a Blériot

142

a speed of 61 mph.

In 1910 hired teams of flyers began to tour the United States giving exhibition flights. The Wright and Curtiss teams rivalled each other in the promotion of their aircraft.

The most renowned American stunt flyer of all was Lincoln Beachey, whom Curtiss taught to fly. Some considered him a 'flying fool', others, including Orville Wright, as 'the greatest aviator of all.' He stopped the breath of crowds throughout the country with his

143

144

143 Houdini about to take off on an exhibition flight, 1910

144 Lincoln Beachey at the controls of his Curtiss biplane, 1912

145 Calbraith Rodgers on his arrival at Pasadena, 1911

146 Calbraith Rodgers about to land at one of the many stages of his seven-week 4,000-mile flight from New York to Pasadena, California

famous vertical dives. He scooped up handkerchiefs from the ground with a wing tip. He set an altitude record by filling his fuel tank to the brim and climbing until he ran out of fuel, returning to earth by gliding. In June 1911 at Niagara he flew over the falls and then under the suspension bridge.

Beachey seems actually to have been highly concerned about safety in the air. His stunts, and those of other barnstormers, helped designers and builders to iron out structural weaknesses in many early aircraft. In 1913 Beachey retired from the air, saying that by his reckoning 22 aviators had met their deaths attempting to perform his stunts. But for some reason he agreed to fly again at

an exposition in San Francisco in 1915. The wings of his Taube monoplane collapsed and 50,000 people saw him plunge 2,000 ft to his death.

In 1911 there took place what must be accounted one of the most remarkable long distance flights in the history of aviation. A speed enthusiast who had raced with horses, motor cars and yachts, Calbraith Rodgers, decided to try for the biggest prize a flyer could then win – William Randolph Hearst's offer of $50,000 for a first coast-to-coast flight across the United States, to be completed within thirty days. He bought a Wright biplane and put in two months' hard practice flying. Before setting out on his prize flight he came to an agreement with the manufacturer of a new soft drink, Vin-Fiz. The manufacturer was to pay Rodgers three dollars for each mile of his flight and supply a special train to accompany him, bearing a team of aides, members of his family, spare parts and rescue equipment. On Rodgers' aircraft, and on the train, the name of Vin-Fiz was painted.

Rodgers set out from New York in his frail aircraft of bamboo, wire and cloth on 17 September. Hearst's offer was to expire on 11 October. It was soon obvious that Rodgers would arrive in California – if he ever did – too late to win the prize, but he pressed on. There were many unforeseen hazards. On the ground his machine suffered the depredations of souvenir hunters and had to be guarded from cows at night, and on more than one stage of the journey he had acute difficulty in taking off from amidst dense crowds of well-wishers. In the air he was blown off course by wind and storm, chased by an eagle,

145

146

and nearly collided with the jagged precipice of a mountain pass; his engine several times had to be held together by hand, and on one occasion exploded, shooting steel splinters into his right arm. At almost every landing, or crash landing, both pilot and aircraft needed patching up. When he arrived at Pasadena on 5 November after a seven week odyssey via Elmira, Kent, Chicago, Kansas City, Fort Worth, El Paso and Tucson, his machine had been repaired so frequently that the only original parts remaining were rudder and

drip pan.

Five months later Rodgers shared the fate of so many like him. On a stunt flight at San Diego he lifted both hands off the controls, and his aircraft went into a death dive.

In a number of European countries, as in the United States, flying burst upon the consciousness of the public in the year 1910. Aside from France and Britain, air meetings were held for the first time in Berlin, Munich, Florence, Bologna, Verona, Milan, Barcelona, Geneva,

147

148

149

150

Brussels, Copenhagen, Budapest and St Petersburg— where Léon Morane flew before the Grand Duke Sergei. There was even a meeting in Heliopolis in Egypt.

In Germany August Euler was the first to hold a pilot's licence, Prince Henry of Prussia proudly flew his aircraft, and Hans Grade started a factory. In Italy Caproni and Agostini made biplanes. In Switzerland Armand Dufaux flew the third aircraft he had built with his brother Henri across Lake Geneva. In Russia Piotrovski and Rossinski flew from town to town.

147 Poster for an air meeting in Milan, 1910

148 Baroness de Laroche in a Voisin

149 Monoplane produced by the Grade factory in Germany, 1912

150 Tabuteau, winner of the 1910 Michelin Prize, in his Maurice Farman

87

151

152

151 Effimoff in his
Farman, Nice, 1910

152 Cody on his 255 mile
flight to win the British
Empire Michelin Prize in
his biplane at Aldershot,
1911

The Dutchman Wijnmalen flew with a passenger from Paris to Brussels and back in 36 hours. The first woman held a pilot's licence – the Baroness de Laroche.

Then came one of the year's worst disasters. The Peruvian Geo Chavez, in seven action-packed months, learned to fly at the Farman school at Mourmelon, took part in a number of meetings from Nice to Budapest, bought a Blériot in which he achieved an altitude record of 8,487 ft – and then, about to land at Domodossola after making the first winged crossing of the Alps, crashed, broke both legs and died four days later.

In France the Michelin Prize was hotly contested for the third time. Since 1908 the brothers André and Edouard Michelin had offered 20,000 francs annually for the longest distance flown in closed circuit, stipulating that it should be at least double that of the previous year's winning performance. Wilbur Wright had won in 1908 with 77 miles at Le Mans, Farman in 1909 with 145 miles in four hours 17 minutes, and now in 1910 it was Maurice Tabuteau with 363 miles in a Maurice Farman.

From 1909 the Michelins offered a British Empire prize, which Moore-Brabazon first won. It is perhaps fitting that this chapter should end with a mention of the winner in 1910, and again in 1911 (with 255 miles) – Samuel Cody.

7 The tragic transformation

Towards 1914 the winged flying machine was turned from an entertaining artefact into a weapon of war. Two main moves contributed to and were part of this transformation. First, the design, construction and flying of aircraft left the hands of individual pioneers and came into the hands of companies. Second, aircraft were built and flown in order to earn profits for industrial concerns and to meet the requirements of government defence authorities. Industrialization and militarization set up their usual partnership.

It is impossible to apportion the extent of these two influences. Both were bad for the idealistic content of the dream of flying.

Aerial bombing did more than any other military invention or procedure to establish total war; war, that is, in which civilians, including women and children, are in the firing line. Mass bombing tore away the last vestiges of differential humanitarianism from the operations of the fighting forces. But the curious thing is that the tragic transformation occurred as part of a kind of gala epoch.

155

153

154

If we look over the years from 1909 – the year when that frail little Blériot monoplane wobbled and stuttered its way across the English Channel – to the outbreak of war in 1914, we see that all the flags are out, all the world interested, astonished and admiring; all the airmen, the designers, makers, pilots, passengers, working and thinking in splendid, optimistic terms, like children with a new toy. Racing, aerobatics, demonstration flying, speed and altitude records, passenger carrying, mail carrying accompanied a positive explosion of instructional flying.

Some memorable flights were made by French pilots. In April 1911 Pierre Prier linked London and Paris, flying from Hendon to Issy-les Moulineaux in four hours 55 minutes in a Blériot with 50 hp Gnome engine. Marcel Brindejonc de Moulinais flew from Paris in June 1913 to pass through six European capitals, Berlin, Warsaw, St Petersburg, Stockholm, Copenhagen, The Hague and back to Paris, in 46 hours of flight. Then on 23 September Roland Garros crossed the Mediterranean. He left from St-Raphaël, hugged the coast of Corsica, crossed Sardinia and landed at Bizerta, Tunisia in his severely battered Morane-Saulnier with 60 hp Gnome engine seven hours 53 minutes later. He had flown 454 miles of which more than 300 had been over sea.

The year 1911 saw a proliferation of international air races which aroused enormous excitement on the continent of Europe. The first inter-capital race, from Paris to Madrid in May, was dramatic. The start was deferred because of the death of the French minister of war caused when an aircraft ploughed into the crowd. Jules Védrines in a Morane was the only pilot to finish; he covered the 1,056 miles in 14 hours 6 minutes of flight. Barely a week after this Lieutenant Beaumont, in a Blériot, beat Garros in a race Paris-Rome-Turin. A million and a half francs was offered in prize money on the occasion of a circuit race that linked France, Belgium, Holland and England. Again Beaumont won

153 Bielovuccic about to take off for his flight over the Alps from Brig to Domodossola in a Hanriot monoplane, 1913

154 Attwood on his famous 1911 St Louis–New York flight in a Wright-type biplane

155 The English pilot Perryon about to take off for a height record in a Blériot monoplane, 1913

89

156

157

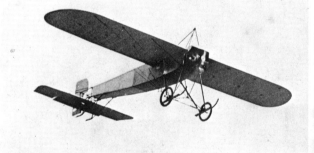

158

159

156 Eugene Ely flying his Curtiss biplane over the exhibition hall of Lethbridge Fairgrounds, Canada, 1911

157 Roland Garros about to win the Grand Prix of the Aéro Club de France in his Blériot 'en vol piqué' in 1912, the year after he crossed the Mediterranean

158 Védrines in his Morane monoplane during the Paris–Madrid air race, May 1911

159 Védrines at the start of the race

information and education about flying. They were also used for aeronautical propaganda.

The meetings positively sparkled with gaiety. They brought far more aerial action to the eyes of the spectators than could have been imagined at the first meeting at Reims in August 1909. This was in some measure an event of curiosity value. There was much of technical interest, but the theatrical side was absent. It was absent, too, from the meetings at Doncaster and at Blackpool in England in the same year. The Doncaster meeting in October 1909 was typically British and took place in an atmosphere of comic opera recrimination between 'officials' and amateur 'interlopers'. Nevertheless it attracted enough attention from flying enthusiasts to infuriate many of those who had organized the 'official' Blackpool meeting.

The Hendon meetings, however, set a pattern and, at the same time, proclaimed a trend. They enjoyed immense success and they worked as a compass card, showing the heading of aviation progress. In fact Hendon became a microcosm of flying. It tended even to shift the world's aeronautical centre of gravity away from France, where it had been since the Montgolfier brothers' work, to England, and from Paris to London. Hendon was the meeting place of all meetings, attracting French, German, American, Belgian, Austrian, Dutch and Danish pilots and setting the pace for other aerodromes. Most important, it outdistanced the static displays.

The aero shows at Olympia, London, beginning in 1909, had attracted the studious, but Hendon attracted

from Garros, both pilots flying Blériots. A circuit race in Germany was won by Koenig, and a race Bologne-Venice-Rimini-Bologne by Captain Piazza, who was followed by two other Italians. There was even a race to Cairo, won by Védrines. A 1,367 miles race through England and Scotland was won by the determined Beaumont in 22 hours 28 minutes of flight.

Meetings were held in many places, and they became extremely popular with a continually growing section of the public. Any piece of level, grass covered ground might be used, but the tendency grew to concentrate the more important meetings at a few well-equipped aerodromes. In France Issy-les-Moulineaux, within easy reach of Paris, was to become an aeronautical amusement place having some resemblance to London's Vauxhall Gardens in the ballooning period. In England it was Hendon, a large open space north of London. The public crowded to these places for the week-end meetings. They became prime sources of entertainment, and of everybody. The prestige of a dynamic meeting, with aircraft performing in the air, far exceeded that of a static meeting, with aircraft displayed on stands. Brooklands had begun to go the way of Hendon, but although great pilots had built up its renown – men like Roe and Pégoud – its commitment to motor car racing had stood in the way of all-out aviation progress. But Hendon would not have gained its place as the signpost of flying development had it not been for the genius of two men, Richard Gates and Claude Grahame-White.

In 1910 Grahame-White was 31 years old and an aviation enthusiast. He had started a flying school at Pau, in France, and believed that the time had come to start one in England. With Richard Gates he began the development of Hendon. Grahame-White was a man of many parts, a first class pilot, an aircraft constructor with original ideas, and a brilliant publicist. His restless energy and his imaginative fervour, backed by the business ability of Gates, made Hendon world famous.

Aspiring aviators, during the midweek, puttered into the air in Caudrons and Grahame-White box-kites and made hesitant and hazardous 'circuits and bumps' – for a high instruction fee. Then, at the week-ends, the star pilots and the star aircraft appeared to thrill the immense crowds of spectators who came from London and further afield by bus and tram, bicycle, train and car. The flags were out, the decorations up. Cafés were opened. The curse of the tea shop descended on the district. Special tickets were sold by touts at exorbitant prices. As the time of opening the aerodrome gates approached, clouds of dust would arise as monster sports cars banged and

160

161

thundered their way through the throng of bicyclists and pedestrians.

Hucks was going to 'loop the loop' Hamel was going to challenge all comers in a race! What light-hearted boy or girl, what solemn scientist or worried engineer, what politician, artist, artisan, business man or bank clerk could resist the lure of a big air meeting?

The events crowded upon one another. A kite-balloon, or tethered man-carrying balloon, might be let up. The Willows airship, the first British airship to fly from

62

163

London to Paris, might appear and cruise at low altitude over the spectators' enclosures. A parachute drop might be done. Parachuting from airships and winged aircraft, developed in 1913, notably by Captain Berry and Major Maitland, was still rather a spectacle than a life saving or practically useful operation, the exception being Grahame-White's demonstrations of supplies dropping by parachute. But parachuting by open-mouth parachute, often of the Guardian Angel type, from balloons was a programme item at many air meetings. The main items, however, were the air racing and the aerobatics. Hendon offered both and can be taken, for our present purpose, as typical of the air meeting places that were drawing crowds all over Europe.

Aircraft first acquired their competitive qualities in racing and attention concentrated upon speed. Climb and load carrying (or duration) came later. Distance events often started or finished at Hendon, but the events which were especially characteristic were the short races

160 Christiaens after one of his successful flights in a Blériot monoplane in Pretoria, South Africa, 1911

161 Ace racing pilot Lt Jean Conneau, who usually flew under the pseudonym André Beaumont, in his Gnome-engined Blériot, 1911

162 Art Smith, popularly known as 'The Human Comet', in his Curtiss biplane, 1913

163 The 1909 Paris Air Show

flown round pylons set up on the aerodrome periphery. They were flown round a course small enough to enable spectators to keep track of all the competitors all the time. The aim was to pull in large crowds by the same kind of cliff-hanging suspense which had attracted them to horse racing and then, at Brooklands, to motor racing. But aerial pylon racing had an added spice of danger.

The great variety in the shapes, sizes and behaviour of the machines contributed to the interest. The spectators pressed to the barriers as the weirdest collection of air-

164

Farman, then the much faster Blériot monoplanes and the even faster Morane-Saulniers. In many of these races a Deperdussin monoplane with 100 hp engine was the scratch or fastest machine and it was frequently piloted by Commander J. Porte who did important work on the design and construction of large flying-boats. Often Porte's take-off time would be when the slow box-kites were completing their first lap. The clash between the handicapped, high speed machines and the low speed ones never failed to produce superb action.

The racers came close to the spectators and the begoggled pilots, scarves streaming, could be clearly seen in their open cockpits, struggling for the lead, juggling with their flimsy aircraft, taking risks, and at the same time demonstrating manoeuvrability and speed. When rounding the pylons, the aircraft would often seem to be within inches of one another, and sometimes flying so low that an undercarriage wheel or a wing tip would brush the grass. It seems extraordinary that there were not more serious accidents. The widely different speeds of the aircraft seemed to invite trouble even though the top speeds of the fastest machines were, or would be thought now, modest.

Next to air racing as a public attraction came aerobatics. Pégoud, the first master of this art, had done almost everything that could be done with the machines of the prewar period. At Brooklands he had looped and done the bunt. The bunt was an advanced manoeuvre for it consisted in a steepening dive ending with an inverted pull-out, the aircraft upside down. In France Pégoud had landed his Blériot on a stretched wire, he

166

167

craft lined up for the start of a handicap pylon race. They were arranged facing into wind, but as close to the spectators as could be managed. There would be a great hurrying of mechanics and pilots, some wearing strange protective head gear, some in reversed cloth caps. Engines would be started. Then would occur the rite of running up. Mechanics, overalls flapping, would cling to the wings or drape themselves over fuselage or empennage to prevent the machines from going forward, while the pilot would open the throttle and check the revolutions. At this time chocks under the wheels were not in widespread use and the aircraft had no wheel brakes.

As the starter dropped his flag the mechanics would spring clear and each aircraft would take off at its allotted handicap time. First might be the box-kites or a Caudron, then perhaps a Maurice Farman or a Henry

had made a parachute descent from it and, some said, he had spun it although this point is in doubt. At Hendon Bentfield C. Hucks, who had taught himself to fly at Filey in Yorkshire, was an apt follower of Pégoud. He looped, flew upside down, did side slips and steep spirals (not true spins). Hucks was a specialist with Blackburn monoplanes, but he used a Blériot for his aerobatics. It had additional 'landing wires' as they were called from the central cabane to the wings to give extra strength in inverted flight.

Gustav Hamel emulated Hucks with his Morane-Saulnier, a splendid-looking, small, rather square little monoplane with rotary engine. The French pilot Chevillard in a Henry Farman did his own particular form of aerobatics, with many almost vertical side slips as part of the repertoire. There were also Brindejonc de Moulinais, in a Morane-Saulnier, and Marcus Manton in a Grahame-White box-kite to give spectators displays of manoeuvrability.

Although aerobatics had begun to develop early – the Russian P. N. Nesteroff is said by some to have looped before Pégoud – it was not until the Hendon meetings that the larger public became aware of them and of how far the control of aircraft in free flight had gone. People became as taken with aerobatics as they are now with a popular song. The interest was shared by Britain's royal family and Gustav Hamel was called by King George V to give a command performance at Windsor. Hamel, a dashing, exceptionally good-looking youth, with a propensity for hurtling about in noisy, high speed automobiles, was the son of one of King Edward's doctors. He was as prominent in racing as in aerobatics and showed his will to win by increasing the speed of his Morane-Saulnier by the simple but highly unorthodox process of chopping large bits off the wing tips. This reduced the span and thus the drag but it also increased the wing loading, making the aircraft difficult to handle and causing it to take a longer run at take-off and landing.

Yet another Hendon indicator of aviation progress were the night flying meetings. Grahame-White had himself given night flying a start in the 1910 London-Manchester race when he took off at night, aided only by car headlamps, in an attempt to gain ground on his adversary Louis Paulhan. The Hendon night flying was a striking example of the almost mystical faith pilots of that time put in their personal aptitude. Today's pilots, in their heavily automated machines, seated in warmed, closed cockpits, specially designed to exclude glare from instrument or other lights, must be incredulous at the fantastic performances of the night flyers of before the 1914-18 war. They went up at night unprotected against glare with the crudest instrumentation and with every-thing optical weighted against them.

Pierre Verrier would take off and fly round to the plaudits of the mob in a box-kite festooned with coloured lights, so that it looked like a levitated Christmas tree. How he avoided dazzle is one of history's unsolved mysteries. To-day it is known that human powers of orientation are unable to cope unaided with darkness, fog or cloud. Yet Captain de Havilland flew aircraft of his own design within clouds without mishap and without a turn and bank indicator or artificial horizon. Later in

168

169

his life he explained this extraordinary feat by saying that when he was young he flew safely within clouds because he did not then know that it was impossible!

Air meetings, therefore, were teaching the world about flying. They were also suggesting to many the part that flying might play if war were to come. And they were sowing the seeds of the fast growing aircraft industries that would be needed to produce the aircraft that would be used in war.

The armies of European countries were beginning to look at aircraft with serious intentions. By 1910 the interest of the German Army in the Zeppelin dirigible airship as an instrument of war was clear, and two years later Germany turned to large scale aircraft production and, like Britain, established a military flying school.

By the end of 1910 the French Army had bought its first aeroplanes and had 60 trained pilots (at this time the

168 Hendon at the start of the Aerial Derby of 1912

169 Hendon, 1911, with a Farman airborne and a 'new' (*left*) and an 'old' Blériot on the ground

qualifications including three cross-country flights of at least 100 kilometres or 62 miles each at an altitude of 300 metres or just under 1,000 ft), and the following year held its first Concours Militaire at Reims for aircraft that could be used in war, a two-seater Nieuport being among the earliest armed machines. Rifles and machine guns were soon to be seen in aircraft of many countries.

In the United States Curtiss pioneered bombing tests with dummy bombs on Lake Keuka as early as June 1910,

and a few months later a Wright machine was used for the first live bomb test, by the US Army, at San Francisco. Bombs were first used in action in the Tripolitanian War of 1911. Lieutenant Gavotti, avoiding rifle fire from the ground at a height of 2,500 ft, dropped four bombs on a Turkish encampment on 1 November 1911. (Bombs were used again against the Turks in the Balkan War of 1912-13, when Bulgarian pilots dropped them by hand on Turkish-held Adrianople.) Another Italian, Captain Piazza, made the first military use of an aero-

170

172

171

plane with his hour-long reconnaissance flight to observe Turkish positions on 22 October 1911.

The year 1911 saw another event fraught with military implications. At San Francisco Eugene Ely landed and took off again from the deck of a cruiser; this feat, together with his take-off from the deck of another cruiser the previous year, constituted the first practice of aircraft carrier technique.

In Russia Igor Sikorsky, born in Kiev in 1889, one of aviation's supreme geniuses whom we shall consider later not only in connection with helicopters but also with flying-boats, entered for a number of military competitions. He decided as early as 1911 that great size increases were needed if aircraft were ever to fulfil their weight carrying potential. He completed in early 1913 his first four-engined landplane. Sikorsky himself did the test flying of this machine. He did the same for his second four-engined machine in 1914, the *Ilia Mourometz*.

The 1914 aircraft made a notable flight between Petrograd and Kiev and return, a distance of 1,600 miles. And Sikorsky machines set world records for Russia in distance, weight lifting and altitude. It is also generally claimed that the Sikorsky four-engined aircraft of 1913 was the first four-engined machine to fly. It was called the *Grand* and it was powered by four 100 hp engines driving tractor airscrews. The wing cells were four-bay with a large overhang, braced by angled interplane struts so that the span of the top plane was much larger than that of the lower plane. The fuselage was of rectangular section and there was a monoplane tailplane.

In Britain Grahame-White, always with his finger on the pulse of the public, began to notice the significance of the drawing together of the kind of aviation he was purveying as a public spectacle and military aviation. Lord Northcliffe, by offering big money prizes through his paper the *Daily Mail* for aviation achievements, races and records, was preaching air power for the sake of national defence. He pleaded, shouted and stormed for ever greater efforts to build more and faster aircraft. Grahame-White rode on this press campaign, introducing at the Hendon meetings simulated war incidents. There were 'attacks' by aircraft on cardboard forts and lath and canvas battleships, there were 'bombing' raids with sacks of flour. It was all designed to suggest the omnipotence of aircraft in war and the need for any country concerned in its own defence to look to its air forces.

Men like Colonel Sir John Capper, who pioneered the use of balloons for army purposes, and Major F. S. Baden-Powell, who experimented with man-lifting observation kites for reconnaissance, gave the popular defence anxieties fostered by Lord Northcliffe a professional military slant. Although the Royal Navy was officially preoccupied with airships as reconnaissance vehicles for battle fleets, there were increasing numbers of naval officers in England, France and Germany who foresaw the potentialities of the winged flying machine in a war at sea. And there was Farnborough.

The Royal Aircraft Factory at Farnborough was another link between aviation as such and military requirements. It emerged from Her Majesty's Balloon Factory whose Superintendent was Colonel J. L. B. Templer. Templer, it was said, was so much in love with machinery that he would take his wife shopping in a trailer towed by a steam traction engine. He and Capper, of the Royal Engineers, must have the credit for forming what has become, under the name of the Royal Aircraft Establishment, one of the outstanding world centres of aeronautical knowledge.

During its early years, Farnborough became embroiled in a controversy which might have destroyed it. For as the increasing demand for aircraft, and the increasing funds which became available for building them, combined to sow the seeds of a large private sector aircraft industry, with the same kind of influences and the same kind of business pressures as other industries, so the authorities at Farnborough set up (as the original name implied) an *aircraft factory* or, in other words, a nationalized industry for the production of all kinds of aircraft but particularly of military aircraft. Several successful designers began work at Farnborough, H. P. Folland and Geoffrey de Havilland among them, and the factory there produced some good machines, which all showed some kind of originality and achieved a measure of success when they were used by the fighting forces – the BE (these initials being later variously interpreted as Blériot or Bristol or British Experimental), the RE (Reconnaissance Experimental) and the FE (Farman or Fighter Experimental), the FE series in-

173

174

cluding the larger two-seat pusher biplanes as well as the very small single-seat pusher, the FE.8. But the national factory plan failed.

Farnborough's bid for monopoly produced something approaching apoplexy in the new English aeronautical press. C. G. Grey had founded the *Aeroplane* in 1911. He was tall, elegant and eye-glassed, cantankerous, packed with prejudice, a master of the memorable phrase and capable of being stunningly rude. He waded into the plans for making Farnborough the centre of a nationalized aircraft industry. Such a move, he argued, would stultify design, eliminate inventiveness, condemn British aviation to perpetual inferiority and Britain herself to vulnerability before other countries with better developed aeronautical potentials.

Whipped up by the writings of journalists like Grey the public became suspicious of government intervention in aircraft production, so that when the defence authorities, the Royal Navy and the Army, began to call for the production of military and naval aircraft in quantity

173 Fischer and two passengers in a Farman at the Concours Militaire, Reims, 1911

174 An Italian Blériot about to land near Tripoli, after a reconnaissance of Turkish forces, 1911

everything was ripe for the formation and the rapid expansion of limited liability companies devoted to this purpose.

Three separate influences were now converging and producing one effect in Britain. There was, first, the education of the public in what winged flying machines were and what they could do in attack and defence. There was, second, the mounting threat of war. There was, third, the vigorous, almost hysterical specialist press contention that private, independent firms were the only

Fortunately many of the pioneers found the change within their scope so that no sharp boundary divided ideological aviation from industrial aviation. A. V. Roe turned from his battling with wood and fabric and wire, striving to coax his ephemeral creations into the air, to the founding of a solid company destined for financial and technical greatness, A. V. Roe Limited. Robert Blackburn, who had begun designing in Leeds after being inspired by the Santos-Dumont *Demoiselle* high wing monoplane, engaged in the production of his

175

176

177

178

ones which would be capable of designing and producing the kind of aircraft that would be needed for the national defence. The transition from peace to war was going on at the same time as the transition from the individual pioneer, who designed, built and flew his own aircraft, to the limited company. The change was from men with few pence in their pockets but many world-shaking ideas in their heads, to commercial organizations with few ideas in their heads but a determination to have plenty of pence in their pockets.

entirely individual monoplanes which were taken up for instructional purposes and put into production for various flying schools.

Frederick Handley Page, who had begun with gliders, founded one of Britain's greatest and longest lived, though not always most profitable, companies. A feature of Handley Page Limited was its insistence upon two qualities which interested Handley Page himself from the beginning—stability and safety. His early monoplanes, which were demonstrated at many meetings before the 1914-18 war, were unusual in having tapered, bird-like wings, with tip warping for control, somewhat resembling the German Rumpler company's Taube monoplanes.

Handley Page saw the stall, or loss of flying speed, as the villain of the piece. The stall was and long remained the chief cause of aerial accidents. Prior to 1914 Handley Page tried various forms of wing taper, wing camber and wing tip 'wash out' or twist, in order to offer pilots an aircraft which, if flown slowly, would not suddenly stall. In much later times he hit upon the best solution to this problem in conjunction with the German Professor Gustav V. Lachmann. This was the wing slot which he patented throughout the world.

The wing slot was a slot let into the wing close to the leading edge and also, perhaps, in the wing flaps. Its effect was to maintain a smooth flow of air over the wing at high angles of attack. An unslotted wing, when it is given a large angle of attack, produces a turbulent flow of air and lift is thus reduced. If the angle is increased further the turbulence increases until the wing loses all

not only because, in seaplane form, it was Britain's first successful entry for the Schneider Trophy race, but also because it was the foundation stone for the world's first successful tractor biplane fighter, the Sopwith Pup. The fortunes of the Sopwith Company were also linked to plenty of other famous military aircraft, the '1½ Strutter', the Camel and the Triplane.

Short Brothers, having started work on balloons, had turned to winged machines by 1909 and by 1913 had become Admiralty contractors. They made many float seaplanes and under Oswald Short's inventive inspiration they introduced a number of devices which have been in use in the world's navies ever since. They introduced folding wings to help in aircraft storage in the confined spaces available in warships and buoyancy bags such as are used by modern small boat sailors. Short's invention of all-metal, stressed skin construction (upon which German engineers were engaged at the same time as Short, but Short was the first to present an aircraft using this form of construction) was universally adopted by aircraft makers everywhere.

Martin and Handasyde, although they never achieved the prominence in the public eye of men like Roe, Handley Page and Sopwith, produced some fine aircraft from 1910 onwards. They built Sopwith one of his first machines. Concentrating originally on tractor monoplanes, they finally switched to biplanes to obtain military orders when the Army rejected the monoplane configuration as being basically unsafe. They used Antoinette engines in their first few aircraft, then went to Gnomes and Beardmores.

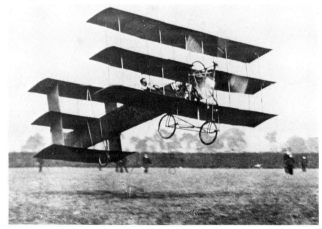

179

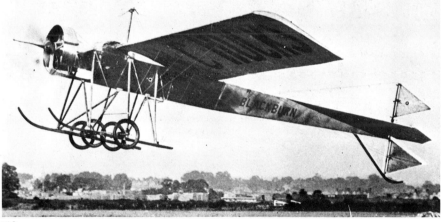

180

lift and stalls. The wing slot, by permitting some air to escape through the wing, delays the breakdown of flow.

T. O. M. Sopwith made his mark at first by his skill as a pilot. Like Grahame-White, he had attracted attention in the United States, particularly in 1911 when he made a tour there with a biplane in which he gave flying exhibitions. He collaborated with Howard Wright in many of his early designs, one of them a twin-engined aircraft. This was flown by the man who threw in his fortunes with Sopwith and became one of the best known pilots of all time, the Australian born Harry Hawker.

The name of Sopwith is associated with some of the most famous aircraft of the 1910-20 decade. There was the small neat, simple biplane known as the Tabloid. It has its place among the finest machines ever devised

One of the Martin-Handasyde pilots, Gordon Bell, became a legend among flying men and is remembered today for his power of surviving crashes and of devising apt and often devastating comments upon them—delivered with his pronounced stutter—for those who rushed to drag him from the wreckage.

In addition to the companies created and led by the pioneers—natural growth companies they might be called—there were the companies that moved into aviation because they saw it impinging upon their traditional interests. Vickers, Bristol and Armstrong Whitworth were among them.

Vickers created an aviation division in 1911 and began by building tractor monoplanes which looked rather like mixtures of Morane-Saulniers and Blériots, but in

179 A. V. Roe's triplane, the first all-British machine to fly successfully, 1909

180 1911 Blackburn monoplane as flown by Hucks

November 1912 the company abandoned the monoplane with which it entered the 1912 military trials when it was given a contract by the Admiralty to develop military aircraft. The biplane which finally emerged was the Vickers 'Gunbus'. This was originally intended to have a Wolseley engine, but was given a 100 hp Monosoupape in service. It was a rather square-looking machine, with pusher airscrew and tail booms and a nacelle for pilot and gunner projecting forward of the wings. In the air it answered well to powerful controls.

181

182

It had a remarkably successful term of service.

Bristol was originally a transport concern and its aviation division, based at Filton, was known as the British and Colonial Aeroplane Company. It founded its long and distinguished line of aircraft upon the Voisin and the Farman types and its Bristol Box-kites were extensively used for instruction, racing and general flying. It produced a series of sleeve-valve, air-cooled radial engines which were used by aircraft manufacturers in many different countries and which were among the most highly developed and successful piston aero-engines ever made.

181 Handley Page *Yellow Peril*, 1911

182 Short No 2 biplane built for Moore-Brabazon who, on 30 October 1909, won on it the *Daily Mail* prize of £1,000 for the first circular mile to be flown in Britain in a plane of all-British construction

183 Flow of air over and through unslotted and slotted wings. Lift increases as angle of attack increases up to the limit set by turbulence. Extension of the limit is obtained by 'natural control' with a leading edge slot (*bottom left*) or slot and flap (*bottom right*)

184 British Military Aeroplane Trials, September 1912. Lt Porte in a British built Deperdussin

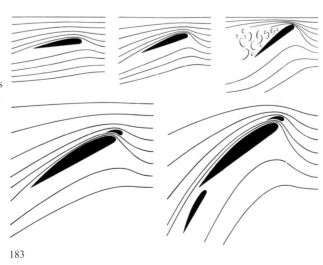

183

Here, then, were the prime origins of the great and wealthy British aircraft industry, an industry that was to swell up during the war of 1914-18 to record proportions, overtaking even France. In Germany as well as in France there had been the same kind of transformation from individual aircraft construction as an art or hobby to multiple aircraft construction as a commercial industry.

In France many of the companies that grew up to meet military demands arose from the work of the pioneers; Voisin, Blériot, Morane, Breguet, Deperdussin, Farman. In Italy several years were to pass before anything that could be called a separate aircraft industry was to appear. The French pilot Delagrange had given exhibition flights in Italy in 1907, but the country of da Vinci was slow to see or to take up the possibilities of military aircraft production.

In the United States no industry grew up comparable with that of Britain, France or Germany because the threat of war there was vague and indirect. Even Italy's aircraft industry was more productive than the American during this war. Also there was the hiatus in US aviation development which had been the outcome of an absence of worthwhile aeronautical publicity. American air meetings of the time tended towards being circus shows rather than essays in a new art.

The handful of US manufacturers that built aircraft during the war comprised mainly the Curtiss and Martin companies and the Wright concern, reconstituted after the United States' entry into the war on 6 April 1917.

The Wrights' first American company had been formed in 1909; a million dollars had been put up by a number of wealthy backers. But after Wilbur's death Orville had sold what was still a small enterprise. In the month of US entry into the war a group of Dayton and Detroit businessmen reorganized the company as Dayton-Wright, and when personnel of the new company were appointed to the Aircraft Production Board, Dayton-Wright came to be the country's biggest producer of aircraft during the war.

Glen Curtiss had begun to produce aircraft in 1908. He supplied flying-boats to the Navy and 'Jenny' trainers to the Army, and by the time of America's entry into the war his concern had developed sufficiently to be given large orders which it was able to fulfil.

Glenn Martin had begun with gliders and made his first powered machine, with a Ford Model T engine,

184

185

186

187

US Liberty engine. The Americans also bought aircraft from Britain and France, among them Sopwith Camels and Sopwith Dolphins.

In May 1914 an event full of dark implication occurred. Gustav Hamel took off to fly across the English Channel to France and was never heard of again. His loss was associated with many nervous wartime rumours; but it is almost certain that the rudimentary navigating equipment of the day proved inadequate for the weather conditions and that he simply flew on over the open sea

188

189

in 1909. He had set up a factory in Los Angeles in 1912, employing three engineers whose names were later to become famous—Donald W. Douglas, Lawrence D. Bell and James S. McDonnell. He supplied tractor biplanes to the Army from 1914, and later built a bomber, too late for use in the war.

The Thomas-Morse Corporation and Gallaudet were other US companies that built aircraft for the war. The founder of the latter, an electrical engineer, had built a biplane in 1909, and in 1912, after visits to the Nieuport factories in France, a monoplane of fabric-sheathed aluminium tubing and fitted with an excessively powerful 100 hp Gnome engine, the *Bullet*, and had been seriously injured while testing the aircraft.

When the United States entered the war the large military appropriations which had passed through Congress had not resulted in the building of aircraft on any scale. The only factory in the whole country capable of producing aircraft in any quantity was the Curtiss. And no American aeronautical engineer knew how to design an up-to-date combat machine. The Americans therefore selected Allied aircraft for production—the de Havilland 4 light bomber in quantity, the Handley Page O/400 and a three-engine Caproni bomber. The DH.4s and Handley Page O/400s were fitted with the

185 The Blériot monoplane flown by Grahame-White at Long Island, New York, 1911

186 Top Sopwith and Howard Wright, with a Wright Avis

187 Sopwith Tabloid, 1913, the third Sopwith plane to appear '

188 Verrier in a Maurice Farman biplane at the British Military Aeroplane Trials, September 1912

189 Military manoeuvres at Poitou, 1912, with Blériots predominating

190 Start of the 1910 Boston Aero Meet. No. 7 is Sopwith in a 70 hp Blériot; No. 3, the winner, is Grahame-White in a 100 hp Blériot; next is the American Earle Ovington in a 70 hp Blériot

190

until his fuel was exhausted as did many other ill-fated British ferry pilots. The third British Aerial Derby was flown a few days later while the tragedy of Hamel was still on everybody's lips. Then came a London to Manchester race in which the American pilot W. L. Brock was the winner. And Brock again won the London-Paris-London race less than one month before the outbreak of war. His victory might have been taken as symbolic of the French-British-American alliance that was to be created by the war.

191

After the colour and *réclame* of the great adventurers and inventors, aviation was plunged into a more studious, more serious, more scientific, more mournful and macabre period of development. Enthusiasts had to bid good-bye to the freaks and fantasies of the uninhibited pioneer and keep to the straight and narrow path which brought them into line with Army and Navy needs.

It is worth bringing together some critical dates for events already touched upon or to be discussed later. The air-

192

craft flown by Santos-Dumont in 1906, it will be recalled, was a canard type but basically a Hargrave box-kite. And for five or six years afterwards the box-kite formula held sway among the working machines over most of Europe while the Wright type biplane appeared alongside it. Outstanding achievements were put to the credit of these types of biplane while the monoplane, which had had a great deal of success among the gliders, remained rather in the background. Henry Farman's circular kilometre in 1908 was done in a Voisin biplane of the box-kite configuration and the Farmans founded their own series of biplanes upon it. In 1908, too, the Wrights appeared at Le Mans with their more elegant-looking

assisted take-off biplane. In 1909 attention was suddenly and dramatically turned from the biplane to the monoplane by Blériot's Channel flight, but, as we shall see, it was a temporary change. Biplanes particularly of the box-kite type were well established. Voisin biplanes were used for the first flights in Italy in 1907, by Léon Delagrange, and in Russia, Sweden and Austria in 1908.

Grahame-White and the Bristol company under Sir George White were both looking to the Hargrave-inspired biplane as the future flying machine. And the Bristol aircraft which was eventually to be called the 'Boxkite' made its first flight in the summer of 1910. Grahame-White's small two-seater with Gnome engine was broadly derived from the same kind of configuration as were his 1913 'Boxkite' (it also used this name) and his 'Charabanc' which was capable of carrying nine passengers. De Havilland's first aircraft, powered by an engine of his own design, was a biplane and the long series of BE machines from the finless BE.2b through the BE.2c with fin and staggered planes, were all biplanes. Perhaps most important from the British point of view, Cody concentrated, except for one inspired period, upon the biplane configuration from the moment of his 'powered kite' to the time of his successful military aircraft.

The biplane form fitted the knowledge and experience of the day. Ash and silver spruce with mahogany for some special parts were admirable woods for structural purposes and their qualities and limitations were well known to the craftsmen of the day. The handling of piano wire and of wire cable for bracing and for control runs was also within the experience of thousands of seamen so that the art of using wire and cable to the best advantage was well understood. And a box-kite biplane was a simple structure, with its cross-braced bays and outrigger booms. It appears in the light of past history that, because of its simplicity as a structure, as well as because of the work that had been done upon its aerodynamics, largely in Australia, the biplane configuration tended to hold the stage and to obscure the more fundamental or *aviational* qualities of the monoplane. There were, however, several interesting monoplanes and these could, with hindsight, be looked upon as pointers to the future.

In America the Walden monoplane made flights from Long Island towards the end of 1909. Although Bristol were concentrating upon the biplane, Henri Coanda, the company's gifted Romanian designer, had been thinking hard about the possibilities of monoplanes and in 1912, profiting from the impetus given by Blériot, he produced a most interesting monoplane design intended for military duties.

This aircraft looked as if it might set a trend but then, in 1912 at Oxford, it crashed killing its two occupants. It is generally supposed that it was this crash that influenced the British War Office when it placed a ban upon the monoplane configuration in the Military Wing of the Royal Flying Corps. The ban had far-reaching effects. It acted against monoplanes for several years and undoubtedly played a large part in causing the first war in the air to be fought mainly with biplanes.

The persistent belief that there was something about

the more bird-like monoplane configuration which gave it greater promise than the biplane was never entirely eliminated. Latham's Antoinette, to the designs of Levavasseur, had been admired by designers everywhere and in 1910 the Martin-Handasyde monoplane appeared with Antoinette engine and was succeeded in 1911 by a second machine which had been built to the orders of T. O. M. Sopwith. He had learnt to fly in a Howard-Wright biplane in 1910, doing so in one day, and he later concentrated upon biplanes. In 1911 another fine-looking monoplane appeared at Brooklands, the Flanders, intended for the Royal Flying Corps while a long and valuable line of monoplanes was introduced by Blackburn, some with Isaacson radial engines, but most with Antoinette or Gnome engines. These monoplanes had handwheel controls not unlike those of the Antoinette

and the pioneer aerobatic pilot B. C. Hucks used them for many of his demonstration flights. Handley Page began his experiments with crescent shaped wings with 'wash-out' at the tips to obtain lateral stability. There were also some exotic design attempts, notably the Lee-Richards annular wing machines, one of them a biplane, the other a monoplane.

Monoplane construction set the designers of this period more difficult problems than biplane construction. The Germans tended to move ahead of the rest of the world with their strictly engineering approach to the cantilever wing form, without external bracing wires. But during the war they employed biplanes and triplanes. They had no special inhibitions about monoplanes or biplanes. Taube monoplanes were being built by several different firms before they went into action in war and the Brandenburg company, which concentrated upon biplanes for its first seaplanes for the German Navy, later turned to monoplanes. The Fokker monoplane,

193 American pioneer aircraft manufacturer Glenn L. Martin

194 Nieuport monoplane, one of the types which inspired Gallaudet's designs for his *Bullet*

195 DH.4 day bomber, 1916

196 Caproni CA-7 four-engined bomber

197 Voisin with an Anzani engine flown in Italy in 1907

198 Cody's Army biplane at Laffan's Plain, 1911

199 Geoffrey de Havilland's second successful aircraft, which he flew in September 1910

200 Japanese biplane, the
'Otori', flying in England
1913

201 The first of Igor
Sikorsky's large aircraft,
the 'Grand' at St
Petersburg, 1913

202 Bristol-Coanda
monoplane, 1912

which made a name as a military aircraft in 1915, was first flown after war had broken out. The biplane Fokker single-seaters appeared later, the D.I in 1917, the D.VI and the Triplane later in the same year. The Mercedes engined D.VII was part of the final German air challenge in 1918.

The early French and British monoplanes had to use wings braced with 'landing wires' stretching outwards and downwards from a central cabane to pick-up points on the wing spars and 'flying wires' stretching upwards

200

201

202

102

and outwards from the underside of the fuselage or even from the main undercarriage members. Where a large wing span was used, as for instance in the Martin-Handasyde monoplane already mentioned, there was need to extend the structural bracing beyond the reach of both landing and flying wires because these could not be used at a very flat angle. In such cases king posts were fitted, mounted to the outer parts of the wings and with bracing wires extending outwards and inwards to produce adequate stiffness in what was often the rather flimsy region towards the wing tips.

It will be seen that the British War Office dislike of monoplanes was not a simple emotional response to the Oxford accident but had with it some sound supporting reasons, not least being the increased difficulty in bracing and producing a structurally sound monoplane wing especially of large span and high aspect ratio compared with the comparative ease of producing a structurally sound biplane wing cell. But in spite of the War Office, the attempts to design good monoplanes continued. And it would be wrong to think that biplanes were at this time showing much improved safety over monoplanes despite official views. C. S. Rolls had been killed in a Wright type biplane at Bournemouth in 1910 and Cody in one of his own biplanes in 1913.

In France, especially, monoplanes of handsome appearance and good performance began to appear in increasing numbers. Among them were the famous Morane-Saulniers. These were developed in various forms, the racers being small, stub winged aircraft with parallel sided wings with no sweep-back but with a longer trailing edge than the leading edge, making for outward sloping wing tips. Gustav Hamel was the outstanding Morane expert up to the time of his fateful Channel flight of May 1914. Moranes continued to win favour and the 'Bullet', as the racing machine was called, was partnered by novel variants, chief among them the Parasol with its single plane arranged above the fuselage. Deperdussin was another successful monoplane designer, whose aircraft at one time challenged the popularity of the Blériots and the Moranes.

But even among the French, who were not influenced by official decisions for or against monoplanes, the biplane gained ground as the war of 1914-18 came nearer. Breguet and Nieuport tended to concentrate upon biplanes.

France remained the dominant producer of aircraft up to the outbreak of war and for some time beyond it. In 1910 there were 350 pilots in France–the highest number of any country. And French aircraft held the speed record (127 mph), the height record (20,400 ft) and the distance record (635 miles). In addition to the successful Blériot and Deperdussin monoplanes, there was the stimulating and highly original Esnault-Pelterie which introduced the 'joy-stick' in something approaching its later form as a vertical column mounted on a universal joint and giving control in pitch and in roll. Control in yaw was obtained from the foot operated rudder pedals or from a rudder bar. Esnault-Pelterie flew his monoplane thus equipped at Buc in 1907 and the scheme went forward uninterrupted so that this designer's work may be said to be represented in the controls of almost every aircraft that is flying.

Engine progress during the period stretching from the date of the Wright brothers' experiments of 1903 to the outbreak of war in 1914 was dominated, just as aircraft progress was dominated, by French designers and constructors. The critical part played by the Antoinette engine and its astonishing 'modernity' have been discussed. The radial Anzani was also a fine piece of logical thinking for it was designed on the principle that the simpler the construction and the fewer the parts, the greater the trustworthiness. And the Anzani not only enabled many of the great pioneering flights in Europe to be made, but it also enabled the United States to initiate their monoplane development with the Anzani-engined Walden.

The Antoinette and the Anzani were power units primarily created for aircraft, though the Antoinette aero-engine was partly derived from engines for racing motorboats. In addition there was the liquid-cooled Canton Unné and a whole range of aircraft engines which came from the French motor car companies, many of them through the stimulating avenue of automobile racing. The English experimenter J. W. Dunne, whose highly original tailless, swept-wing biplane has been discussed, turned to French engines for his experiments and installed Buchet power units in one of his most important models. The Buchet was a straight-forward liquid-cooled, in-line engine highly successful in small cars. It was rather heavier for its power than some of the specialized engines – the Antoinette for instance – but it was trustworthy. Cody was impressed by the Buchet and tried to obtain one for his powered kite.

But undoubtedly the greatest advance in aero-engines was the air-cooled Gnome rotary, with its successor the Gnome Monosoupape. The Gnome and Monosoupape engines were the most successful power units of the 1914-18 war. They and their derivatives and imitations were employed in tens of thousands of aircraft, German and Allied. The French Le Rhône engines were legitimate offspring of the Gnome. The German Oberursel and the British Bentley were offspring of the Gnome but less obviously legitimate.

There were also stationary power units of more conventional design than the rotaries. Among these again the French were in the van: the air-cooled Renault, in different powers from 80 hp upwards, was used extensively by Britain in training and operational machines. Farnborough produced its RAF engine which was an obvious imitation of the Renault while the Cirrus light aircraft engine of the postwar period used Renault parts. The Cirrus helped to make the reputation of Major Frank Halford who later designed the famed Gipsy piston engines and all the de Havilland turbojets.

Germany showed a national preference for the in-line, liquid-cooled stationary engine and her Mercedes units were almost certainly the best in this class. They were normally six-cylinder engines and they added first rate reliability to reasonable lightness for power. Austro-Daimlers were used extensively in German aircraft during the early period, but the Mercedes, though similar, was developed in a slightly different direction. Italy also sought to develop aero engines of the in-line

203

205

kind and the name of Fiat became established in the aviation world. But from whatever angle engine development is looked at before and during the 1914-18 war, the French effort stands out far beyond all others.

French engines made flying. Britain had tried hard with the Green, the Isaacson, the ABC and, later, Beardmore, Napier and Rolls-Royce; but until late in the war they were insignificant contributions compared with France's achievements. America seemed to be incapable of thinking in terms of low frontal area and high power to weight ratio until her Liberty liquid-cooled V engine, designed with extraordinary speed and skill in 1917, resulted in a very effective 400 hp motor used in thousands for more than a decade thereafter.

204

203 65 hp Austro-Daimler four-cylinder engine, 1913

204 Fokker M.5L of 1915 with Anthony Fokker in the cockpit

205 Testing the propeller thrust on a Martin-Handasyde monoplane at Brooklands, 1911. Handasyde is crouched under the wing

8 War in the air

206

Flying received an enormous quantitative impulse from the war of 1914-18 as it did again from the war of 1939-45. Aircraft multiplied, so did pilots. Aircraft constructing companies increased in size and in numbers. More scientists, technical men and workers were engaged upon aeronautical tasks. More information about flying made its way to the general public. More aerodromes were established. Yet we must note that the development of flying *as such* was undoubtedly held up by the war. Progress made during the period of hostility was concerned more with military achievement than with aeronautical.

It was in Europe that flying was to march to war, backed up by a great and growing production industry. The United States, which was destined to become the greatest of all the world's air powers, was at this time an aeronautically backward nation. Apart from the efforts of half a dozen men, Glen Curtiss among them, there were few signs that the Wright brothers' initiative was being followed. After nervously buying one Wright biplane in 1909 the United States government hastily closed its coffers against aviation. Grahame-White's visit to the United States in 1910 and his call by air upon President Taft had generated public excitement in the Americans but had done little to induce in Congress any desire to call for government participation in flying and had done even less to bring about the foundation of an aircraft industry. It was not until March 1915 that the Advisory Committee for Aeronautics (which later became the National Advisory Committee for Aeronautics or NACA, and ultimately the National Aeronautics and Space Administration or NASA) was

104

established to 'supervise and direct the scientific study of the problems of flight, with a view to their practical solution.'

When war was declared France was still in the technical and numerical lead. She had three times the number of qualified pilots of Britain and about four times the number of practical aircraft. Britain was about level with Germany with 400 pilots. The United States had fewer than 200.

France and Germany saw aviation as an integral part of armies and navies, like a new kind of gun. In Britain, however, a separate corps was formed on 13 April 1912 within the British Army; it was called the Royal Flying Corps; its Central Flying School was opened two months later in Wiltshire. It had a seemingly anomalous 'Naval Wing' but this was soon transmuted into the Royal Naval Air Service to become as much a part of the Royal Navy as the RFC was of the Army. And the Navy was determined not to be left behind in training. Just before the formation of the Central Flying School Mr Winston Churchill, then First Lord of the Admiralty, announced in the Navy Estimates (March 1912): 'The buildings and sheds for the Naval Aviation School are in course of erection.' He was referring to Eastchurch.

Tweedledum and Tweedledee exhibited a no less ludicrous rivalry than the RFC and the RNAS. And it went on and on in jealous squabbles through most of the 1914-18 war and appeared again even after the Royal Air Force had been formed on 1 April 1918.

As good a way as any of telling the strictly aviation story of the war years is to trace the career of a sample

The often dangerous methods which had to be adopted for turning out qualified military pilots had a lasting influence on flying instruction after the 1914-18 war and onwards even to the present day. The process of learning, at the flying schools of Europe, was progressive. The pupil would learn to run the engine, to operate the controls, to read the two or three rudimentary instruments. He then undertook rolling exercises. He would position his aircraft at the lee side of the aerodrome and make runs into the wind at progressively higher speeds. Then there would come short hops, in which the pilot would allow his machine to lift a few inches from the ground and bring it down again still on the same heading by cutting the power. The manoeuvre of turning in the air was the next and the most difficult and dangerous stage.

There was urgent need for an instructor who could not only take the pupil up as passenger and give him advice, but also help him to learn how to use the controls in the air and, above all, save him if he used them wrongly. So after the plain gamble which the learners on Caudrons at Hendon, on Bristol box-kites at Bristol and on Voisin, Caudron and Farman biplanes at Issy-les-Moulineaux undertook, there came in dual control.

But many training machines were without dual control even after the outbreak of war. Some of the pusher biplanes had the instructor-pilot's position in front of the small nacelle with the pupil-passenger sitting behind him and on a higher level so that the passenger's knees and feet were on either side of the pilot's body. Although the pupil could reach over and place his hands

207

service pilot—it may be modelled upon the experiences of many—from the time he was taught to fly, to the time he entered a first line squadron and went into action and from there through his combat experiences to his end when he was either shot down or transferred to non-operational duties. If we succeed in sketching it truthfully, this sample service pilot's career in 1914-18 will reflect the course of flying's progress during this restless interlude.

on the control stick and wheel—they were called the 'spectacles'—used for elevator and ailerons, and although he also had duplicated engine throttle, he had no means of learning by example how to operate the rudder. On aerodromes all over the engaged countries, thousands of young volunteers were assembling to be taught to fly in this manner.

The preferred aircraft for elementary training in Britain was the Maurice Farman Longhorn. This was

207 Robey-built Maurice Farman Longhorn in service with RNAS, 1913

a biplane with a much larger span top plane than bottom, with a biplane empennage, two rudders and with two elevators, one in the empennage, the other carried well forward of the main wing cells on outriggers. The undercarriage had two twin wheels and there was a tail skid. The number of struts and wires needed to hold this contraption together must have set an all-time world record. The rigging was described by cynics as 'built-in resistance'.

The engine was usually the air-cooled V Renault and

experience. Having learnt how to get a floppy old Maurice Farman Longhorn into the air, how to make it fly properly, how to climb, to turn, to descend and to land, the pilot would apply his knowledge to faster, more sensitive, more demanding types of aircraft. Finally he assembled experience in the air, experience of different types of aircraft, experience of cross country flying, map reading and navigation, and experience of night flying. After all this our pilot would be adjudged ready to go into the fighting line.

208

mounted behind the nacelle it drove a pusher propeller. The pilot, sitting in front of the nacelle with the pupil immediately behind him, was protected by a windscreen. But the passenger, with the upper part of his head permanently exposed to the blast of the relative airstream and with the propeller churning energetically inches behind the back of his neck, was less luxuriously accommodated.

The time spent by each novice before going solo was astonishingly short. Men who had never before been up in an aircraft, who might never even have seen one, went solo after one hour and a half of instruction and sometimes less time than that. After the first world war, the time before going solo in the flying schools, where the trainers had full dual control and speaking tubes, was normally eight to ten hours. The early pilots were given crash courses of instruction and the accent was woefully often upon the word crash.

A pilot who survived his elementary instruction had to go through a course of advanced instruction and then to take up a post in which he could accumulate air

In Chapter 2 a difficulty was mentioned which sometimes puzzled the pioneers: the relationship between the free flying aerodyne and the ocean of air within which it is suspended. This difficulty also faced the pupils of the war period. It had to be hammered into them that an aircraft in free flight is not only *in* the air, but also *of* the air. Air speed, for example, is hardly ever the same as speed over the ground. The pupil had to learn that when once he had taken off his aircraft was suspended in an ocean which had its own tidal streams but that these streams would have no effect on the aircraft's movements except in relation to the land. His machine would be making its own wind–a relative wind–and that would be blowing all the time, almost directly from nose to tail.

At take-off and at landing, however, with the aircraft at the interface between earth and air, the pupil had to pay close attention to the natural wind. Early aircraft, with top speeds not much more than average natural wind speeds, had to be pointed exactly into the wind. And this preoccupation of pilots with the natural wind led to the introduction of what has become known throughout the world as the emblem of aerodromes and landing strips – the wind sleeve or wind sock, a fabric cone open at both ends and hoisted on a flag staff or high post, an indicator not only of wind direction but also of wind strength and state of turbulence. Modern aircraft approaching to land at high air speeds, over 200 ft per second, can take off and land safely with large cross wind components. But a Maurice Farman Longhorn pilot, wobbling and waffling in on his approach glide at 65 or 70 ft per second, became as he touched down a plaything of the natural wind.

Our typical service pilot, having learnt to fly a Maurice Farman Longhorn in the hazardous manner outlined, and just as he was beginning to like it and to have confidence, would be whisked away by the military authorities for advanced training. This was the time when either the joy of flying would come to him and possess him completely or when he would develop antipathy for it and seek to give it up. He would be likely to find himself flying the Avro 504, probably powered by that *prima donna* of early engines, the 60 or 80 hp Gnome rotary. Everything would seem different to our pupil. The beautiful little Avro was in contrast to the flimsy, spidery, tangled, cat's cradle Longhorn. The Gnome was much less reliable than the Renault, but it buzzed in a curiously attractive manner and flung out hot castor oil, which gave it a clinging perfume all its own.

So the pupil, after a period of nervousness at attempting to fly this elegant fast (80 knots perhaps!) biplane, would come suddenly to adore it. He would suddenly become aware of why men, over the ages, had striven to realize the dream of winged flight. But once again, just as he was gaining confidence, just as, armed with information given him in lectures, he had achieved a few modest cross country flights, he would be whisked away from his advanced training and put in some job in which he would get plenty of flying hours and plenty of air experience. In Britain, the posts suitable for this stage were many, but we will place our prototype pilot in one of the most interesting, one which not only enabled the pupil to gather flying experience quickly, but also to make the acquaintance of many different types of aircraft. This was the post of ferry pilot for the armed forces in France.

The first units of the Royal Flying Corps left for France on 11 August 1914, a few days after the outbreak of war. From that moment on there developed a ferry service for moving new aircraft made in England to the aerodromes in France and a body of ferry pilots was built up, starting with a few officers stationed at Farnborough. They were presented with a feast of flying machines. Had it not been for the shadow of war, ferry piloting

210

211

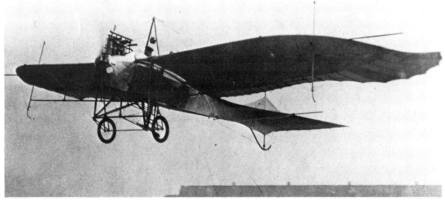

212

offered the enthusiastic airman a perfect opportunity for practising and developing his art.

In the first stages of the war monoplanes were used a great deal. Number 1 Squadron of the Royal Flying Corps was equipped with Morane-Saulnier Parasols, a delicate but highly efficient monoplane with the wings mounted on a *cabane* well above the top of the nicely streamlined fuselage (hence the name 'Parasol'). The French were using the ordinary high wing Morane-Saulnier which was almost the same as Gustav Hamel's racing machine and, later, the midwing 'Bullet'. The Moranes had Le Rhône rotaries, some of 80 hp, some of 110. The Germans were using their Rumpler Taubes and, shortly afterwards, their Fokker Eindeckers or monoplanes with Oberursel rotary engines.

209 Morane-Saulnier Type P parasol monoplane, 1916

210 Morane-Saulnier Type G with 80 hp Gnome engine

211 Morane-Saulnier Type BB biplane, 1915

212 Rumpler Taube taking off at Cologne, 1913

209

Although ferry pilots immediately after the outbreak of war had to be familiar with the handling of monoplanes, they soon found themselves flying biplanes as a result of the official decision of the British military authorities, who, turning a blind eye to the birds, took it into their heads that monoplanes were basically unsafe and forced British aircraft makers to concentrate upon biplanes. So the ferry pilots of the 1915 period onwards found themselves flying the oddest assortment of biplanes across the water that Louis Blériot had first conquered in a monoplane.

Although the United States Congress had authorized the creation of an aviation section of the American armed forces in July 1914, British, French and German aircraft were in an overwhelming majority. The first US Aero Squadron was sent to the battle zone in August 1917. The Curtiss trainer known as the Jenny was the only American landplane to attract much attention in Europe. It was used by the RFC and the RNAS. As we shall see when marine aircraft are considered, Curtiss flying-boats, with Curtiss engines, were early on the scene and were a stimulus to world flying-boat progress. Also US engineering abilities were devoted to the production of power plants, the Hispano-Suiza, for instance, being built under licence by Wright-Martin. The 400 hp V12 Liberty engine was, as we have seen, US designed.

All aircraft of this period can be divided into two classes: pushers and tractors. The Maurice Farman Longhorn, as we have seen, had its engine and airscrew mounted *behind* the nacelle accommodating pilot and passenger so that it was a *pusher* biplane. But the Avro

504 had its engine and airscrew out in front, with the airscrew *pulling* the aircraft through the air. It was a *tractor*. With the coming of jet engines the distinction between pushers and tractors disappeared but until then it was fundamental. Strictly speaking we should confine the term 'propeller' to a pusher airscrew, but the word has been debased and is now used indifferently for both pusher and tractor airscrews.

In addition to the wing cell configuration – biplane, triplane, etc. – and the drive configuration – pusher or

215

tractor – there were other flying machine sub-divisions, among them the manner in which the planes of a multiple aircraft were superimposed. They were usually given forward 'stagger', meaning that the top plane was arranged ahead of the lower one, but they could have backward stagger as in the famous backward stagger DH.5 designed by de Havilland in 1916 and much used in France, the Sopwith Hippo and a few others.

At first military aircraft designers were especially concerned with the choice between pushers and tractors. Their choice was affected by what was eventually recognized as a fundamental, unchanging principle of aerial combat.

In order to come to grips in aerial battle, aircraft crews had to be able to bring weapons to bear. But aircraft were awkward bases from which to fire guns or rockets. Naval officers believed that in an engagement aircraft would fly alongside one another on nearly parallel courses and fire guns pointing out from the sides – equivalent to the battleship's broadside. The alternative of pointing the whole of an aircraft directly at another

213

213 Curtiss Jenny (JN-4) in camouflage, 1918

214 Liberty motors being built at Packard works, 1918

215 De Havilland DH.5, 1916

216 Lewis gun installation in an RE.7

214

seemed fraught with difficulty. How could fire be brought to bear directly in the line of flight?

If a gun were mounted in any of the monoplanes, Morane, Blériot, Deperdussin, Blackburn, Fokker or Rumpler, the airscrew blades would get in the way of the bullets. Guns firing aft, as from the observers' seats of BEs, REs and Sopwith 1½-Strutters, could not be used for attack, only for defence against another aircraft coming up from the rear.

It was an excruciating problem for the designers of the

217

219

tractor aircraft – monoplane, biplane or triplane – to fire forwards without risking shooting off the airscrew blades. One solution was stunningly simple. The French pilot Eugène Gilbert fitted steel deflector blocks to the airscrew blades of his Morane and successfully used a St Etienne machine gun mounted immediately behind the airscrew, on top of the fuselage, in front of the pilot's eyes where he could aim it. Gilbert, with this gun or with a similarly arranged Hotchkiss, shot down an Aviatik in January 1915. Those serving in RFC squadrons at

this time believed that the Germans learnt of Gilbert's invention from the machine of Roland Garros when he was shot down and that they copied it in their Fokker monoplanes. But the idea was soon superseded by proper interruptor or synchronizing gear (described later).

A host of small, quick aircraft with forward firing guns began to appear: Sopwith Pup, Sopwith Camel, Sopwith triplane, DH.5, SE.5, Nieuport, Spad, Albatros, Fokker monoplane, biplane and triplane, Halberstadt, Pfalz, and others.

We now return to our sample service pilot to find out how these gunnery and aircraft configuration theories worked in actual battle. We left him on ferrying duties, flying new aircraft from factory aerodromes to military stations and across the Channel from England to the French aircraft parks at St Omer, Candas and other places. He had become familiar with a wonderfully varied selection of machines. He had acquired practical knowledge of rotary and stationary, air-cooled and liquid-cooled engines and most important of all, he had begun to learn how to find his way in the air.

Navigation was mostly by guess and by God, with a bit of map reading thrown in. Our pilot will have lost

day. Mounting a gun high on the top plane could take it outside the airscrew disc, but this entailed remote control of the gun and other difficulties. In the end a radical arrangement was introduced in Britain. The whole aircraft was replanned to produce the Pusher Scout, a single-seat fighter exemplified by the DH.2 and the FE.8.

The aircraft was made to fit the gun, rather than the gun to fit the aircraft. The pilot was seated in a small nacelle stuck out in front with engine and airscrew behind. It was an essentially Farnborough solution. Colonel Mervyn O'Gorman was steering the Royal Aircraft Factory, as it was still called, towards technical pre-eminence and a whole series of FE aircraft, all pushers, was produced. ('FE', commonly thought to be an abbreviation of Fighter Experimental, is stated by Harald Penrose, himself a noted aviation pioneer and test pilot, to mean 'Farman Experimental'.) The small FE.8 pusher biplane was a highly sensitive machine, but in action the pusher scout concept was mainly represented by the DH.2 (Captain de Havilland was still at Farnborough).

Although the pusher scout was a brilliant intellectual exercise – giving its pilot a completely uninterrupted field of view and of fire in a forward direction and combining this with quick manoeuvrability – it was soon displaced by tractor scouts offering a different solution to the fighting in the air and gun fire problems. The prime reason for this displacement was aeronautical. Higher speeds, higher rates of climb and superior manoeuvrability were obtained with the tractor arrangement, whether monoplane, biplane or triplane. There had never been difficulty about providing an uninterrupted field of forward fire when air performance and manoeuvrability were of secondary importance. The earliest Voisins had it, with their observer-gunners well out in front. The FE.2b two-seater also had its observer-gunner so sited and so did the Vickers Gunbus.

The problem remained how to enable the pilot of a

217 Voisin pusher biplane with cannon, 1917

218 British Deperdussin military two-seater, 1913

219 De Havilland DH.2 fighter, 1916

himself when trying to deliver aircraft not once, not twice but at least a dozen times. He will have learnt how visibility can play tricks with map reading.

The lengths to which airmen went when they lost their way were hazardous and sometimes comic. A pilot whizzing over the confused pattern of the countryside, hopelessly lost, would come down and, to the consternation of the commuters waiting for the nine-fifteen, would fly very low past a railway station in order to read the name of the station.

223

220

224

221

222

225

220 Vickers FB.9 Gunbus

221 Aviatik C.1 trainer, 1915

222 Fokker in the cockpit of an M.5 ready for a demonstration of its synchronizing mechanism for firing through the propeller

223 Sopwith 1½-Strutter, 1915

224 Sopwith Pup, 1916

225 Pfalz D.III, 1916/17

reached a scale never known before and not exceeded by the casualty rate of the second world war. The artillery bombardments never ceased so that the ground in the battle areas was utterly devastated and evoked a shock of horror in airmen who looked down on it for the first time. Over these ghastly, mutilated areas of France's beautiful land, military pilots were enjoined to debase the art of flying.

Let us now look at these small, fragile, vulnerable, sensitive flying machines as they meet and swirl in aerial battle and speed out and back on their reconnaissance, artillery observation, photographic, bombing, close support and other duties.

The opposing pressures were clear. An aircraft would go to reconnoitre or to spot for artillery and the immediate defensive demand would be for it to be driven away or shot down. Anti-aircraft guns and small arms fire were soon found to be inadequate as a defence against enemy aircraft. All was set for a clash of opposites.

Gabriel Voisin relates the details of the first conclusive aerial combat in his autobiography. Joseph Frantz and his mechanic Quenault, in a Voisin pusher biplane on 5 October 1914, saw an Aviatik below them. They dived

Having painfully assimilated this kind of practical navigational knowledge, having survived several forced landings–as much by luck as by judgment–our pilot will be adjudged qualified and will receive his 'wings'.

Our pilot is posted to an operational squadron in France. There the slaughter of infantry soldiers had

upon it. The Aviatik observer had a rifle but his field of fire was restricted by the Aviatik's empennage. Quenault took aim with his Hotchkiss and pressed the trigger. The first victims of aerial combat fell in flames on the French side of the lines. It was the beginning of the end of aviation's benign image. This incident preyed on Gabriel Voisin's mind and eventually caused him – one of the greatest air pioneers and most successful designers and constructors – to abandon aviation altogether.

Next came what English language newspapers called the 'Fokker scourge' when German pilots in Fokker monoplanes with forward firing guns attacked Allied BE.2cs and RE.8s and shot them out of the sky. French and British aircraft were called 'Fokker fodder'.

The Allied reply was made with DH.2 pusher scouts at first, then Sopwith Pup and Nieuport scout tractor biplanes with forward firing guns. The Pup mounted a Vickers gun with mechanical interruptor gear which momentarily checked firing as the airscrew blades passed. Fighting in the air exploded in furious multiple combats.

Often aerial battles would start when, say, an Allied formation was sent out on photographic reconnaissance. A flight of two-seater FE.2bs might go out with an escort of Sopwith Pups and Nieuports. When over the region to be photographed they would be swamped with accurate German anti-aircraft fire from ground batteries and then attacked by the German fighters.

Fokkers, Albatros V-Strutters – small tractor biplanes with forward firing guns and Mercedes or Austro-Daimler engines – and Halberstadts with Argus engines would rush in upon the FEs in steeply diving attacks. The Pups and Nieuports, reinforced later by the backward-stagger DH.5s, would then go to the rescue. The German fighter pilots engaged with immense dash. Allied pilots were stubbornly courageous. Ever more machines were involved. Formations of 20 and 30 and then of still larger numbers clashed in whirling, swooping conflicts, the aircraft glinting in the sunlit air at as much as three miles above the brown, battle-scarred countryside.

During the first three years of the war the single-seat fighter aircraft bore individual markings and in 1916 and 1917 these reached high levels of fantasy, the whole of the aircraft often being painted in some special design. Here and there paintings of some artistic merit were to be seen on the wings and fuselages of Pups, Nieuports and other aircraft. Elaboration carried this decoration far beyond the original purpose, which was to allow the pilots to identify one another in battle. Later these markings were mostly given up for stylized squadron markings.

We have seen that, at the outbreak of the war, monoplanes were in use on both sides. Britain, in spite of the War Office disapproval of the monoplane, was using French machines of this type partly because they were the best available. The Germans were using their Taube monoplanes of various makes. But as the war in the air built up so the trend towards the biplane, artificially stimulated by the War Office decision, asserted itself. The Royal Flying Corps replaced its Moranes with DH.2s and FE.8s, then with DH.5s,

Sopwith Pups, Sopwith Camels, Sopwith Dolphins and SE.5s. The Royal Naval Air Service reinforced the Royal Flying Corps as the war proceeded and brought in Nieuport biplane fighters, Camels and triplanes. The French, after their Moranes and Nieuports, introduced their Spad biplanes. Italy's 140 mph Ansaldo fighter, with six-cylinder in-line engine, played a part.

But here may be noted a development which seemed to emerge from the exigencies of aerial combat because both Britain and Germany were involved in it at almost the

226

227

same time. Striving for yet higher performance and yet greater fighting power, British and German constructors took to the triplane. Sopwith produced the Sopwith triplane and Fokker, the Dutchman working for the Germans, produced the Fokker triplane. The Armstrong Whitworth and the White quadruplanes were attempts to go one further, but they failed.

The triple configuration was championed for various reasons; chiefly because it allowed higher aspect ratio planes (i.e. long, slender wings) than biplane or monoplane while retaining the structural advantages of the easy box girder bracing of the biplane. The Sopwith triplane was produced in 1916 and it attracted the admiration of experienced pilots for its high performance, its excellent

226 Sopwith Camel, 1916

227 Nieuport XI

111

handling qualities, particularly at height, and its good—though specialized–field of view. The three high aspect ratio planes were arranged with one below the fuselage, one on top of it and the third raised above upon a dual strut centre section.

Various engines were used, mostly the Clerget, and with this the top speed was 120 mph. The armament in the early models was a single Vickers gun, with interruptor gear and later synchronizing gear to enable it to fire through the airscrew disc without hitting the blades.

229

230

228

231

232

The handling qualities of the Sopwith triplane were especially attractive and there was never any trustworthy evidence to support the rumour that this aircraft was weak and that structural failure could occur through the twisting of the upper plane in a steep dive. It was partly prejudice that prevented it from coming into service in such quantities as the SE.5.

Germany's Fokker triplane, which came out about a year after the Sopwith and was often supposed to be a copy of it, had certain special features, among them uneven plane lengths. The lowest plane was shortest and the next one slightly longer with the top plane longest of all and fitted with horn ailerons. The Fokker's wing section was different from that of the Sopwith and the aircraft was able to do a somewhat higher speed with the German Oberursel rotary engine, though its performance at altitude was generally assessed as being somewhat less satisfactory. It was fitted with the Spandau machine gun firing through the airscrew disc, twin guns being fitted to the later models.

These two triplanes proved to be exquisite flying machines, and the subsequent disappearance of the small triplane is not readily accounted for because it was the kind of aircraft that might have been expected to interest and attract postwar civilian pilots, particularly those who were taking to aviation as a form of sport.

The fundamental problems of handling aircraft in close combat have not altered over the years. The speeds of 1914-18 machines in level flight were low, perhaps

228 Hermann Goering in his all-white Fokker D.VII

229 French Morane-Saulnier BB in German hands, 1915

230 SE.5a, a type widely used by the Royal Flying Corps, 1917

231 Spad XVI of the Armée de l'Air

232 Line-up of Italian Ansaldo SVAs at the factory, 1918

90 up to 110 mph, and the heights modest, perhaps 8,000 to 25,000 ft, but the manoeuvring followed the pattern of the Pégoud aerobatics of the prewar period. And the loads to which pilots could subject their bodies were as high in 1914-18 as in 1939-45 because, although top speeds were down, the turning radius of the small scouts of 1914-18 was extremely tight so that crews were subjected to high g forces, that is high multiples of the force of gravity.

The excitement and anxiety caused to those taking part in these extraordinary 'dog fights' were intense. The aircraft manoeuvred at close range, the pilots under high g forces, pressed down into their seats, 'weighing' three or four times their normal weights, looking into the cockpits of their opponents as they hurtled past one another then lifting from their seats against the shoulder straps in minus g manoeuvres. It was, as it were, 'hand to hand' fighting.

Collisions were frequent. Deliberate ramming was

112

sometimes tried, notably in 1917 by Captain Oliver Sutton in a Pup. Fire in the air was frequent when incendiary and tracer bullets found the fuel tanks. When fire came, it was a horrifying reminder of what it was all about. Although the American A. Leo Stevens had demonstrated a free parachute in 1912 and although others, Berry, Maitland, Pégoud and Newell, had shown it was possible to make a parachute descent from an aeroplane before the outbreak of war, and although during the war parachutes were used by kite balloon crews, Allied aeroplane crews did not have parachutes at any time in the 1914-18 conflict. Nor did German aeroplane crews until near the end.

So an aircraft on fire was, for its occupants, a burning at the stake. For pilot, observer or gunner there was no escape. The flames roared round him, rapidly enveloping the whole aircraft and leaving a comet's tail behind it. His choice was simple and absolute. Either he jumped to his death or he was roasted alive in his cockpit.

Tactically nearly all major air battles, after the first frantic exchanges, resolved themselves into pairs of aircraft duelling together. These duels usually conformed to the same formula, the circular chase. The two pilots would circle, each using all his skill to hold height and to bring his machine in on a smaller radius of turn or to make it go faster so as to overtake and to 'get on the tail' of the other. Once in that position, behind the adversary, the forward firing gun could be used with a fair chance of hitting the target and finishing the combat. In these desperate duels, the fact was repeatedly emphasized that however good an aircraft's armament,

235

236

it was its *flying* qualities that won battles. The faster, better climbing, more acrobatic machine was superior in combat.

The big air battles of 1917 and 1918 emphasized another tactical lesson. The Germans had thought out their air war doctrine better than the Allies and had discovered a way to obtain more useful results from the deployment of fewer fighting machines. They adopted the 'flying circus' system. The first and most famous circus was commanded and led in battle by Baron Manfred von Richthofen; but the basic idea is sometimes attributed to the great German air leader, Oswald Boelcke.

Richthofen assembled an elite of German fighter pilots. They were given the highest speed, fastest climbing machines the extremely able German designers could produce. At first they were Albatros V-Strutters, then Fokker biplanes and later the lively, fast manoeuvring (with a wing span of only 23 ft), light-weight (at only 815 lb) Fokker triplanes. These were painted in different colours and in individual designs. Richthofen's own machine was all red.

He would keep his circus at an aerodrome well behind the land battle lines and would be ready, at a moment's notice, to take to the air and challenge any Allied formation that had been reported. These economical fire-brigade tactics were effective against the predominantly British offensive patrol or provocation tactics. Every German fighter thus attained a higher productivity (in this context the word should surely be

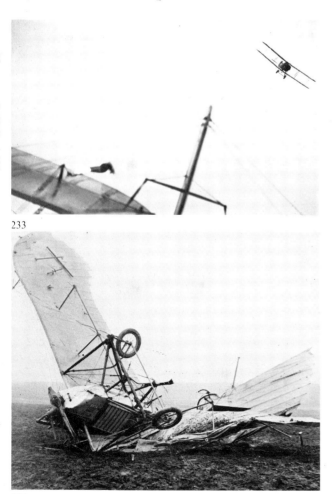

233

234

233 Demonstration of aerial fighting with Bristol Fighters

234 Crashed Rumpler Taube near Weimar, 1914

235 Fokker Dr I triplane, 1917

236 Sopwith three-seater triplane fighter, 1916

113

237

238

239

240

described, bombing was also under development. It has its interest here because of the light it throws upon weight lifting and endurance. It is the power to lift great weights into the air that gives an aircraft its peaceful value as a passenger or freight carrier, and the ability to fly great distances without refuelling.

It was in the last year of the war, particularly during the final seven months after the Royal Naval Air Service and the Royal Flying Corps had been amalgamated to form the Royal Air Force, that strategic bombing had its real beginnings. Neither the French nor the Germans were as favourable to the concept of a separate air force or to the value of strategic bombing as were the British. It was largely the obstinate dogmatism and – as some think – the farsightedness of General Hugh Trenchard, commander of the RAF, that brought this about. Yet the German aircraft designers were, on the whole, ahead of the British in the quality of their large size, weight

carrying machines. The Gotha and the Friedrichshafen bombers were fine aeronautical achievements.

Both were twin-engined and both used the trustworthy and efficient 260 hp Mercedes liquid-cooled, in-line power units. People in Britain were made aware of the scope of these aircraft in June 1917 when a squadron of Gothas made a daylight bombing raid on London. People in France were made aware of the Friedrichshafen bombers when raids were made on Paris. By the standards of the day these were very large aircraft, both of them with wing spans of some 80 ft. Although this measurement was less than the span of the British Handley Page O/400, at 100 ft, the British machine had a much smaller lower plane, being, in fact, closer to a sesquiplane than a true biplane.

Towards the end of the war there were efforts in Britain and in Germany to produce aircraft with greater range and load carrying capacity in order to step up bombing attacks. The Handley Page V/1500 with four Rolls-Royce engines and a span of over 130 ft was ready as the war ended, and in Germany the Zeppelin biplane bomber was almost ready. It had five Maybach engines, two in tandem on each side of the fuselage and one in the nose. This aircraft was not fast, but it was designed for an endurance of ten hours and it was intended to carry over its full range a bomb load of more than two tons.

The military load of these aircraft may be likened to the payload of civilian machines. It was varied in the same manner according to the distance that had to be

'destructivity') than the Allied fighters.

Richthofen's circus specialists were formidable in combat, tearing into the fray with a determination and seeming recklessness which could strike fear into their opponents. The circus system was the most notable of the pioneer examples of operational research into the war in the air. But the Germans also obtained larger results from their bomber forces, aircraft for aircraft, than did the Allies. In support of this is the continuing hold the Germans maintained in the air up to the time when they were numerically outmatched by more than two to one. At the war's end, although the RAF had an absolute total of all aircraft types of 22,000, the French and British together had only 8,000 aircraft in the first line. But the Germans were down to 2,500 first line machines.

While aerial fighting was evolving in the manner

237 Handley Page O/400 bomber seen from the rear gunner's cockpit of another Handley Page, 1918

238 Austrian Albatros-Renn biplane, 1914

239 Hermann Goering's AEG G.III bomber is inspected by the Crown Prince

240 Caproni 1001 bomber

114

241

242

flown. Thus the disposable load was made up of two weight variables, fuel and bombs which translate into fuel and payload for commercial aircraft. The early bombers were the first aircraft to provide proven operating figures for designers, telling them how much a big machine could carry, how far, how fast and at what fuel cost.

These machines were capable of delivering a bomb load of half a ton to a ton at ranges of the order of 300 to 350 miles and, as mentioned, this bomb load could be put up at shorter ranges. The Handley Page V/1500 was exceptional in being able to take a military load of over four tons. The Friedrichshafen, it should be noted, was built by the Zeppelin company at a time when the German heads of staff, as will be seen in the next chapter, were beginning to see the limitations of the large rigid

241 Gotha III of 1916, predecessor of the widely-used G.IV and G.V bombers

242 Friedrichshafen G.III, one of the principal types of bomber used by Germany in 1914-18

airship for strategic bombing missions.

France, with her army traditions, was never en-amoured of strategic bombing by large aircraft. Her most important bomber was the Voisin pusher biplane spanning only 48 ft, with a single Renault or Salmson engine. Its military load was of the order of 650 lb. It was also, as we have seen, used as a two-seat fighter aircraft. The Hotchkiss machine gun, mounted in the front part of the nacelle, was later sometimes replaced by a 40 mm shell firing cannon. Voisins achieved fame partly because

and then flown at a progressively increasing angle of incidence and diminishing speed, cocking up its nose more and more steeply until the wings stalled and it settled on the ground in a 'three-point' landing. But the tricycle undercarriage entailed a touch-down on the main wheels and then a rotation forward until the nose wheel came down. In this way the lift was taken out of the wings by reduction of the angle of attack instead of by increase of this angle to the stalling point. The Voisin, on landing, *rotated* or tipped forward on to the two front wheels of

243

244

243 De Havilland DH.9a two-seat day bombers, in RAF service 1918-31

244 Breguet 14, used in enormous numbers 1917-30

they were successful night operating machines. But they were full of interesting features, structurally in the way metal was used and aerodynamically in their controls and in their four-wheel undercarriages which introduced the modern rotational landing technique.

Until the arrival of the tricycle undercarriage before the second world war, aircraft mostly landed in a nose-up attitude, on two main wheels and a tail wheel or tail skid. The aircraft landed by being brought close to the ground

its four-wheel undercarriage just as a modern aircraft tips forward on to its nose wheel.

In addition to their Voisin aircraft the French used the Breguet 14 for night bombing and for reconnaissance. It had a liquid-cooled Renault engine and was a conventional two-seater with ring gun mounting for the observer who was seated behind the pilot. Metal construction was used. The Breguet 14 two-seater was supplied to the United States squadrons when they came to France. Another French aircraft used for bombing was a twin-engined version of the Caudron trainer. It had two curious features. It was a tractor biplane, yet it had tail booms and it was powered by rotary engines—one of the extremely few bombers ever to have been used with this type of power plant.

In aviation's first experience of war the pseudo-romantic side was prominent. All the belligerent countries had their heroes and among the most highly regarded and the most widely publicized were the flying champions or 'air aces'. Some of them were gifted leaders of men, but many were also or alternatively lone fighters who exploited strictly individual skills. Even when large formations were common in all the main theatres of conflict, these men would go out on lone sorties. And

116

they had many outstanding successes when flying alone.

Baron von Richthofen's success as a tactical innovator and creator of his famous 'circus' was matched by his success as a lone fighter. Richthofen was credited with 80 victories and comes at the top of the list. René Fonck is credited with 75 and the Englishman Edward ('Micky') Mannock with 73. But we may depart from the official lists to pick out those pilots who contributed something memorable to the manner in which aircraft were used in combat. The greatest of these was the delicate, melan-choly Frenchman Georges Guynemer who shot down 53 German aircraft.

At first rejected by the French authorities on account of his poor health, Guynemer contrived in November 1914 to join the Army in the ranks. He learnt to fly at Pau and, although said to be an indifferent pupil, he took his pilot's certificate in April 1915. Almost immediately his extraordinary combat gifts were shown. On 19 July 1915 he won his first victory. He flew Nieuport scouts, which had V struts not unlike those of the German

245 Albatros D.IIIs of a German Fliegertruppe, 1917

246 Ernst Udet as a lieutenant

247 Georges Guynemer with his *Vieux Charles*, 1917

245

246

247

Albatros, and then Spads. His most remarkable engagements were when he was using this type of fighter. It was a two-bay, tractor biplane with Hispano-Suiza liquid-cooled engine and it had a machine gun fixed to fire through the airscrew disc under control by synchronizing gear. The Spad was fast–about 135 mph–very strong and could be dived vertically from great heights, while its controls were effective all through the speed range. Guynemer nick-named his own particular Spad 'Vieux Charles' and he fitted a 40 mm shell-firing cannon in place of the machine gun.

In this Spad he performed prodigies of courage. He was often shot down and he was wounded more than once, but he never flinched from combat or retreated before superior numbers. His was always an introspective character, but shortly before he was lost his strange melancholy became very noticeable. Also noticeable was the amount of hard thinking he had put into the task of fighting in the air. This close study of aerial fighting technique was characteristic of French war pilots, particularly Charles Nungesser, Georges Madon and René Dorme. Guynemer won his last victory in August 1917, and in the following month went out never to return.

England's Albert Ball, who shot down 43 aircraft, had some similarities to Guynemer. A sensitive, violin-playing, romantic-minded, rather delicate youth, he joined an operational squadron at the time of the Fokker 'scourge' and won almost every British and Allied military decoration, the VC, the DSO, the MC, the Légion d'Honneur and others. He used various aircraft,

248

one designed by himself, but many of his successes were when he was flying SEs. His final sortie was made when he had changed to a Sopwith triplane. Lothar von Richthofen, Manfred's brother, is supposed to have shot him down.

Among the great German pilots Ernst Udet was probably the best known after Richthofen. His name became almost as famous in the second world war (when he committed suicide) as in the first. He was a highly skilled flyer and one of the world's most brilliant aerobatic pilots. Max Immelmann, although he does not figure high in the official lists, gave his name to a tactical manoeuvre which he used to good effect in battle. It was the 'Immelmann turn' and is best described as a turn through 180 degrees made by a mixture of half loop and half roll.

Every country in the 1914-18 war had its flying aces.

248 The United States undertook a punitive expedition against Pancho Villa of Mexico in 1916. This bombing biplane was tested at Sunnyvale, California in that year

249 Two British observer officers in the basket of a kite balloon. May 1918

118

Captain Kosakoff of Russia is said by W. E. Johns in *Fighting Planes and Aces* to have had 17 victories and Major Francesco Baracca of Italy 34. Captain 'Willy' Coppens was Belgium's best known flyer. Major Raoul Lufbery was probably America's although Captain Edward Rickenbacker was given the highest score with 26. He flew a French Nieuport–a later version than the V-Strutter. Americans entered the air war alongside the Allies before the United States had declared war officially on 6 April 1917 and the Escadrille Lafayette was their own squadron in the Armée de l'Air. Numerous American pilots served with the French and transferred to their own squadrons later. One for mention here because he specialized in shooting down observation balloons, a much more difficult enterprise than might be thought, was Frank Luke.

An American force had aerial responsibility for a sector of the front in the summer of 1918; it was commanded by Colonel William Mitchell, who after the war was to make strenuous attempts to awaken his country to the growing role of air power and argue passionately for a stronger air force. He suffered heavy losses against superior German strength. Inspired by Trenchard's aggressive air strategy, he conceived the idea of a huge parachute assault over the German lines, and the project was being planned when the war ended.

Tactics became highly developed and scientifically worked out. Combats between fighters were not hazardous slamming matches, but carefully contrived confrontations. The lone fighters went to extraordinary lengths to effect a surprise. The use of sun and of cloud, the manner of the approach to suit the different kinds of quarry and a thousand other matters were most carefully studied by fighter pilots.

During the 1914-18 war aircraft performance increases were small when the extent of aircraft production is taken into account. In general terms it may be said that fighter speeds increased from about 80 mph to 125 to 135 mph. Ranges and loads cannot be expressed in any similar round terms because the aircraft of the fighting powers differed so fundamentally.

Biplane construction was favoured by France, Britain and Germany for the construction of both heavy and lighter day bombers. They were nearly all closely related

249

to the biplanes of the Voisin and the Wright types.

Attempts were made to provide them with gun positions which the crew could man during bombing sorties in order to beat off fighter attack. But the belief that the heavier, slower aircraft could defend itself against the lighter, more manoeuvrable faster aircraft by means of gunfire was proved to be an illusion. This was one of the lessons of the first war in the air that had to be learnt a second time in 1939-45. For the American air forces were at first convinced – in opposition to or in

by October 1918 – a larger labour force than in the years following the second world war when the figure fluctuated around 250,000. Rate of output was high though here the relative simplicity of the early aircraft must be taken into account.

Note that this was a quantitative growth. There was no *comparable* technical or aerodynamic advance. On the contrary, the war sometimes seemed to put the brake on progress in the strictly flying capabilities of aircraft. The Sopwith Pup was one of the best of the early tractor

250

ignorance of what had happened in 1914-18 – that suitably armed heavy bombers could defeat fighter attack by gunfire.

Bombing aircraft were developed rather slowly but they were produced in quantity. The situation went against the spirit of experiment, studying new ideas and new wings and wing sections, new configurations. The box-type biplane was there and was the only form thought suitable for big bomber production.

Fighters were in a somewhat different situation. They were small and consequently there were, now and again, attempts at novelty and originality. Among the fighters used by France, Britain, Germany and Italy were many machines with attractive flying qualities and fairly good performance. But even among the fighters there was no swift progress on the technical or aerodynamic sides. The factories had to be kept roaring, there was little time to change the production lines.

The 1914-18 war was the generator of large aircraft industries, particularly in France, Britain and Germany. France produced 67,982 aircraft and 85,317 engines; Britain 55,093 and 41,034. An Italian industry also started to grow and produced during the war 20,000 airframes and 38,000 engines. The United States as a late starter turned out 15,000 airframes and 41,000 engines.

Industrialization therefore received a powerful stimulus from the war. From a few small works with a few dozen workers, the British labour force had risen to 347,112

biplane single-seat scouts or fighters. Its top speed was 110 mph. One of the best performers as the war ended was an improved French Spad. Its top speed was raised from 95 mph of the original model to 135 mph. The Sopwith Dolphin was not far short of this speed. The Fokker triplane could do only 120-125 mph but it had an exceptionally good rate of climb, attaining 15,000 ft in 17 minutes against the Pup's 30 minutes and the Dolphin's 20 minutes.

It must be said, however, that there were aircraft designed late in the war which exhibited remarkable qualities as flying machines although they never went beyond the prototype stage.

Flying after the war was over started with a huge production industry and many people with some knowledge of how to fly. The numbers of pilots and those under training as pilots were vast – the RAF alone had 22,000 men under pilot training. So the stage was set for a great outburst of flying. What actually happened will be related in due course, but first an entirely separate aeronautical activity must be discussed, for it overlapped the 1914-18 war and continued for many years afterwards, showing flashes of promise but also moments of disaster. It was the activity concerned with 'ships of the air', both those lifted by what Cayley called 'balloon floatage' – airships, and those lifted by wings – flying-boats.

250 The American 11th Aero Bombardment Squadron in France with their DH.4s, 1918

9 Ships of the air

Two attempts were made to develop the size of aircraft. In the aerostat or lighter-than-air field they focused upon airships and in the aerodyne or heavier-than-air field they focused upon flying-boats. Both attempts to introduce much bigger craft attracted a massive technical, financial and constructional effort. Both attempts failed in circumstances which were either tragic or perverse.

The world's navies were the earliest supporters of airships and of flying-boats. They saw them both as direct offspring of surface vessels. Many naval officers, as early as the time of the Giffard, Krebs and Santos-Dumont airship flights, began to picture to themselves immense ships of the air, suspended in the atmospheric ocean, navigating over the high seas just as their surface ships had navigated.

It was a fine idea. And great efforts were made, particularly in Germany, the United States and Britain, to realize it. Germany began it all with airships of large size, given a rigid frame, covered by an envelope containing lifting ballonets and powered by a number of

251

251 Zeppelin landing in the presence of Count Zeppelin and the Crown Prince

engines carried in gondolas slung below the envelope. The name of Ferdinand, Count Zeppelin is without doubt the greatest in the story of large airships. His vision came to him late in life, when he was already an old man. But it was a blazing, irresistible vision.

Zeppelin believed that the large rigid airship was a safer, more efficient and more economical transport vehicle than any other. And from the time of his pioneer commercial services before the first world war to the time of the great British experiment in world communications by airship in the 1920s and 1930s Zeppelin's belief seemed repeatedly to be on the brink of practical proof.

The large rigid airship was a vehicle which had a magnetic attraction for transport experts. It seemed to offer a means of conveying people and goods from point to point without having to fight the frictions which are unavoidable for land or sea vehicles yet without having to waste power upon maintaining altitude as an aerodyne must do. Airships were lifted and held aloft statically, by the buoyancy of the gas used in their ballonets. All that remained for the engines to do was to overcome aerodynamic drag and to drive the vessel along.

Large rigid airship development overlapped that of heavier-than-air flight. It branched from the aerostatics of the early days, the balloons and the non-rigid dirigible airships. Mathematical studies seemed to show that airships, if only they were to be made large enough, would become superior to winged aircraft in almost everything but speed over a short course. The arguments were so convincing that during the first world war Germany spent large sums in a vast manufacturing effort to build large rigid airships and their associated bases.

These machines were launched into warlike operations on a big scale. They were hailed by the Germans as a prime instrument of victory over the Allies. The Imperial German Navy found airships of value for fleet reconnaissance and they were constructed for independent bombing raids. Immense bases for them were created, some, like that at Cuxhaven, with revolving sheds so that the vessels could be man-handled in or out of the shed whatever the wind direction.

The war of 1914-18 very nearly wrote the whole story of the large rigid airship. It was a story of heroism by the German crews, of commanders such as Heinrich Mathy, Peter Strasser, Captain Linnarz and Treusch von Buttlar. They took their enormous, fragile, highly inflammable cylinders over France and over England, usually at night, to be highlighted in searchlight beams and made the target for infernos of anti-aircraft fire. On 19 January 1915 two airships of the Imperial German Navy attacked Yarmouth, Cromer and Kings Lynn on the east coast of England. On 31 May 1915 the airship *LZ 38* raided London, causing 41 casualties.

The beginning of the end of the large rigid airship's part in war was when Sub-Lieutenant Warneford of the Royal Naval Air Service shot down the *LZ 37*. The debris fell on a convent and there was only one survivor. He was the helmsman, who came down with a part of the airship, went through the convent roof and finished up unhurt on a bed.

252

In 1916 it was decided in Britain that the appropriately armed winged machine was the antidote to the large rigid airship. Aeroplanes were fitted with Lewis machine guns firing explosive and incendiary bullets and also with bombs; for it was thought at first that Zeppelins might be bombed. Also, it is of historical importance to note, aeroplanes were fitted with rockets and explosive darts. The darts were the invention of a naval commander called Rankin, the rockets of Le Prieur. Rocket missiles, therefore, were by no means an invention of the 1939-45 war.

A reconnaissance 'egg' was devised, to be lowered on a wire cable far below the airship which could remain under cover of the clouds while the observer in the 'egg' made his notes. This had little success.

Airship bombing was the occasion for incessant arguments about the moral justification for attacks upon open towns. The German crews, men of the highest courage, were condemned by the British as 'baby killers' and an utterly unjustifiable public fury was aroused against them. It led to incidents of a particularly horrible kind. The best known example of this was the destruction of the airship *L.19* under Captain Loewe in February 1916. This airship came down in the North Sea. A British trawler was in the vicinity but its master, although begged to do so, refused to save any of the Germans on the grounds that there was a risk of his ship being taken over if he allowed them on board. All the Germans were drowned.

Some of the dreadfulness of war thus rubbed on to the large rigid airships. But their period of military effectiveness was brief. Allied fighter aircraft were coming to grips with them. Zeppelins were being shot down in increasing numbers, most of them in flames. This did not prevent the British Royal Navy from trying to copy German airship work, for naval commanders of most countries obstinately held to their belief in the usefulness of large rigid airships for fleet reconnaissance. Vickers built airships and British constructors copied one of the German airships which had been brought down on English soil almost undamaged.

After the war Britain undertook a courageous and imaginative scheme. It was for the building of two extremely large airships, the *R.100* and the *R.101*, and their use to start a prodigious system of British Commonwealth air communications.

252 *Z.4*, a German rigid dirigible, on the military parade ground at Lunéville, 1913, after it had landed inadvertently on prohibited territory

Few official documents have the breadth of outlook and the daring displayed in *The Approach Towards a System of Imperial Air Communications* presented to Parliament by the Secretary of State for Air, then Sir Samuel Hoare, in October 1926 and considered by the Imperial Conference. It offered a vision of a British Commonwealth stronger and more closely knit than the Empire had been, and brought and held together by rapid, regular and safe air communications. Passengers, mails and freight were to move freely—mainly on the

253

254

253 British C-class non-rigid airship of the RNAS escorting a convoy, 1917

254 Grand Salon of *R.100*, 1930

255 Construction shed at Cardington where the *R.101* was built

ocean routes—between any points in the Commonwealth. Trade and social links were to be forged by means of air travel. And the large rigid airship was to blaze the trail. It was nothing less than a plan for an Aerial Empire.

Not long after the British Government had published its plan, German airships performed feats which vividly endorsed it. They sustained the view that the large rigid airship could indeed be the prime instrument of a great system of world communication—a cohesive of common-

wealth. A first commercial flight across the Atlantic was made in 1928 by the *Graf Zeppelin* commanded by Dr Eckener, carrying twenty passengers from Fried-richshafen to New York, and the same ship flew from Lakehurst, New Jersey, to Germany and thence to Tokyo the next year and then on round the world, completing nearly 22,000 miles in 21 days. This was just before the launching of the *R.100*, which was longer and larger than the *Graf Zeppelin*, had six engines and was capable of a speed of 80 mph. The year after launching she made an out-and-back Atlantic crossing.

Political issues affected the airship programme as they did so many aviation activities. The *R.100*, largely designed by Sir Barnes Wallis and built by Commander Dennistoun Burney's company, was taken, politically, as representing private enterprise, the *R.101* as repre-senting state enterprise and they were thus set almost in competition with one another instead of being in alliance.

These big vessels were designed to offer luxurious travel, with large dining rooms, lounges and even a smoking room. They had promenade decks with big windows from which the passengers could look down on the scenery; their catering and cuisine arrangements were not far short of those on big ocean liners. The prospect of really civilized passenger travel on long commonwealth routes, at reasonable costs, and of the high speed carriage of first class mails and of special freight, looked favourable. But here a word must be interpolated about a basic feature of the airships of this period.

255

They were filled with inflammable gas and, as was emphasized during the war operations, they could readily be set on fire in action. It was the contention of the airship enthusiasts that this tendency to catch fire was an exclusively war risk; that with proper design there was almost no risk of fire in commercial operation—at any rate no greater risk than in a ship or a train. Nevertheless in the United States the claims of non-inflammable gas, which was available in America, were pressed. The American *Shenandoah*, which was a Zeppelin, had been filled with helium and thus was seen as a demonstration of how even the fire risk could be reduced to near zero and the airship established as a safe commercial air vehicle. The *Shenandoah* did crash with the loss of 14 lives before the British experiment got under way, but the crash had nothing to do with the type of lifting gas. However, expert opinion did not insist upon non-inflammable gas – partly because of the scarcity of helium outside the United States and partly because it gave slightly less lift.

It was on 5 October 1930 in the early morning at Beauvais, north of Paris, that the end came to the great British airship experiment and to the hopes for Commonwealth passenger, mail and freight services run by lighter-than-air craft. The *R.101*, pressed into use by the government though far from airworthy, set out on her maiden voyage. About seven and a half hours out of Cardington, flying in a strong south to south-westerly wind and some rain, she lost height and would not respond to elevator corrections. On hitting the ground an explosion or series of explosions occurred. Fifty-four people were on board and six survived. Among those killed were Lord Thomson, the Air Minister, and Sir Sefton Brancker, who had done more than most people to advance civil aviation in Britain.

It was the end of large rigid airship services in Britain; but not in the world. There was still a belief that the Germans might understand these vessels better than the peoples of other nations and many remarkable flights by German airships commanded by Dr Eckener sup-

ported this view. The trans-Atlantic passenger and mail service started in 1936 with the *Hindenburg* as one of the ships. Then, in May 1937, came the accident which not even German loyalty and enthusiasm could overlook. The *Hindenburg*, which was larger than the *R.101* in both length and girth and had carried a thousand passengers across the Atlantic, was coming to its mooring mast at Lakehurst, New Jersey, after a journey with 97 people on board. Before thousands of spectators the airship, as she made contact with the mooring mast,

256

257

256 Wreck of the USS *Shenandoah*, the first US Navy rigid airship, near Marietta, Ohio, 3 September 1925

257 *Viktoria Luise* over Kiel Harbour, 1912

burst into flames and thirty-five people perished.

This disaster spelt the end of large rigid airships for Germany. For the United States it is probable that the *Akron* and the *Macon* disasters were the turning points. The *Akron*, after attracting attention by carrying 207 people for a ten-hour cruise, crashed with the loss of 73 out of a complement of 76 men in April 1933.

Less than two years later the *Macon* crashed. Although she had 125 men on board the death roll was comparatively light, only two being killed; but the effect

was contributory to the atmosphere of doubt and distrust about the safety and competence of large rigid airships, whether helium filled or not. In France the faith in these vessels had never been high and when the *Dixmude*, the best known French large rigid airship, crashed with 52 men there was no attempt and, seemingly, no desire to attempt further developments with this type of aircraft.

We have now another story of courage and ingenuity in the development of large size aircraft closely related

258

259

260

258 *Graf Zeppelin* over the Colosseum, Rome

259 Italian dirigible in Tripoli, 1912

260 The *Hindenburg* disaster, 6 May 1937

to ships; and of aircraft which did great things, showed great promise, then faded – the big flying-boats. Although they did not suffer that absolute extinction that was suffered by the large rigid airship, the large flying-boats also went completely out of favour. Just as the airships had done, they pioneered long distance routes; they offered passenger conditions superior to anything that could be had in other types of aerodyne. But unlike the airships they proved themselves to be extremely safe. Unlike the airships, the big flying-boats had no fearful disasters, no explosions and flaming crashes etched in their history. They are believed by many – though comprehensive statistics are unobtainable – to have been the safest form of flying machine ever to have been introduced into general service. Yet they failed.

The reason could have had to do with the principle that a landplane has something basically superior in cost-effectiveness to the flying-boat. It could *not* have been that the landplane has any superiority to the flying-boat in safety and in comfort for its occupants. One other possible explanation lies in the factor that has always played a part in determining the way design will go – air performance. Small float seaplanes led the way in speed development for many years; but large flying-boats were generally somewhat slower than large landplanes.

Germany, which had pioneered the large size airship, also pioneered the large size flying-boat. The Dornier company produced, not long after the publication of the British plans for commonwealth airship services, a twelve-engined flying-boat, the *Do X*. This by its ability to carry many passengers – up to a hundred according to

the accommodation offered – attracted world wide attention. It was within its limits a success but as day-to-day working aircraft rather smaller flying-boats exerted a stronger influence upon progress. An originating example in Britain was the White and Thompson, built for racing before the 1914-18 war and capable of 85 mph. It was followed by whole families of Short, of Blackburn, and of Supermarine flying-boats. The developments which led to these aircraft belong to the early pioneering period.

H. F. King, in his *Aeromarine Origins*, relates how Peter Nissen, in 1903, tried to cross Lake Michigan in a 'balloon-like' contrivance in which some critics claim there was a forecast of the cushion craft or hovercraft. It is certain that Clément Ader in 1904 presented a design for a hydrofoil which had air cushion characteristics. Also the Wright brothers did some experiments with hydrofoils in 1907. Usually priority for the first flying operation from water is given to Henry Fabre and is dated 28 March 1910. It was at Martingues. After that there came the Glenn Curtiss biplane of January 1911 and the Curtiss 'hydro' as it was called which flew in January 1912. The Voisins produced the first successful amphibian and this was flown by Maurice Colliex in August 1911. It made out-and-back trips between the waters of the Seine and the land aerodrome at Issy-les-Moulineaux.

Glen Curtiss expended more effort than almost any other pioneer on marine aircraft. He was working upon practical designs in 1908 though full success did not come to him for over two years. It was in January 1911

261 Dornier Do X twelve-engined flying-boat, 1929

262 Romar flying-boat designed by Rohrbach, on the Baltic near Travemünde at the start of flight tests, August 1928

263 Dornier Superwal in service with Luft Hansa

264 Curtiss's first float-plane, early in 1911

261

263

262

264

that he flew his float seaplane at San Diego, California and this was the outcome of the thinking that he did after innumerable experiments with flotation devices fitted to what were essentially landplanes.

The 1911 seaplane was a three-bay biplane with outriggers to carry forward control surfaces and tailbooms for the empennage. This empennage was of the conventional cruciform shape and gave elevator and rudder for control in pitch and in yaw. Control in roll was by means of ailerons mounted between the upper and lower planes.

The undercarriage combined simple flotation gear with members intended to act as hydrofoils and to enable the aircraft to rise as it made its taking off run and to plane on the water until flying speed was reached and it became airborne.

The hydrofoil was arranged forward under the outriggers and the flotation gear consisted of two floats. The aircraft embodied the float seaplane conception of the period which assumed that hydroplaning would be possible only with the aid of special hydroplane surfaces whereas later the simpler and more logical concept of integrating floating gear, whether hull or floats, and hydroplaning surfaces came into general use. Thus the bottoms of floats and of flying-boat hulls were given the 'steps' which eventually became characteristic of hydroplanes and were made to do the work of lifting the aircraft partly out of the water while it accelerated for take-off.

After his 1911 seaplane had been modified and used for trying various different arrangements of the flotation

265

gear, Curtiss turned his attention to a more ambitious project, a seaplane which would be suitable for all kinds of private flying. It was in fact his first flying-boat for it dispensed with floats and employed a boat hull. Upon this hull was mounted the biplane wing cell and tailbooms were used, as in the earlier machine, to carry a cruciform tail. This flying-boat which was called the 'family hydro' had a single engine but, somewhat in the manner of the Wright landplanes, this was used to drive two tractor airscrews by means of chains. The aircraft flew in January 1912. And although it did not carry the empennage on the hull but had, as already explained, separate tailbooms, it may be said to be a major achieve-

265 The first practical flying-boat, flown by Curtiss on 10 January 1912

ment in the development of the flying-boat idea.

It was the work of Curtiss upon these two aircraft in particular that won him the Robert J. Collier Trophy, awarded by the National Aeronautic Association of America, in 1911 and again in 1912. The official citation refers to his work on the 'hydroaeroplane' for the 1911 Trophy and on the 'flying boat' for the 1912 Trophy. Some believe that Curtiss was the first to introduce the term 'flying boat'. Certainly he was one of its most energetic and successful advocates during the early years of its progress.

In the 1914-18 war and immediately after it there were large numbers of seaplanes and a few amphibians. There were some fairly large flying-boats. The Porte three-engined flying-boats had a wing span of 125 ft (the wing span of a modern Boeing 707 is little more). The United States and Britain paid increasing attention to the large flying-boat, seeing in it great possibilities for long range journeys entailing ocean crossings. When the airship experiment failed, the tendency for the countries involved in aeronautical projects was to turn to the flying-boat as its successor and substitute. The National Advisory Committee for Aeronautics in the United States, established by act of Congress in 1915, after the war began to steer American aviation in the directions which it believed to be best suited to American interests. The Committee placed large hopes in the flying-boat for long distance work.

The flying-boat offered scope for size development because of the unlimited natural runways offered by stretches of sheltered water and because large weights could be supported by water in circumstances in which difficulties arose if they were to be supported by wheels and tyres on hard surfaces. But there were other matters of interest.

At this time the retractable undercarriage had not come into use though its possibilities had been widely canvassed. But at first the mechanical complications put off designers. The flying-boat hull contrived to combine in a single structure the landing gear *and* the body, including the cabin and other accommodation. And it had a planing bottom for preliminary lift at take-off. It did its jobs without creating additional drag in the air. This looked like a bonus for the flying-boat.

Most important for passenger carrying was the inherent safety of the large flying-boat. A forced alighting after power failure in a flying-boat could be safely accomplished at any time provided only that a patch of water was within gliding range. A boat could alight on land without catastrophic damage. The hazards faced by landplanes after power plant failure had no parallel in flying-boats.

Flying-boats, during their entire period of development, lived up to their promise for trustworthiness and for long range capabilities. It is not always remembered that the first aerodynes to fly the Atlantic were flying-boats. Alcock and Brown and Lindbergh, who used landplanes, are much better known to the larger public than Commander A. C. Read who, in a US Navy Curtiss flying-boat, made the first crossing in May 1919. Three boats commanded by Commander J. H. Towers started and the flight was made in stages; but that does not detract from its importance. And it demonstrated the high degree of safety of these machines for two were forced down upon the water. One crew was rescued by a British steamer, while the other crew was picked up by a US destroyer and Towers taxied the aircraft to port.

The position of the flying-boat in the transport vehicle hierarchy when the great British airship communications scheme was abandoned was not clearly defined. But the firms of Short Brothers and of Supermarine had been steadily developing this form of aircraft

backing of Sir Charles Wakefield to make a survey flight round Africa in one of these aircraft with the object of collecting data upon which Imperial Airways, which had been formed on 1 April 1924, could prepare schemes for regular services. By the end of 1928 the Singapore was ready. Cobham found more than fifty possible seaplane bases in and around the African continent and during his 23,000 miles of flying he showed again and again the flexibility and the safety inherent in the flying-boat.

266 Arrival of the one remaining NC-4 flying-boat (three had set out) at Lisbon after the first air crossing of the Atlantic, May 1919

267 Francis K. McLean in a Short floatplane flying through Tower Bridge, London, 1912

266

268

267

269

in a successful and imaginative way. The early Short flying-boats were mainly biplanes but Oswald Short was looking far ahead in constructional methods and introducing all-metal stressed-skin construction with special planing bottoms to the hulls and corrosion-resisting alloy panels and fittings.

Sir Alan Cobham decided that the Short Singapore flying-boat would be an excellent vehicle for a trailblazing long distance flight and he obtained the financial

When the Empire Air Mail scheme was launched by Imperial Airways in 1937 the flying-boat was the chosen machine on the long range routes. Once more then, flying was to be put to the test as a means of high speed communication between places remote from one another. And this time the flying was to be done by aerodynes and not by aerostats.

Unfortunately for Britain the whole project failed as the previous airship project had failed, but not in this

268 Short Type 827 seaplane serving with No. 8 Squadron, RNAS in East Africa, 1916

269 REP monoplane with floats which made very fast times at the St Malo seaplane competition in France, 1912

127

case because of the failure of the chosen vehicle. The flying-boat proved supremely competent and successful as a mail carrier on the long Empire routes and also, a little later, as a passenger carrier.

Priority for the realization that air mails might be an important factor in future communications, not only between units of any single empire or commonwealth, but also between units of different nations, was not with Imperial Airways for already the Dutch, with the KLM mail service between Amsterdam and Batavia, had begun

to profit from flight speed potentialities while in the United States the Post Office was encouraging air mail services by appropriate financial inducements to those lines that would accept them. The story of the development of these air mail services is told in Chapter 12.

Indisputably at the head of the firms which produced flying-boats and in a position of leadership and authority throughout the world in the design and construction of flying-boats was the British firm of Short Brothers, with their works on the River Medway. In 1934 and 1935 Short Brothers prepared to meet an order which, for that period, was extremely large. It was for a total of more than 40 four-engined, monoplane flying-boats, officially named the Imperial Flying Boat, but usually called the Empire Boat. The larger part of the order came from Imperial Airways, but the Australian line Qantas also bought a number of these machines. Thus, out of a specification which started with the modest requirement of a carrying capacity for 24 passengers and one and a half tons of mail, there came into existence an aircraft which had its place near the top of all types of civil transport machine.

The boats, as the large airships had been, were splendidly luxurious in a manner which met the demands of the long distance passengers of those days. They had two decks with a large promenade section with windows along the port side. The seats in the forward cabin were large and comfortable. An aft cabin with six seats and two sleeper cabins, with bunks, were available and right forward, under the flight deck, which was in the upper nose of the hull, was the smoking room with five seats

270

271

270 Albatros D.3 being brought to the slipway at Wilhelmshafen in April 1913 during an inspection by the Kaiser

271 Short Calcutta of Imperial Airways before her maiden flight from Rochester, February 1928

and with tables for use at meal times and for writing or other purposes.

The Atlantic was the flying-boat's next challenge. In 1937 a survey of the North Atlantic was conducted with Empire flying-boats. Both Imperial Airways and Pan American Airways engaged in studies of passenger and mail services. But the range-load factor was seen as restrictive. How could the flying-boat be given the range plus the load to make an Atlantic service–or for that matter any long distance service–economically viable?

In the 1930s an answer was given to this critical question. It was in two parts, one a brilliant, strikingly original invention and the other an air development of a known transport services device. The first was the Mayo composite aircraft; the second refuelling in flight.

Major Robert Mayo, in England, was an engineer with wide piloting experience. He noted that an aircraft, once it was in the air, could carry a much greater load than it could take off with. He noted that the take-off and the climb to operating height were heavy drains upon the fuel carried. He saw the ideal of having the aircraft somehow divorced from the mundane business of taking off and climbing and somehow carried aloft to its operating height without the use of its own fuel. Mayo proposed to place one seaplane on top of another; to lock them together for take-off and climb, and then to release the upper one for the mission.

Thus came into being the extraordinary Short-Mayo Composite Aircraft, an inventor's dream if ever there was one–an 'impossible', 'ludicrous', 'mad' solution to a difficult problem yet a solution which proved to work

272

under full scale practical trial. A clean, fast, four-engined float seaplane was mounted upon the top of a Short Empire flying-boat. The float seaplane was called *Mercury*, the flying-boat *Maia*. The two aircraft worked *in concert* for the take-off, both contributing thrust and lift, each a component of a *composite* machine.

Maia was launched in July 1937 and this extraordinary invention went forward in the following year with almost no major difficulties or interruptions to achieve resounding success. Just before the outbreak of the second world war the Mayo composite aircraft achieved a performance of outstanding merit. After composite take-off *Mercury* flew from the taking off point at Dundee

272 Italian flying-boat, the Savoia 10

273 The first Short Empire' flying-boat, *Canopus*, 1936

273

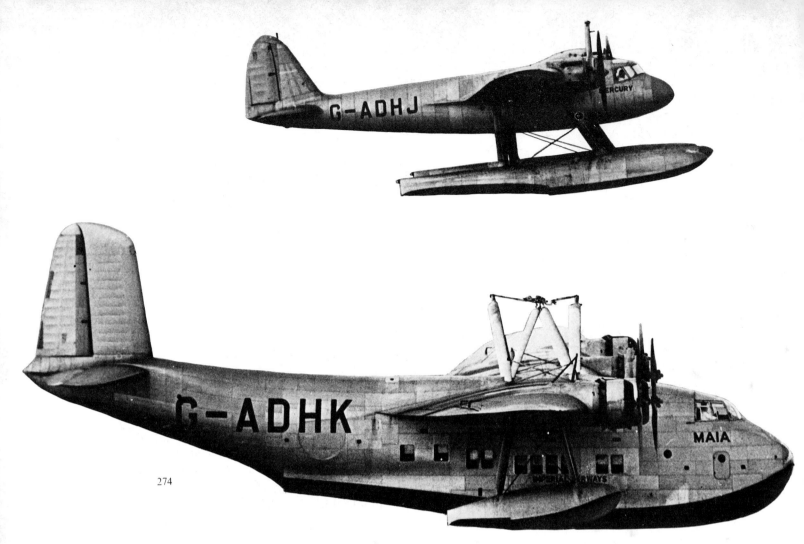

274

to Alexander Bay, South Africa, an official international seaplane distance record of just over 6,000 miles which stood for many years.

Yet this wonderful invention was cast aside never to be used again. And in the same way the large flying-boat, after showing great promise and after demonstrating capabilities which were beyond those of any kinds of landplane, was abandoned. The decisive influence in this was probably the progress made by America with landplanes.

Here the effects of the 1934 MacRobertson race from England to Australia must be mentioned. It was not so much the victory of the de Havilland Comet (the racing aircraft must not be confused with the later jet liner) that impressed the aviation world as the behaviour of the Douglas DC-2 landplane airliner entered by the Dutch company KLM and flown in the race almost as if it had been on a normal passenger carrying service. This undoubtedly tended to turn the eyes of operators away from flying-boats and towards landplanes just as it turned their eyes towards the genius of Donald Wills Douglas. In addition the energy and enthusiasm which the United States now began to display in the advancement of commercial flying had their influence upon the way the managers of British airlines looked at their tasks. America – a land power – was using landplanes and showing that they could be successful. In the end Imperial Airways found itself carried the American way.

So the work that had been done on flying-boats was cast aside. The British Overseas Airways Corporation,

successor to Imperial Airways, committed itself to the landplane. For America, too, there was a wastage of design and constructional effort. For flying-boats had received concentrated attention in the United States and some exceptionally fine machines had been produced. Two companies had devoted a large effort to these machines in particular, Boeing and United Aircraft. In addition the Consolidated Catalina twin-engined amphibian flying-boat had earned a high reputation for use in the services and work on marine aircraft had been done by Glenn Martin and Leroy Grumman.

The Boeing company's products will be treated in more detail when the progress of civil airliners is being examined; but the United Aircraft boats must be referred to here because they were to the designs of one of the greatest men aviation has produced, Igor Sikorsky. Born at Kiev in Russia in 1889, Sikorsky will come to our notice chiefly for his unique accomplishments in the advance of rotorcraft; but he by no means concentrated his attention solely upon this type of aerodyne. He was interested in large size aircraft, and he had built extremely large machines in his early days. The possibility of ocean trade and passenger routes being operated by large marine aircraft fascinated Sikorsky as much as it did the British and Americans. He designed and built a twin-engined amphibian, the S-38, and then went on to aircraft intended to meet Pan American Airways requirements. The S-40 and the S-42 were dated 1931 and 1934 and were produced by United Aircraft. The idea was to establish routes between the Pacific coast of America

274 Short-Mayo Composite aircraft, the upper component of which, *Mercury*, crossed the Atlantic on a commercial flight in July 1938 non-stop from Foynes, Ireland, to Montreal

and Hawaii and Asia. The S-42 led the way to the Boeing 314 flying-boat of 1938 (described in Chapter 12).

The industrious and increasingly vigorous American aircraft industry, however, looked with greater kindliness upon the landplane and lavished its genius upon it. And the big American airline operators, including Pan American, also turned towards the landplane and away from the marine aircraft. And so in due course the fine American clipper ships—as Pan American liked to call them—were superseded by landplanes.

But during the second world war the big flying-boat had one more fling before it went to its grave. Out of the

320 ft—and it had eight engines against the Empire boat's four. It made one brief flight but was not a success.

Then there was the more practical, more aeronautically successful Saunders-Roe Princess flying-boat which, had the politicians had the courage to hold to their purposes, might have brought the type back into regular commercial service. It had a wing span of 220 ft and it was powered by ten coupled turboprop engines. Flown at the Farnborough show in 1952, it could accommodate 250 people though the original scheme was to carry fewer people in superior conditions of comfort resembling those of the big airships. The only serious trouble with

275

276

Short Empire flying-boat the Short Sunderland military flying-boat was developed. It became an important aircraft for the protection of the Allied trade routes, for communications and for general transport, reconnaissance, anti-submarine and a thousand other duties. Ultimately, however, this successful representative of a successful class of aircraft was abandoned, just as the commercial flying-boat had been.

There were one or two gallant, terminal efforts to keep the large size flying-boat going. One of the most adventurous was the American Howard Hughes H-2 flying-boat of 1947. This had an enormous wing span— nearly three times that of the Empire flying-boat at

the Princess flying-boat was with the Bristol Proteus engines. These were causing difficulties and delays. The Princess, many of those with flying-boat experience believe, could have succeeded had it been operated on the trunk air routes.

With the disappearance of the Princess the last discernible chance of the large flying-boat ever coming into regular, passenger carrying service disappeared. With it went the chance of ever meeting the ideal accommodation obstinately visualized by the cantankerous air tourist— a cabin so large that aspidistras and a grand piano could be put in the main lounge.

275 Consolidated Commodore of the New York, Rio and Buenos Aires Line, 1929

276 Sikorsky S-42 Flying Clipper of Pan American which first flew in 1934

10 Sport and speed

Between the two world wars uninhibited exploration of all forms of flying machine and every manner of flying attained a peak. It was flying's golden age. Hordes of wild-eyed, dedicated amateurs learnt to fly in thousands of amazingly varied types of machine, some small, cheap and simple; others large and dear. The crazy essays of the early inventors were followed by further essays, fully as imaginative, but somewhat less crazy. There was a widespread belief that flying was to become the universally accepted form of personal transportation. The heady thought entered the minds of countless young men, among them many demobilized war pilots, that they would one day own their own private aircraft which they would use as a car, but on the much enlarged scale made possible by moving in the all-covering ocean of the air.

Aviation industries in the United States, in Britain, in France and in Germany had been geared to high production by the war of 1914-18. An interval of disruption was inevitable immediately afterwards. The great pro-

277

277 Alcock and Brown land at Clifden, Ireland, nosing over in a peat bog, after the first non-stop Atlantic crossing, 1919. This event was a spur to public interest in flying

278 London's welcome for Alcock and Brown

ductive capacity of the constructing companies, and the design genius of their staffs, had to be switched to the potential market offered by the up-and-coming private flyers. Governments supported a sword-ploughshare policy. There were subsidies and, more important, money-prize competitions sponsored by governments to encourage the development of good transport and personal aircraft. There were plenty of valuable prizes for those who won races and who set records.

Fighting and bombing aircraft had been developed

without consideration of cost. But now cost was to become a critical factor. So the aims of the aviation enthusiasts began to focus upon the same objectives as those which Santos-Dumont had had in view long before the outbreak of the first world war – the objectives of convenient, pleasurable and rapid personal transport.

Before the war there had been probably some hundred and fifty or more types of aircraft having the characteristics of a private transport vehicle. But the Santos-Dumont *Demoiselle* held a promise which the others did not appear to fulfil. One difference was cost. When the *Demoiselle* was shown at the Paris Salon de l'Aéronautique of 1909 it was priced at £300. A Blériot monoplane could be bought complete with Anzani engine for £480 and a Voisin for £780. These were the list prices and they showed that the attempt was being made before war broke out to attract the private and personal buyer.

While the war was on, a small aircraft which had in it the characteristics that were expected to appear in the postwar private aeroplane was made and flown successfully. It was the Grain Kitten. Captain W. H. Sayers was associated with this miniature machine. It had a 40 hp engine and was a handy little machine of great design and constructional merit.

A. V. Roe had a delightful small monoplane and also the historic Avro Baby biplane which was used by Roe's chief test pilot, the Australian Bert Hinkler, for long distance proving and pioneering flights. And in the years from 1920 to 1930 many other British designers turned out some efficient small, low powered machines intended for the private owner market.

German designers were prevented, as a result of the outcome of the war, from competing in powered aircraft

278

at this time, but Anthony Fokker, who had designed such successful German war machines, had resumed his Dutch nationality and was among those who set themselves to this task. Among French designers the name of Henri Mignet makes its first appearance, though his notable contribution to private flying was to come much later and will be examined at the end of this chapter.

In the United States after the war aviation, associated in the public mind with violent death, went into particularly severe eclipse. One veteran flyer, asked at this time

279

280

281

to name the greatest hazard in aviation, replied: 'Starving to death'. In this climate a number of war pilots took to barnstorming once more, buying unwanted ex-Army machines such as Curtiss Jennies and DH.4 bombers. But their audience was more demanding than before the war, and all kinds of circus antics had to be resorted to – wing walking, parachuting, 'plane changing' in mid-air. A crowd thus attracted would usually produce a few bold spirits willing to pay for a ride.

While Billy Mitchell of the US Army Air Service made

282

283

himself thoroughly unpopular with his chiefs – at what personal cost will be seen later – in his furious attempts to arouse professional concern for the state of the nation's air force, the barnstormers did something to sustain the public's interest and faith in aircraft. It was not to be until the 1930s, however, that private flying attained popularity in the United States.

The practical proof of the various British aircraft was made at a series of meetings, many of the most important in southern England. There were gliding meetings at Itford Hill, where the design of low drag high lift wings and low drag fuselages was studied. Simultaneously the Germans produced some admirable sailplane work at the Wasserkuppe gliding site in the Rhön mountains. Once again the *Daily Mail* newspaper came forward with money prizes for gliders. Alexis Maneyrol won the prize in the first year (1922) but was killed when competing

279 Curtiss JN-4 of the 'Great American Flying Circus'

280 Curtiss-built Martin NBS-1 racing at St Louis

281 Parachute jump from a DH Moth, January 1932

282 Avro Baby, 1919

283 Crazy flying by Avro 504Ns of the RAF, Hendon, 1931

in the following year. His duration flights and those of other successful glider pilots made it clear that the margin between gliding and genuine soaring flight was small. If a Maneyrol could remain in the air, circling, S-turning, climbing, gliding, for hours on end without having an engine of any kind, surely the ordinary private owner-pilot might expect to be able to make flights with extremely low powered, low consumption engines?

The Lympne competitions of 1923 and 1924, government sponsored and supported again by *The Daily Mail*

a given distance and what small engines could give high speeds. Two small aircraft were W. A. Shackleton's ANEC and W. O. Manning's English Electric Wren, with an ABC engine of 398 cc capacity. It was found possible to maintain level flight (not to take off or climb) on only three and a half horsepower. The Wren achieved the astonishing fuel consumption of 86 miles per gallon.

For general utility an aircraft had to be able to take off after a short run and not be too particular about the smoothness of the runway. The 1924 Lympne competitions produced some two-seat aircraft with wide speed range, this being assessed by relating the stalling speed to the top speed. Speed ranges attained the three to one and even four to one ratios which were to become standard practice through the following generations of civil aircraft, private owner machines and large commercial aircraft.

But now a new feature entered into all these attempts to produce a suitable private owner transport vehicle. It was a difference of opinion between those who drew up the conditions of the numerous competitions and races—and they included some of the most able technical men—and those who believed that they could see farther ahead to the kind of aircraft that the practical flyer would demand.

The official trials placed much emphasis upon economy and therefore upon flying with low engine power, whereas the designers who called themselves more 'practical' believed that flying could not be satisfactory unless there were ample margins of power even if these entailed higher running costs. It was a sharp division of thought

284

285

284 Geoffrey de Havilland (*left*) and Frederick Handley Page, 1920

285 De Havilland Moth, 1925. This classic design gave rise to the flying club movement and, later, to the Tiger Moth military trainer

and with encouragement, financial and other, from the Duke of Sutherland, Lord Wakefield and Sir Philip Sassoon, produced some aeronautical economies of quite startling importance. They showed just how little power was needed to fly and how little fuel was needed to cover

and it led, in the end, to the disappearance from general use of the small, light, totally economic aircraft of the 1924 Lympne trials type. It led to the appearance of a somewhat cruder, heavier machine.

The idea of the more robust, work-a-day aircraft was

most vigorously upheld by Captain Geoffrey de Havilland. In the early days at Farnborough he had designed military aircraft, as we have seen, including the DH.2 pusher biplane fighter. But now he had visions of a small personal aircraft capable of long distance flying, yet outside the category of the bombers and converted bombers on which he had done successful work, something much smaller, yet not so small as the Lympne competition machines, not so small as his own DH.53.

He refused to enter the 1924 Lympne competition in spite of its reasonable-looking rules and he hid himself away in secret contemplation of what the private pilot would really want. As an experienced, active and skilful pilot himself he saw things from the pilot's point of view. It was out of de Havilland's mental anguish during this period of contemplation that there arose the most successful private flyer aircraft of all time, the true pioneer of the genre, the de Havilland Moth.

It had a wing span of 30 ft and an empty weight of 770 lb. This wing span was the same as that of the light weight, competition type DH.53 but the 53 was a monoplane whereas the Moth was a biplane. And the weight was about double that of the smaller machine. Most important the engine, instead of being a motor cycle type, was more nearly a car type unit, the Cirrus. It harked back to the Renault but was a single bank, in-line engine giving 60 hp.

Sturdiness and simplicity were prime qualities in the Moth. The tandem seating of wartime aircraft was adhered to. The wing cell was a single bay, box girder biplane with a centre section above the fuselage with hollow steel struts. As in so many of the aircraft intended to usher in the age of universal air travel—as it was seen by the optimists—the DH.60 or Moth had wing folding for easy storage.

It would be difficult to overestimate the influence of the de Havilland Moth in the development of flying. It showed what an aircraft was capable of doing as an independent, personal transport vehicle. It showed that a small machine, inexpensive in first and running costs, could cover the entire world, overflying all those natural barriers which had until that moment proved to be insuperable. The de Havilland Moth was robust, not difficult to fly, easy to move about on the ground, trust-

286

worthy, safe, not uncomfortable. Yet it brought to its owner the entire gamut of aerial locomotion. Its popularity was assured by the new government subsidized flying clubs in Britain, most of them selecting the Moth.

The club movement was so successful in Britain that other Commonwealth countries imitated it. Australia decided to give government subsidies to flying clubs and afterwards India and New Zealand did the same. The nations outside the British Commonwealth, although equally interested in the progress of aviation, never took to the club movement in the same way. France created clubs, but they were entirely different things from the British clubs. The United States, true to its belief in the virtue of individual effort unbacked by government subsidy, was not enamoured of the club idea at first and preferred to let the pressures of an open market take their course. This held back American private flying; but in the end, as we shall see later, the Americans produced some of the world's most successful personal flying machines.

Meanwhile the private flying that had been so largely founded upon the de Havilland Moth prospered. Because of the Moth's success, the Avro Avian, which was about £100 cheaper than the Moth, and the Bluebird, in its metal framed form, also attracted pilots and were used in trail blazing flights all over the world. There were now and then, however, incidents which caused the wider public to exhibit sudden anxieties. One of these was a collision between two light aircraft, a Bluebird and a Westland Widgeon, during a pylon race in 1927. Both pilots were killed.

287

There was a period of conflict between the view that flying was dangerous and difficult, demanding skill and daring in high measure, and the view that it was a simple, ordinary, everyday affair within the capability of anyone who could drive a car. This was where the champion pilots played such a large part. For notable, newsworthy, trail blazing flights demonstrated the rapidly growing powers of aircraft while at the same time they set in the centre of public attention personalities of more than

286 Amy Johnson beside her Moth, 1930

287 Bert Hinkler's Avro Avian, with wings and undercarriage folded, before his London-Darwin flight, 1928

288 R. V. Thomas was the first pilot to land an aircraft in the Grand Canyon, 1922

289 Departure of Poulet for Australia in a Caudron C.IV from Issy, 1919

290 *L'Oiseau Canari*, the Bernard of Lefèvre and Lotti, which flew from Maine to Spain in 1929

ordinary interest, dedicated men engaged on a do-or-die mission, preparing to pit their skills in this relatively new art of flight against tremendous and largely unknown dangers.

The success of John Alcock and Arthur Whitten Brown in their non-stop Atlantic flight, in a Vickers Vimy bomber with Rolls-Royce engines, became the centre around which revolved many other attempts. Their flight had been from St John's, Newfoundland, to Clifden, County Galway, Ireland, on 14 and 15 June 1919, a

Then there was the non-stop flight with directional limitation, prevailing winds making west to east easier than east to west, then non-stop *solo* flights, non-stop flights between capital cities, linking flights between France and the United States, Germany and the United States, formation flights and flights by women pilots.

The US Army flight across the Atlantic via Greenland in 1924 was one part of the first round-the-world winged flight. This was undertaken by four Douglas biplanes. Two of them landed at Seattle on 28 September having covered 26,350 miles. Lieutenant Lowell H. Smith and Lieutenant Leslie P. Arnold were the leading crew members. During this flight the Douglas machines were at times converted into seaplanes by having floats substituted for the wheels of their undercarriages. The American airmen were still on their way when the Italian Locatelli, with a crew of three in a Dornier Wal flying-boat, attempted an east to west Atlantic crossing. His craft was forced down but the rescue of Locatelli and his crew was another piece of evidence of the basic safety of flying-boats. They were picked up unhurt after three days and nights on the water.

It was again in a Dornier flying-boat, this one with Napier Lion engines, that Major Franco and a crew of three made a successful crossing as part of a flight from Spain to Buenos Aires in 1926. A year later came the first of a series of Atlantic tragedies and also the first and most notable of a series of Atlantic successes.

Captain Charles Nungesser, a French fighter ace of 1914-18 and another French air force pilot Captain François Coli, in a Levasseur aeroplane, took off on

288

289

290

291

292

291 Dornier Wal flying-boat used by Locatelli on his attempted round-the-world flight, 1924

292 Charles Nungesser in his wartime Spad

distance of 1,890 miles in 15 hours 57 minutes – or 119 mph average speed.

In the twenty years which succeeded the absolutely first Atlantic crossing by air – that by Commander Read in early 1919 – we can easily find one hundred Atlantic aerial exploits of note. We can distinguish several groups of North Atlantic flight during this adventurous period. The first was the non-stop flight between continents.

136

8 May 1927 to fly from Paris to Newfoundland. After they had left and set course over the Atlantic there was no news. Rumours multiplied. They had landed at some uninhabited point on the Atlantic seaboard; they had been picked up by a ship with no radio; they had turned back and crashed in an inaccessible, mountainous region. Gradually the truth dawned: they had been swallowed by the 'never surfeited sea' and the manner of their deaths would never be known.

Then came the great success: Captain Charles Lindbergh, not many days after Nungesser and Coli had disappeared, flew non-stop from New York to Paris in a Ryan monoplane with a single Wright air-cooled engine. Lindbergh had a rapturous reception from the French on his arrival. The entire world hailed his achievement with an enthusiasm and unanimous acclaim not proffered to any previous flight – that of Alcock and Brown included. This prodigious outpouring of public applause can be traced to a number of features of the flight.

In the first place it was a solo flight. It has always been evident that a solo achievement appears to most people to have an innate superiority to a crew or team achievement. And in Lindbergh's trans-Atlantic non-stop flight the accent was inevitably and markedly upon one person: Lindbergh himself. He planned it, he assembled the materials with which to make it, and he did it.

Next there was the 'rounded' quality of Lindbergh's achievement. The flight was from points close to two great capital cities, New York and Paris, and no previous flight had seemed so clearly to link continents, countries or cultures.

Lindbergh had learnt to fly before joining the US Army. For his Atlantic flight he received the support of Mr Raymond Orteig, who offered a prize of $25,000 for the first non-stop Paris-New York or New York-Paris flight, and of a group of business men in St Louis. The United States press was less helpful. It tended to be its cutting and critical self when it reported on the plans and some newspapers insisted upon calling Lindbergh the 'flying fool' presumably because of his former activities as an exhibition and aerobatic pilot. But the courage and skill of the man overcame.

Then there was the aircraft itself. Alcock and Brown had flown a wartime bomber, a biplane with a rather old-fashioned appearance. But Lindbergh's Ryan, the *Spirit of St Louis* with its elegant high wing monoplane configuration, was modern. It was the kind of aircraft that

293 Breguet 19A-2 *Point d'Interrogation* (Question Mark), flown from Paris to New York by Costes and Bellonte, September 1930

294 Three Douglas World Cruisers over New York on the first round-the-world flight, 1924

293

294

137

fitted the conception of a machine that could be used by individual travellers for ordinary touring.

Lindbergh's success and fame encouraged other pilots to attempt the same feat or some variation of it. There was a New York-Berlin attempt by Chamberlin and Levine which ended at some distance from the German capital. There was the unsuccessful attempt to fly from England to Canada, which cost the lives of F. F. Minchin, an especially skilled British pilot, L. Hamilton and Princess Loewenstein-Wertheim.

Baldonnel to Labrador.

Two months later the young American Miss Amelia Earhart, with two companions, made the west-east flight in a Fokker monoplane; four years later, in 1932, she made her solo flight in a Lockheed Vega. The distinguished pilots Jean Mermoz and Charles Kingsford-Smith laid the foundation stones to their later fame on the Atlantic, the former making the first postal crossing of the South Atlantic in a Latécoère, the latter crossing the North Atlantic, east-west, in a Fokker. These flights

Hardly less tragic, though less theatrical, was the failure of another fine British pilot, Captain W. G. R. Hinchliffe of Imperial Airways, and the Hon. Elsie Mackay. Hinchliffe was one of those buccaneering characters who seem to be able to overcome by sheer genius the handicaps of physical disability; for he had only one eye and, like Nungesser's navigator Coli, always wore over his blind eye a black patch. But he claimed to be able by his own methods to overcome the difficulties of distance estimation which are held to arise from the absence of the binocular, range-finding faculties of the two eyes.

Now the challenge of the non-stop Atlantic flight began to lose its *réclame*. There was one more absolute first, the first east to west non-stop crossing by a winged machine on 12 April 1928. It was made by the German Captain Hermann Koehl, supported by the substantial financial and prestige background of Baron Gunther von Huenefeld and with the help of a wild and charming Irish pilot Colonel James Fitzmaurice. They flew from

295 Charles Lindbergh taking delivery of his specially built Ryan monoplane, *Spirit of St Louis*, at San Diego before his solo Atlantic crossing, 1927

296 Junkers F.13 *Bremen* in which H. Koehl and others first crossed the Atlantic from East to West, 1928

297 Amelia Earhart

138

298

were made in 1930 by which time the menace and the challenge of the Atlantic ocean had been somewhat dimmed though by no means eliminated.

But contemporary with the Atlantic trail blazing, there had been trail blazing in many other parts of the world and in various other forms.

The French Lieutenant Roget had given flying a post-war boost when in April 1919 he flew from Paris to Rome in a Breguet XIV, nearly half of the 930 miles he covered being over sea. He went on to fly from Paris to Kenitra, Morocco and from Paris to Warsaw. The following year a fleet of four Capronis and seven SVAs set forth from Rome in a daring bid to reach Tokyo. Two of the SVAs, piloted by Ferrarin and Masiero, reached Tokyo nearly three months later. The Frenchman Georges Pelletier Doisy flew from Paris to Tokyo in a good deal less time (just under seven weeks) four years later in a Breguet. He had an eventful journey, changing engine at Hanoi and being lent another Breguet by the Chinese when he damaged his own aircraft in a Shanghai ditch.

The Far East continued to beckon. In 1925, in what must be the longest aerial journey ever undertaken, de Pinedo and Campanelli flew a Savoia flying-boat 34,000 miles. They flew from Lake Maggiore to Tokyo, circumnavigating Australia on the way, and then took a more direct route home again. In the same year Pelletier Doisy flew from Paris to Peking in a mere seven days.

The Swiss Walter Mittelholzer gave his two and a half month flight from Zurich to the Cape a scientific character by taking with him two geologists. His machine was a Dornier Merkur with BMW engine. He flew via the Nile and the great East African Lakes.

In the United States a number of Army pilots, fired with Mitchell's crusading zeal, achieved historic flights. In September 1922 Lieutenant James Doolittle flew from

299

Jacksonville, Florida to San Diego, California in a DH.4 in 21 hours 20 minutes, stopping only once for refuelling and a quick breakfast in San Antonio, Texas. Eleven years before, the gallant Cal Rodgers had taken seven weeks to make the first winged crossing of the continent.

In May 1923 Lieutenants Oakley Kelly and John Macready set America alight by making the first coast-to-coast non-stop flight—2,500 miles from New York to San Diego in 26 hours 50 minutes. Their aircraft was one of the Army's Fokker T-2 monoplanes with single Liberty engine. Two weeks previously Kelly and Macready, timed by Orville Wright, had set a world endurance record in the same machine, remaining in the air for just over 36 hours.

The Dutchman Anthony Fokker, in whose aircraft

298 Abe and Kawashi on arrival in Paris, 1925, having flown a Breguet 19A-2 from Tokyo. The Japanese Ambassador to France stands below them

299 Brutin and Moenck beside *Alsa*, the Farman 190 in which in 1931 they flew from Paris to Tokyo and back in 250 hours

many pioneer flights were made by American flyers, had settled in the United States after the 1914-18 war. Before the war, having offered his services in vain to the Dutch, British, French and Belgian governments, he had been snapped up by the Germans, and for the German Army during the war he built 8,000 aircraft, supervised the building of 6,000 more, and produced a method of synchronizing machine gun fire through a propeller. After the Armistice he returned to Holland, smuggling out of Germany sufficient materials to start an aircraft factory. Some of his aircraft manufactured in Holland were bought by the US Army, with whom they proved popular, and he was invited to build aircraft in the United States – but not under his own name.

It was at an air meeting in St Louis that the aviation publicist Harry Bruno first revealed the identity of the builder of the T-2 to the American public. Gaining control of the loudspeaker system by a stratagem, Bruno directed attention to a T-2 which was standing unnoticed at the edge of the airfield, referred to the recent flight in this machine by Kelly and Macready, had Fokker himself stand beside the aircraft, and then 'Ladies and gentlemen!' he shouted to the tumultuous and wildly enthusiastic crowd, 'Meet the great designer of the T-2 himself, Anthony Fokker, the Flying Dutchman.' The Army struck back by entering the T-2 in a race for bombers, in which fast twin-engine Martins were guaranteed to leave the T-2 well behind. But as the T-2 was being lapped the wily Bruno noticed that its time scarcely varied from lap to lap, and he immediately announced to the assembled pressmen that they were

301

302

300

300 Lieutenant Maughan's Curtiss PW-8 which flew the 'Dawn to Dusk' flight across America, 1924

301 The American Lieutenant Commander Byrd, with Roald Amundsen, checking equipment before taking off in his Fokker Trimotor to make the first crossing of the North Pole on 9 May 1926

302 Refuelling the Fokker C-2A *Question Mark* over Imperial Valley, California, during its 150 hour flight of January 1929

witnessing an unprecedented display of consistent flying. The Fokker T-2 it was that got the headlines.

The American genius for publicity was seen again in June 1924 when Lieutenant Russell Maughan raced the sun by flying 2,670 miles from New York to San Francisco in a Curtiss machine in just under 18 hours at an average speed of 150 mph including refuelling stops.

Another Fokker triumph came on 9 May 1926 when the Americans Lieutenant Commander Richard Byrd and Floyd Bennett made the first flight over the North Pole in a Fokker trimotor, having taken off on skis from Spitsbergen. More navigational history was made the following year by Lieutenants Lester Maitland and Albert Hegenberger, who in a Fokker C-2 trimotor flew 2,400 miles in just under 26 hours from Oakland,

California to Honolulu, using a radio beam – which turned out to be far less efficient than the crew.

A number of flights by US army and naval pilots made significant contributions to technological advance. In 1929 a crew of five kept a Fokker C-2 trimotor, the *Question Mark*, in the air over California for 150 hours, the aircraft being repeatedly refuelled by a hose lowered from another aircraft. In the same year Lieutenant Doolittle made the first take-off and landing on instruments, and in 1935 Hegenberger and Akers made the first blind landing on an aircraft carrier.

The conquest of the Pacific came in 1928. Two Australians, Squadron Leader Charles Kingsford-Smith and Flight Lieutenant Charles Ulm, with Americans Harry Lyons and J. W. Warner as navigator and radio operator, made a spectacular nine-day flight from America to Australia; their route was Oakland-Hawaii-Fiji-Brisbane. In the same year Captain Bert Hinkler of the Royal Australian Air Force, in a frail Avro Avian, flew from London to Darwin, Australia in a mere two weeks, and Ferrarin and del Prete flew 4,500 miles from Italy to Brazil non-stop in a Savoia flying-boat.

The American pioneer flights across the Atlantic and around the world were done, as has been related, by formations of aircraft. But the formations were small. Without much question the greatest pioneering formation flight was that achieved in 1933 by Marshal Italo Balbo with twenty-four Savoia Marchetti S 55 twin-hull seaplanes fitted with Isotta-Fraschini engines. Twenty-three of them completed the journey from Italy to Chicago and back. Designed by Alessandro Marchetti and first built in 1922, the seaplane was of strikingly original conception, half flying-boat, half float seaplane having something of a catamaran appearance, with the two engines mounted in tandem on pylons above the centre section.

This aircraft had earlier been turned down by the Italian government, but Balbo, when commanded by Mussolini to stimulate and build up the Italian air force, decided to concentrate upon this aircraft. He formed his

303

304

305

306

squadrons at Orbetello and was ready to start in July 1933 with a formation of eight 'platoons' as he called them, each of three aircraft, each aircraft with a crew of four except for Balbo's own machine which carried five.

The whole affair took place in an atmosphere of high heroics, emotional ecstasy and comic opera extravagance. The figure of Mussolini and the exaggerated patriotism of Balbo and his men, leading finally to a march of triumph along the Piazza Venezia in Rome, were sneered at by the peoples of some other nations, but the fact remains that this formation flight was a supreme aeronautical achievement. It marked the development of aircraft up to the point when a large formation could make a controlled and well regimented long flight.

303 Fokker C-2 Trimotor, the type in which Maitland and Hegenberger flew from Oakland to Honolulu, 1927

304 Fokker F.VII/3m *Southern Cross*, in which Kingsford-Smith, Ulm, Lyons and Warner conquered the Pacific in 1928, being serviced at Oakland, California

305 Bellanca *Miss Veedol*, in which Clyde E. Pangborn and Hugh Herndon made the first non-stop flight across the Pacific from Japan to the United States, 1931

306 Marshal Balbo's twenty-four Savoia Marchetti S 55s before taking off on their flight from Italy to Chicago and back, 1933

141

While Marshal Balbo and his considerable force were preparing for their flight two Americans, with a contrasted lack of ceremony, flew round the world in eight days. They were Wiley Post and Harold Gatty. They started from New York in the early morning of 23 June 1931 and flew by way of Harbour Grace, Chester, Berlin, Moscow, Novosibirsk, Blagoveshchensk, Khabarovsk, Fairbanks and Edmonton back to New York in 16 hours and 15 minutes over the eight days. Their aircraft was a Lockheed Vega with Pratt & Whitney

307

Wasp engine.

These pioneering flights built up confidence in the powers of aircraft. They were followed by countless trail blazing flights by pilots who used light aircraft in the Moth class. Among these the Englishwoman Miss Amy Johnson, later to become Mrs Mollison, attracted attention. A shorthand typist by profession, she brought together her meagre resources and, inspired, so it was said, by the Hollywood movie *Wings* which glamorized the first war in the air, started her lessons in September 1928 in a Cirrus Moth. Although not a particularly promising pupil she was so bent upon proving herself that she decided on a flight from England to Australia. Her route was by way of Vienna, Constantinople, Baghdad, Karachi, Calcutta, Bangkok, Singapore, Java and Timor to Darwin on the north coast of Australia where she arrived on 24 May·1930. Nor did she pause afterwards. She made numerous other long distance flights, always planning thoroughly and handling her aircraft skilfully. She caught the imagination of Britain and then of the world.

Also with the knack of capturing affection and attention was the remarkable James Mollison; but his claim to fame was built upon different foundations. He specialized in taking appalling risks. But his flights

307 Lockheed Vega *Winnie Mae*, in which Post and Gatty flew round the world in eight days in 1931. In front is Post, blind in one eye, who flew *Winnie Mae* solo round the world in well under eight days two years later

308 The Deperdussin in which Prévost won the first Schneider Trophy contest, 1913

309 The Sopwith Tabloid, piloted by Pixton, which won the 1914 Schneider Trophy

142

were remarkable for the skill with which they were conducted. A soft-spoken Scot, cultivated, seemingly rather retiring and shy, he was a tremendously expert pilot and navigator and about the toughest human being imaginable. Together he and Amy Johnson did much for personal flying and for the private aircraft.

Personal aviation was and is closely allied to sporting aviation. Racing performed the function of stimulating technical and piloting progress. Between the world wars it attained its highest point of development. After the second of these wars air racing declined in aeronautical importance although it has been kept going as a purely entertainment and sporting activity.

But at the very beginning, the pylon races and the races between capital cities situated at such distances apart that they tested the range capabilities of the competing machines, were a real means of advancing the art of aircraft design not to say the skill of pilots and of air navigators.

Two events stand out as representative of the most highly developed forms of these two kinds of air racing: the Schneider Trophy series and the MacRobertson Trophy race from England to Australia, already mentioned for the boost it gave landplane development for airlines. The first was the more influential. In the United States pylon racing became popular and there were many events, as we shall see later, drawing good entries and huge crowds of spectators; but as a world stimulus to aircraft progress no other event can be rated as highly as the Schneider Trophy.

Although when Jacques Schneider presented the Trophy in 1912 the race was intended to encourage seaworthiness in marine aircraft as well as performance, speed soon became dominant. The outright win enabling Britain to retain the trophy in perpetuity was the consequence of three victories in a row in 1927, 1929

308

309

and 1931. All the races were flown under the auspices and rules of the Fédération Aéronautique Internationale.

The Schneider Trophy race was flown twelve times, starting in 1913 and with a gap for the war, the last event being in 1931. The nations engaged were Britain, France, Italy and the United States. The winner's speed – Prévost for France – in 1913 was 46 mph and the winner's speed – J. N. Boothman for Britain – in 1931 340 mph. Engine power went up from 100 hp to 2,350 hp.

The first winner, Prévost's Deperdussin monoplane,

competitors. Eventually the United States government entered the field.

So in 1923 to Cowes, in the Isle of Wight, America sent a team with full government backing. D. Rittenhouse, in a Curtiss CR-3 seaplane with Curtiss engine, demolished the opposition, winning at a speed of 177 mph. In 1924 the race was postponed by the Americans in a true sporting spirit because the British and Italian entries were not ready. In the following year, 1925, at Baltimore, a pilot whose name was to become

310 Fokker D.VII completing a loop

311 Lieut. Rittenhouse and his Curtiss CR-3, winner of the 1923 Schneider Trophy

310

was a remarkably clean aircraft with a bulbous nose cap for streamlining the Gnome rotary engine. The 1914 winner, the Sopwith Tabloid, piloted by C. H. Pixton, was a biplane. It was the inspiration for the wartime Sopwith Pup. After the war England was the race venue, and England lived up to her reputation for generating the world's worst fogs. Held at Bournemouth, the race was annulled because all the competitors lost themselves in a dense fog. At first however it was thought that an Italian had completed the course and consequently Venice was selected for the 1920 event. The Italians proved their skill in marine aircraft design with a Savoia seaplane flown by L. Bologna. French opposition was eliminated by the seaworthiness tests. In 1921 the Italian G. di Briganti in a Macchi with Isotta-Fraschini engine won the race at a speed of 110 mph. Britain had her second success in 1922 at Naples with the Supermarine Sea Lion flying-boat designed by R. J. Mitchell (Napier Lion engine).

Public interest in the Schneider Trophy was mounting. It was the outstanding speed contest of the world. The publicity which the winner received increased continually and the winning aircraft was taken as an example of a country's aeronautical competence. Governments were forced to consider whether they should help

known worldwide won – James Doolittle, again in a Curtiss, at 233 mph.

The Italian government supported a great effort in 1926 when di Bernardi in a Macchi with Fiat engine won, thus ensuring that the next race would be held in Italy. It was a rush to Venice where the race was to be flown over the fashionable waters of the Lido, the course taking the aircraft close past the golden beaches and along in front of the glittering luxury hotels.

311

The Italian Macchi M.52 aircraft were beautiful to look at, their wings lacquered, their ailerons french polished, and their pilots were the stuff from which national heroes are made—Guazzetti, Ferrarin and the great di Bernardi. Britain had two Supermarine monoplanes and one Gloster biplane and her pilots were Flight Lieutenant Worsley, Flight Lieutenant Kinkead who flew the biplane, and Flight Lieutenant Webster.

The race day was a frantic fiesta. Bands played, flags fluttered, the beaches of the Lido were black with people.

down to a modest 50 degrees. The less spectacular British method proved the more effective and at one turn Webster overtook Guazzetti while actually rounding a pylon.

The winner was Webster in a Supermarine. He completed the seven laps of the course (he made one extra lap because he felt unsure whether he had counted correctly) at a speed of 282 mph. Worsley came second. All the Italians were forced to retire to the tragic disappointment of the huge crowds of emotional spectators.

312

313

312 The Curtiss R3C-2 in which Lieut. Doolittle won the 1925 Schneider Trophy and also set four world speed records

313 Macchi M.39 flown by di Bernardi, winner of the 1926 Schneider Trophy

314 Boeing F4B-4s of the US Navy, 1933

315 Jean Batten's Percival Gull, 1935

316 Ford Trimotor, continuously in use since 1930, taking off

317 Waco S-3HD, 1936

318 Replica of the Lockheed Vega *Winnie Mae* of 1931

319 Curtiss Robin, 1929

320 The first Fokker F.VIIA of KLM, 1925

The Italian pilots made their turns at the pylons in dizzy Immelmann turns, zooming up to 500 and 600 ft and then over and down almost to the water surface to hurtle into the next leg of the course at top speed. The British pilots, however, instructed by a special research on turning methods made by Farnborough, maintained a constant height on the turns and kept the angle of bank

Early preparations for the 1929 race over the waters of the Solent promised an even more significant and exciting event. French, Italian and US entries were promised. They came to nothing and H. R. D. Waghorn won at 329 mph. His Supermarine seaplane had a Rolls-Royce engine. In 1931 there was a sour comedy before the event when the British government, in a sudden fit

314

315

317

319
320

316

318

321

323

322

324

325

326

of meanness, decided it could not give the necessary financial support to the British entry. Lady Houston, a rich widow of firm and fiercely expressed patriotic and political views, promptly wrote out a cheque for £100,000 and the race went on. J. N. Boothman completed the course in a further refined Supermarine with Rolls-Royce engine at an average of 340 mph. He had no opposition and he thus concluded the whole series and put a final full stop to grand scale, government supported air racing.

Speed, the objective of the Schneider Trophy series, remained the most important aircraft performance parameter. Advances in speed were demonstrated and signalled to the world not only by races but also by means of international and world records. Many of the most important speed records–defined as averages of opposite runs over a measured course–were set by Schneider Trophy racing machines.

In 1923 A. S. Williams of the United States in a Curtiss took the world air record speed to 267 mph, and in 1927 di Bernardi in a Macchi with Fiat engine took it to 319 mph. A. H. Orlebar and G. H. Stainforth, both Schneider Trophy team pilots, in Supermarine seaplanes of Schneider type with special Rolls-Royce engines achieved 358 and then 407 mph in 1929 and 1931, the last two Schneider years.

In the United States air racing was resumed after the 1914-18 war with the first Pulitzer Trophy Race in 1920.

It was the great rivalry between the Army and the Navy that sustained tension in this series and spurred pilots and manufacturers to ever greater speeds. The first year, at Long Island, Lieutenant Corliss Moseley won in a Verville-Packard racer at a speed of 156 mph. The 1922 race, won by Russell Maughan at Detroit, Michigan in a Curtiss biplane at a record-breaking 205 mph, featured the first aircraft with undercarriage retracted into the wings–two Verville-Sperry racers. (The first modern fully retractable undercarriage had been seen in 1920 on the American Dayton-Wright RB monoplane which competed for the Gordon-Bennett Trophy in France; the wheels retracted into the fuselage.) In 1925 the race was won by the same Curtiss machine that, fitted with floats, took Doolittle to victory in the Schneider Trophy later that year–the R3C-2 biplane. In the National Air Races the two leading trophies were the Thompson, for the fastest speed in a closed circuit race, and the Bendix, for victory in a transcontinental race.

These races attracted huge crowds to witness constant record-breaking by renowned speed pilots such as Jimmy Doolittle, Al Williams, Frank Hawks and Roscoe Turner.

In France in the 1930s the Deutsch de la Meurthe Trophy races, for aircraft not exceeding eight litres engine capacity, gave an impulse to speed and were influential in French design. A special 'Deutsch de la Meurthe Trophy type' was designed for Caudron-

321 Supermarine Spitfire fighter in 1940 markings

322 De Havilland Mosquito VI fighter bomber

323 Hawker Hurricane IIB single-seat fighter, seen postwar

324 North American Harvards (AT-6 Texan) of the RAF, 1953

325 Avro Lancaster I bomber, 1942

326 Supermarine S.6B, winner of the 1931 Schneider Trophy and thus the outright winner of the Trophy for Britain

327 Curtiss R2C-1 flown
by Lieut. Alford Williams
to win the 1923 Pulitzer
Trophy

Renault by Marcel Riffard. The winning speed in 1933 was 201 mph by Georges Détré in a Potez 53 with Potez 270 hp engine, and in 1935 275 mph by Raymond Delmotte in a Caudron-Renault C 460 with Renault 330 hp engine. A French national heroine at this time was Hélène Boucher, who held the world open speed record over 1,000 kilometres in 1934, raising it successively to 276 mph.

In both Europe and the United States, aerobatics was popular with the public in the early 1930s. The German

Here the achievements of balloonists intervened, particularly the record of Captains O. A. Anderson and A. W. Stevens of the US Army Air Corps in 1935 – 72,394 ft or nearly 14 miles. The last world height record by an aeroplane before the war was 56,046 ft in 1938 by an Italian Caproni 161.

Distance records are less informative than speed and altitude records because there must always be an element of loading choice. But absolute distance in a straight line produced some remarkable performances. Lindbergh's

327

329

328

330

328 Kirsch takes off in his Nieuport-Delage competing for the 1920 Gordon-Bennett Trophy

329 American ace racing pilot Frank Hawks with his Laird Solution biplane, winner of the Thompson Trophy, 1930

330 James Doolittle and his Gee Bee Super Sportster in which he won the Thompson Trophy in 1932

Gerhard Fieseler and the Frenchmen Michel Détroyat and Marcel Doret thrilled France in 1933 and 1934 with their competitive virtuosity, the programme sometimes requiring each entrant to change aircraft with his opponent. Aerobatic displays were also performed by teams. French, Italian, British, Polish, Czech, Yugoslav and Romanian pilots competed at Turin, Brussels, Hendon, Vincennes, Zurich and Bucarest. In the United States Claire Lee Chennault's Flying Trapeze and the Navy Sea Hawks were favourites, and Cleveland was the famous venue for international competitions.

Altitude records were pursued at the same time as speed records; not so eagerly, but still with much energy.

331

332

333

the early 1930s. In France the government began in 1931 to assist flying clubs and the purchase of aircraft by amateurs, and a whole line of small private machines arose – Potez, Morane-Saulnier, Farman and the popular Caudron Luciole and Phalène. From Germany came the Klemm and from Czechoslovakia the Avia.

In the United States the Daniel Guggenheim Fund for the Promotion of Aeronautics had been set up in 1926. It furthered aviation education, encouraged commercial aviation, sponsored the Safe Aircraft Competition, and eventually assisted the growth of flying clubs. Among the most popular American small private aircraft were the Parks P-II two-seater of 1929, the Taylor Cub, and the Stinson Reliant of 1937 which carried five.

In the Flying Thirties, with their air free from the restrictions of later times, many Americans owned aircraft and took part in sports flying which ranged over a wide variety of activities from the sublime to the ridiculous: inter-club racing and parachuting, country cruises in fleets of aircraft, the flyers spending the night and holding parties in remote spots, mock-bombing, bursting free floating balloons with propellers, cutting rolls of toilet paper released in the air. At the same time private aircraft came to be widely used in business.

Women eagerly participated in these American flying clubs. They thronged the air. After Amelia Earhart who perished in the Pacific in 1937 having completed the major part of her attempted round the world flight in emulation of Wiley Post – Jacqueline Cochran's is perhaps the most illustrious female name in the history of American aviation.

At first she suffered one misfortune after another. She got lost flying over the Rockies, stranded in Romania in the London to Melbourne race, was forced down in the 1936 Bendix race (she was the first woman entrant in the event) after taking off in a machine against the advice of both the manufacturer of the aircraft and the manufacturer of the engine, and just managed to make a forced landing in the next year's Bendix race after her aircraft had caught fire 12,000 ft up. Then for three years, from 1937, she was selected as the world's outstanding woman aviator by the International League of Aviators, was placed first in the Bendix Trophy race of 1938, and at one time held three out of four open class records in the United States against men. In the second world war

New York-Paris flight of May 1927 was given a record by the Fédération Aéronautique Internationale at 3,600 miles. A Soviet flight of 6,400 miles in July 1937 was of interest because it joined Moscow and San Jacinto, California in a trajectory over the North Pole; it was made by a crew of three in a fine-looking, slender ANT.25-1 monoplane. The British distance record of November 1938 has technical merit because the Vickers Wellesley aircraft in which it was done were built to the Barnes Wallis patented geodetic form of construction. The route was Ismailia to Darwin, a distance of 7,158 miles.

Private flying developed on the European continent in

331 Balloon in which Capts Anderson and Stevens of the US Army Air Corps attained a world record height of 72,395 ft in 1935

332 Delmotte, winner of the 1935 Deutsch de la Meurthe Trophy, beside his Caudron-Renault monoplane

333 1930 Bulte trainer, registered in Belgium

this formidable woman served with the British Air Transport Auxiliary and then became head of the US Women's Airforce Service Pilots.

While hosts of races and world records and competitions were in progress, light aircraft development all too soon began to take an unexpected turn. It moved towards the complications and elaborations that were

of all kinds, from the big commercial machines, where the added complication was justified, to the small personal machines, where it was not always justified.

At a time when most pilots had given up the thought of ever keeping private flying simple and cheap and were resigning themselves to increases in complexity and cost, Henri Mignet – who has already been mentioned as the designer of an early light aircraft on the Lympne trials pattern, made his own little machine and published in Paris in 1934 his book *Le Sport de l'Air*. It had the sub-title *Pourquoi et Comment j'ai construit le Pou-du-Ciel*. At first the book seemed to have little impact; then suddenly it hit the aviation world with a bang.

Mignet had penetrated the very minds and aspirations of millions who longed to fly in their own way: who longed to imitate, but with success, the feats of the pioneers. They saw in the sharply original, vigorous yet firmly logical approach of Mignet the salvation of true personal flying and the realization of the dream of the individually owned and operated aircraft. *Le Sport de l'Air* was translated into almost every language under the sun.

Anyone, in the Mignet philosophy, could build a safe and effective aircraft if he had a hammer, a saw, a chisel and a screwdriver and a few bits of wood, ply and other, a couple of children's scooter wheels and tyres and some fabric. For power unit he need not go to the sophisticated and expensive aero-engine makers. Any good engine would do provided it was not too heavy. Motor cycle engines were the obvious choice and for his first machine Mignet selected a 500 cc Aubier-Dunne twin horizontally

334

335

334 Howard Hughes and his Racer. In 1935 he set a world landplane speed record of 352 mph and in 1937 made a trans-continental flight, eastwards from California, of 7 hours, 28 minutes and 25 seconds (average speed of 327·5 mph)

335 The famous Blériot 110 *Joseph le Brix* in 1935, with indication of its many distance and duration records

invading commercial flying. The idea of the individual owner, going where he wanted, when he wanted, landing on any suitable flat field, untrammelled by traffic control orders or detailed regulations, waned.

It followed that small personal aircraft became more complicated, more heavily equipped with all kinds of aids. The memorable adage of the early American automobile manufacturer – 'what you don't fit don't give no trouble' – was forgotten. More and more instruments and more and more equipment filled aircraft

opposed two-stroke. Many other engines were used in the Mignet type machines later, but all of them were straightforward comparatively cheap motor cycle or small car engines.

Mignet did, of course, have a wide aerodynamic knowledge. He was by no means the ignorant amateur he liked to pose as. He built a successful glider in 1923. But he did, all the same, keep largely to his scheme of simplicity and the avoidance of technical mumbo jumbo – a straight, logical approach. His aircraft, the

337

338

339

Pou-du-Ciel or sky louse, primly translated by the Air League of the British Empire as the 'Flying Flea', was unlike other aircraft. It was neither a biplane nor a monoplane, but a tandem plane, the lifting surface being divided between two small, equal-sized low aspect ratio planes arranged one behind the other. The front plane, of 13 ft span, was higher than the rear plane. A large vertical rudder, worked by the control stick instead of by pedals, was fitted. The body of the aircraft was a small nacelle taking a single occupant hung below the forward plane with engine and airscrew at the nose. The two rubber tyred wheels took the weight on the ground with a small tail wheel. Control was ultra-simple: Mignet did without ailerons or the ordinary elevator. Tilting of the planes produced the control in pitch while the marked dihedral angles on the planes gave inherent lateral stability and enabled turns to be made on rudder alone.

Mignet took a month to build his first *Pou* in his outdoor workshop and he flew it in 1933. A British pilot, S. V. Appleby, built one in England and flew it in 1935. The number in use in Britain rose to over a hundred one year later and continued to rise. Mignet flew across the Channel from France and with Appleby travelled

336 Taylor Cub, one of the first practical light monoplanes, 1930

337 Air meeting in Cologne with a Focke-Wulf 44 Stieglitz flying before a crowd of 100,000 people, 14 July 1935

338 Formation flying at the RAF Pageant, 1931

339 Mock bombing. Sopwith Snipe at the 1924 Aerial Pageant, Hendon

all over England giving demonstrations at air meetings.

Although the *Pou* had its effects upon aircraft design – the United States Aeronca for instance – and although Mignet insisted upon the rightness of his tandem configuration and simplified controls, the accidents – a dozen of them within eighteen months – smothered his enthusiasm in the end. It was full circle from the Santos-Dumont *Demoiselle* to the *Pou-du-Ciel*.

Flying as an individual way of getting about, comparable to motoring, went out as the complicated private aircraft with all its fittings and accessories came in. To be a private pilot to-day entails a good deal of study. Examinations have to be passed and licences obtained. Nevertheless there is one comparatively new kind of flying which has a right to be called a sport and in recent years has attracted ever increasing numbers of people; this is aerobatics.

We must be clear about what is meant by aerobatics in the context of competition flying. It has almost nothing to do with exhibition flying or with formation air drill. So although air force formation teams are usually called 'aerobatic' teams it is a misnomer. Nor has aerobatics anything to do with the sound and fury of the exhibition pilot in a high powered jet, tearing round an aerodrome, splitting the ears and dazzling the eyes of spectators. Aerobatics is a form of flying of enormous complexity and great difficulty. It is best compared with virtuosity on a musical instrument and it exacts the same kind of continual practice. Or you could say it has a relationship to figure skating, the aircraft being made to trace involved patterns in the sky and to meet strict criteria in each figure.

'Aerobatics,' says the British Standards Institution's *Glossary of Aeronautical Terms*, are 'evolutions intentionally performed with an aircraft, other than those required for normal flight.' There are two main classes, the stalled manoeuvres and the flown manoeuvres. Flick rolls, spins and stalls are stalled manoeuvres when the aircraft is so flown, at big angles of attack, that the airflow over its wings ceases to be smooth and to produce ordinary lift. Loops, inverted flight, the bunt (downward

340

340 Mignet's *Pou-du-Ciel*, 1933

341 Meeting of British-made Flying Fleas, 1936

341

loop), the spectacles and slow rolls are flown manoeuvres. Few foundation novelties have appeared since the pioneer aerobatic pilot, Pégoud, but the variations and elaborations have been endless. The 'fin sling', shown by Zurakowski at Farnborough, in which asymmetric engine power is used in a twin-engined machine to produce a form of cartwheel, could perhaps be called a new aerobatic. The 'lomçevak', devised by Czech aerobatic pilots and consisting in a form of flick roll about the lateral axis – a wildly improbable, difficult and

world championship series, in which entries steadily went up, the number soon approaching a hundred with many women among them. It was held in different countries. In Moscow the Yak aircraft showed that the Russian manufacturers were able to do as well as the Czech in the design of these specialist machines. It was held also in Bratislava, Budapest, Bilbao and at various aerodromes in England. Sixteen different countries sent teams of pilots to the 1966 contest, which was won by Martiemianov of the Soviet Union.

342

fantastic manoeuvre seen in most of the last five world championship contests – is certainly a new aerobatic.

Modern aerobatics began with the International Aerobatic Competition for the Lockheed Trophy held at Coventry airport in 1955. At first France dominated with that absolute master of aerobatic techniques Léon Biancotto winning. In subsequent years Swiss pilots won the contest and then, in several successive years, Czechoslovak pilots, although German, Polish, Hungarian, Spanish and, later, United States pilots were highly placed. The Czech pilots were to some extent aided by their Zlin aircraft, among the best aerobatic machines in existence.

Eventually the Lockheed Trophy aerobatic competition, after ten successful contests, turned into the

Aerobatics are not entirely useless; but they have little or no commercial value. They come near to fulfilling the early definition of a sport and they are popular in the flying clubs all over the world – though perhaps less in the United States than in other countries. And because the aircraft best suited to them are small machines, sensitive, with powerful controls, they offer the joys of flying for its own sake in the highest degree.

Flying for touring and for personal travel has suffered the diminutions that have been mentioned. Aerobatics have helped a little to maintain the purely piloting interest. But they can never occupy more than a small corner of aeronautical activities. We now turn to one of the most technically inventive of aviation's developments, moving wing aircraft.

342 Czech Zlin 526, 1956

153

11 Moving wings

Men who must be placed in the front rank of world inventive and engineering genius have devoted prodigious intellectual studies to moving wing machines. The effort began, as was shown in an earlier chapter, with mathematical and design approaches to the so far unsuccessful form of moving wing machine, the ornithopter, but it eventually oriented itself to the finally successful form of moving wing machine, the helicopter.

Inevitably Leonardo da Vinci must appear once more with his vertical-lift helix drawing. It was an imaginative thought rather than a real design. The little working model made towards the end of the eighteenth century by Launoy and Bienvenu with its two four-bladed rotors has already been mentioned. Sir George Cayley and Enrico Forlanini both had schemes for helicopters powered by steam engines. But then came the petrol engine and the first genuine man-lifting helicopter.

Louis Breguet, in a four-rotor helicopter he had designed and had built with Richet in 1907 made, in September of that year, the first helicopter flight. This

343

helicopter was tethered during the flight, being partly restrained by a ground crew, although it did without question perform flight. It did so four years after the Wrights had made their fixed wing aeroplane experiments at Kitty Hawk and one year after Santos-Dumont had made his first officially observed fixed wing aeroplane flight at Paris.

After Breguet's achievement rotorcraft progress entered a period of unique contrasts. It was a period of wonderful schemes and operational stagnation. There were hosts of ingenious and unusual designs: single rotor, multi-rotor, co-axial, intermeshing and two-,

three- and four-bladed rotor craft, of the weirdest shapes and configurations; but not one of them surmounted that high barrier between the brilliant invention and the practical, dependable aircraft.

Henry Berliner in the United States had been working on helicopters two years before Breguet's flight, but by 1908 he had still done nothing further than develop mainly theoretical ideas. In fact it was not until 16 July 1922 that Berliner made his successful hovering flight before military observers. Even Igor Sikorsky, one of aviation's supreme geniuses, had achieved little success in his home town of Kiev. His 1909 helicopter had co-axial rotors and embodied promising features, but neither it nor his 1910 machine reached practical, consistent dependability in the achievement of flight. The years passed; the inventors continued to invent–the Marquis de P. Pescara in Spain, Etienne Oemichen in France, de Bothezat in the United States, Brennan in England. They could not obtain the practical breakthrough. Something was holding up the entire rotorcraft effort. Its nature was a mystery.

It was left to a genius who can be put alongside Sikorsky for the size of his original and inventive success and for the flexibility and inspiration of his work, to resolve the mystery. He contrived to look at the rotating wing as a means of obtaining lift from a totally new and previously unthought of angle. He was the Spaniard Don Juan de la Cierva.

His contribution was indirect because it came through his own invention of the Autogiro and the Autogiro is not a helicopter or indeed any other class of flying machine except, uniquely, the Autogiro class. Cierva discovered a new way of flying. Embodied in the design of the craft for that new way of flying were secrets which, until then, had been hidden from helicopter experimenters.

The Autogiro was called by pressmen the 'windmill aircraft', and for once this journalistic reader-catching term was an exact description. The Autogiro was not lifted by a helix as da Vinci's helicopter was supposed to be and as Breguet's was, but by a freely spinning windmill. It seems doubtful if anyone before Cierva had appreciated that a freely rotating windmill, if drawn through the air, will turn and generate lift. This was Cierva's starting point. He mounted a freely rotating windmill above an ordinary aeroplane fuselage–an Avro fuselage was used in much of the early work–and he mounted the ordinary engine and airscrew in their customary positions. He then had a machine which could be accelerated and drawn through the air by the ordinary engine and airscrew while above it, umbrella-

344

345

346

347

348

349   350

351

like, turned by the action of the relative wind and *not* by engine power, was the freely spinning windmill. The body or fuselage with its accommodation for the pilot and its engine and airscrew were slung below the lifting windmill.

Juan de la Cierva Y Codorniu was born in Murcia in 1895. He built gliders in 1910 and then started work on a powered fixed wing machine in 1911. He built military aircraft at the time of the first world war and it was about then that he developed his obsession about the dangers of the stall. But although he thought of the way to defeat the stall in 1922 it was not until 1923 that his first Autogiro made successful flights–at the Getafe Aerodrome near Madrid on 17 January. From then on progress with this new form of flying machine was rapid.

Cierva acted as his own test pilot for much of the development period, but he was also associated with the noted British test pilot, who had been working at Farnborough, Captain Frank T. Courtney. Other of Cierva's collaborators were Wing Commander R. A. C. Brie and, later still, the American Harold F. Pitcairn who gave the Autogiro its impetus in the United States.

The early flights of Cierva's first Autogiros showed at once the difficulties of achieving stability and control. It was in solving these difficulties that Cierva injected into all rotorcraft design the life-giving ideas which led to the helicopters of to-day. His original patent fore-shadowed what was to come although only in incomplete and ultra-simplified terms. For the patent indicated that the lifting windmill should be so arranged that it would attain *automatically as it turned an equilibrium between centrifugal forces due to rotation and the forces of lift* coming from the relative airstream over the windmill blades.

If one imagines the principle of a rotor moving along a horizontal path while at the same time delivering lift to counteract gravity–a simple lifting airscrew moving along through the air–one sees at once that on one side of its axis the blades are advancing and on the other side they are retreating. Clearly an advancing blade relative to the motion of the whole thing through the air is moving faster than a retreating blade. One side of the rotor or screw is therefore in a faster relative

353

354

355

airstream than the other side. Other things being equal the faster moving side will lift more than the slower moving side so that the whole airscrew or rotor will tilt over and eventually topple.

Complicated schemes had been tried to even out the lift on the two sides of a rotor passing through the air. But Cierva saw the simple solution. It was to allow the

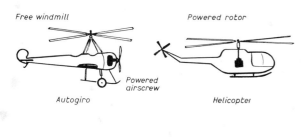

Free windmill   Powered rotor

Powered airscrew

Autogiro   Helicopter

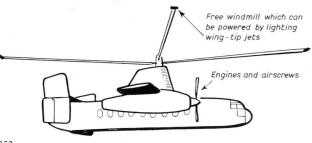

Free windmill which can be powered by lighting wing-tip jets

Engines and airscrews

352

352 Different types of rotary-wing aircraft, and a compound aircraft or convertiplane

353 First free-flight helicopter, flown by Cornu, 1907

356

blades of the rotor (which are no other than sections of an airscrew) freedom to flap. He hinged the blades of his lifting rotor. And because his rotor was a windmill and not power driven, the blades rose and fell as they rotated under the impulsion of the centrifugal and aerodynamic forces. The advancing blades rose, the retreating blades fell and the amount by which they rose and fell was a form of natural balance. The Cierva Autogiro was not only a *rotating wing* aircraft, but also and inseparably a *flapping wing* aircraft. And neither the rotation nor the flapping was directly power operated. The rotation occurred because the machine was drawn through the air by an ordinary airscrew; the flapping because the blades were free to balance themselves in the matter of lift and drag and centrifugal force.

As development proceeded, the freedom to flap became a highly complex form of multiple articulation. It worked at first only in Autogiros or windmill lift machines, not in powered helicopters. Directly power was applied to the rotor, the natural stability and natural flapping motion failed. But in the end the essentials of Cierva's invention were modified and adapted so that the power driven rotors of helicopters were able to benefit from Cierva's inventions and his mathematical analyses and, so doing, to obtain their long delayed success.

The Autogiro derives lift from a *free* spinning rotor or windmill, the aeroplane from fixed wings and the helicopter from a power driven rotor or screw. Both fixed wing aircraft and Autogiro must have translational speed in order to remain in the air. *Neither Autogiro nor fixed wing aircraft can hover in still air.*

The Autogiro was not–and there is wide misunderstanding on this–a plumb vertical ascent/descent machine

though it could come close to doing these manoeuvres. That was the practical, operational difference between it and the helicopter. But Cierva saw the importance of vertical take-off. So he determined to introduce it into his machine. Already he had arranged clutching systems for giving the windmill an initial spin before take-off. He now decided to accentuate that initial spin and to use it in a different way.

Reference has been made to the complex articulation which gave the blades of the Autogiro's lifting windmill its inherent stability. Not only could the blades flap within limits, but they could also change pitch by the angling of one set of hinges. This pitch changing was used in conjunction with engine power to produce the jump take-off machine. It had its first public demonstration in England, on Hounslow Heath, on 23 July 1936, still long before the conventional helicopter had made real progress towards general use or even full flying success.

What those who were present saw was this. The Autogiro, stationary on the ground, in the midst of a small clearing with bushes and trees all round, had its engine started. The wheel brakes were on. The engine power was then clutched in to the main lifting rotor. The arrangement of blade hinging ensured that as power was applied to the rotor, the blades turned to zero incidence. So they went round without producing any lift at all. In this way the rotor was spun to a prescribed rate, the Autogiro still motionless on the ground. The critical condition was now reached when the spinning rotor stored a large amount of inertial energy. At that moment the pilot declutched the rotor from the engine and instantaneously the blades of the lifting rotor–now a freely spinning windmill–acquired incidence and de-

354 The Oemichen 2 helicopter flying a kilometre, May 1924 at Arbonans

355 Cierva's first practical Autogiro, the C-4 at Getafe, January 1923

356 RAF Pageant, 1931. A Cierva C-19 is in the centre, with the Handley Page Gugnunc and the Westland-Hill Pterodactyl I, a tailless aircraft

veloped lift. The whole machine leaped vertically up from the ground about 20 ft, and then the ordinary airscrew and engine performed their normal function of drawing the whole aircraft through the air, and a relative wind blew over the rotor which from then on proceeded to windmill as in normal horizontal flight.

These jumping Autogiros, now almost forgotten, were major inventive achievements. Their manner of take-off was highly spectacular and constituted a demonstration of the original, unconventional and daring qualities of Cierva's technical thinking. He had achieved vertical take-off in his Autogiro without compromising its basic character. The landing, however, could not be absolutely vertical in still air nor could the machine hover in still air; but these were the only remaining basic differences in the performance of Auto-giros and of helicopters. In other ways the Autogiro was ahead of the helicopter, particularly in speed. It remained at the head in speed right through the development of rotorcraft, and when Doctors Bennett and Hislop went on to devise compound aircraft, incorporating both helicopter and Autogiro features – the Gyrodyne and the Rotodyne – they relied upon the Autogiro method of flight to obtain high speeds.

Cierva prepared designs for a long line of machines and his work was carried on by the Autogiro Company of America and by Pitcairn, by French, Italian and other companies specially set up or by existing aviation companies which acquired licences.

Autogiros were turned out in increasingly large quantities. They were used for military purposes – especially after the introduction of radar when they performed calibration functions which would have been difficult with fixed wing aircraft – and they were used for private flying. Large numbers of pilots in many countries qualified to fly Autogiros. Nor has the Autogiro principle ever faded away. It continues to be in use in the 1970s, with a number of new designs being launched in the United States and in Britain, France and Italy.

There now appeared, amongst the numerous names in the patent records for moving wing aircraft inventions, two which were to leave a profound mark in the story of rotorcraft development, Focke and Igor Sikorsky, both of them successful fixed wing aircraft designers, both with great achievements in the building of large size flying-boats to their credit.

If the thousands of different kinds of helicopter doing their thousands of different duties to-day can be traced back to the creative thinking of a single person, that person would be Igor Sikorsky, designer of Pan American Airways' famous S-42 flying-boats, builder of one of the first successful US passenger aircraft, builder of the first successful twin-engined amphibian, and then in 1939 producer of a helicopter. He had, as already noted, started his aviation career in Russia by working on helicopters, then devoted himself for many years to fixed wing aircraft, mainly flying-boats, and then after Cierva's work he returned to helicopters.

It is necessary, before going more fully into Sikorsky's rotorcraft successes, to refer to the successful helicopter which pre-dated by three years his Vought-Sikorsky 300, the Focke-Achgelis 61. The FW 61 appeared early in 1936 and was demonstrated before General-Major Udet of the German air force by a highly skilled woman pilot, Flug Kapitan Hanna Reitsch. It was the helicopter break-through and it had been brought about, as Professor Focke acknowledged, partly as a consequence of the advances made in the treatment of lifting rotors by Cierva. In fact the Autogiro companies and the German Focke-Achgelis company had been in close contact with one another at the time the new helicopter's designs were being prepared.

357

358

Then, in 1938, Sikorsky made his return to the rotor-craft with his Vought-Sikorsky 300 single-seater. With the restless energy of Sikorsky behind it the helicopter began to make progress. In 1940 Kellett introduced an interesting twin, inter-meshing rotorcraft, and in 1943 the Austrian Doblhoff produced his comprehensive proposals for a jet driven helicopter rotor. Landgraf devised his cyclic lift control whereby the pitch of the rotor blades could be adjusted in their angles of attack, and in 1946 a notable step was taken when the United States Civil Aeronautics Administration granted the first

357 Cierva's jumping Autogiro at Hanworth, 1939

358 Focke-Achgelis 61 helicopter, 1936

159

commercial licence to Bell. The helicopter had finally been established as a practical aircraft capable of carrying passengers safely. Sikorsky had taken it into a region of normalcy comparable with that of the fixed wing aircraft, his R-4 being representative in basic rotor configuration of many thousands of subsequent helicopters.

It is curious that the special abilities of the helicopter took so long to make their value known. When in 1931 Lieutenant Alfred Pride of the United States Navy made

361

359

360

the first deck landing by a rotating wing aircraft he used a Pitcairn Autogiro. Wing Commander Brie, when he made landings on the Italian cruiser *Fiume* in 1935, also used an Autogiro, the C-30. These were the first indications of the big future that existed for rotorcraft working with ships. Gradually the navies of the world turned their attention to rotorcraft, and their turning was accelerated when the helicopter became a complete success. The Autogiro's inability to hover in still air was a slight disadvantage for naval work and so the helicopter was substituted for the Autogiro as soon as it proved practical.

There now started an era in which the helicopter proved itself in hosts of specialized duties for which no other vehicle was suited. Aerial survey had already proved successful with ordinary fixed wing aircraft;

359 Sikorsky R-4, the first helicopter to enter large-scale production, 1945

360 Aérospatiale Alouette 3 landing on an offshore drilling platform

361 Focke-Achgelis 223, largest helicopter in use in the second world war

but the helicopter brought to it a wide range of ancillary operations which called for hovering flight. There were, too, the innumerable services associated with oil drilling rigs located at sea. These could be supplied conveniently by helicopter and their crew changes could be made by helicopter. Police in many countries found the helicopter of high value for traffic control and for other duties. Agriculturalists used it for crop dusting. It was used for forest fire fighting. Perhaps the most satisfactory work which the helicopter came to perform was rescue, on sea and on land.

The air forces of most countries of any size formed special sections or divisions equipped with helicopters and trained to specialist rescue duties. Projects for refuelling helicopters by pressure from surface ships were introduced and arrangements were made whereby helicopters in United States Naval and Coast Guard service could employ orbiting satellites for passing signals from location beacons. The co-operation of the different countries using helicopters was achieved through the Global Rescue Alarm Network (GRAN) first advocated by the United States Coast Guard.

One further duty which helicopters came to perform to an increasing extent was crane work for construction sites. As the lifting power of helicopters increased, so large building projects found them of increasing value.

After the second world war there were to be many pressures upon aircraft designers and makers to introduce vertical take-off and landing (VTOL) aircraft and these led to the full success of the helicopter. There would also be pressures in favour of short take-off and landing (STOL) aircraft, with variable sweep wings, suction wings, slipstream deflection and other methods. As urban areas extended their built up regions so the need for aircraft which did not demand wide open spaces for the processes of landing and taking off became more urgent. Modern helicopter developments, and the rise of VTOL and STOL aircraft, are described in Chapter 16.

Part Two

The Colossus

Bill Gunston

12 Birth of the airlines

While the Zeppelin airships had sustained regular, scheduled passenger air services from March 1911, and a small passenger flying-boat airline had operated in Florida in 1914, commercial aviation proper had to wait until after the Armistice of 1918. In the ensuing months most of the developed world suffered from a surfeit of unemployed warplanes and unemployed pilots. Most of the aircraft were anything but suitable for use as civil transports, and there were not many would-be airline operators with the capital required to pay for specially designed commercial machines.

Boards of a score of famous motor companies that had been pressed into making aircraft or aero engines during the war soon rid their factories of work which they considered to have no future, and they got down to making cars, trucks and buses. The entire world civil aviation market amounted to a handful of struggling individuals with little to offer but enthusiasm.

Many of these enthusiasts did form air transport companies, and most of them gave up within a year. But a few survived, and this harsh selection process, by eliminating all but the best and fittest operators, left a good basis on which to build. At first the embryonic airlines had no basis of experience, and the ones that survived were those that had a professional accountant and plenty of common sense. Passengers were advised to wear a heavy leather coat, goggles and ear-defenders, because the first airliners had open cockpits. The payload was seldom more than two or three adults, and the only cargo was usually a bag or two of mail.

One of the biggest factors in putting the airlines on some sort of secure footing was the merging of the numerous small and precarious operators into bigger groups which often enjoyed the status of a national political instrument. Thus in 1924 British Marine Air Navigation, Daimler Hire, Handley Page Air Transport and Instone Air Line – the survivors of a much larger group – amalgamated to form Imperial Airways, one of the first and greatest national 'flag carriers' in the new commercial ocean of the air. A similar process took place in most other European countries, with the notable exception of the Netherlands whose KLM was a single national company from the start in 1919. In the United States the merging of the many small lines into today's giant carriers did not begin in earnest until 1930, while Air France did not emerge until 1933.

In the matter of the technical development of civil transport aircraft the major nations adopted quite dissimilar philosophies in the two decades between the wars. All started level in 1919 with relatively crude aerodynamics, structures of wood with occasional aluminium

363

364

365

or steel parts at the principal joints or concentrations of stress, a covering of doped fabric and liberal use of tension wires to brace the whole assembly and increase its rigidity. But several visionary engineers were by this time developing more advanced structures which appeared to point the way to future development.

One of these was Professor Hugo Junkers. From the earliest days of powered flight he dreamed of cantilever monoplanes, with a wing having a section deep enough for it to have sufficient strength and rigidity without external bracing. By 1910 he had been granted a patent

362 Pan American Martin 130 *Philippine Clipper* at San Francisco, 1936

363 Benoist flying-boat opening the St Petersburg-Tampa Air Boat Line, Florida, 1914

364 First US air mail flown by Curtiss pusher in 1911

365 Boeing's design office in 1918

163

366 Caudron C.23 flying the first Paris-Brussels service, 10 February 1919

367 Airco 4a about to take off from Hounslow to Paris, 1919

for an even more futuristic idea: an all-wing aircraft in which the single large wing housed fuel, engines, crew and payload – a perfectly feasible idea, as was shown several decades later. In 1915 Junkers produced the J.1, a small cantilever monoplane made wholly of metal (almost entirely steel, despite this metal's very high density), which evoked an official German response ranging from indifference to hostility. Undeterred by this predictable reception, Junkers produced improved designs built of duralumin, the new alloy of aluminium,

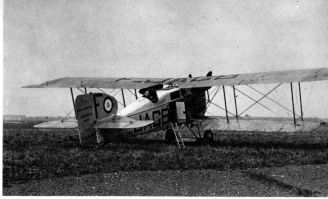

368

366

369

unbraced by struts or wires and the whole structure was duralumin, the skin being corrugated in a way that was soon almost a Junkers trademark.

In Britain Short Brothers, who had produced a fine series of float seaplanes during the war, caused a sensation at the Aero Show at Olympia in 1920 by exhibiting the Silver Streak. This little biplane was remarkable in its method of construction, which was more advanced than anything Junkers had done. The fuselage and most of the wings were not only made of duralumin but they were covered with a 'stressed skin' of the same material. The principle of the stressed-skin aircraft is that the skin is made to bear a considerable proportion of the loads that in earlier machines were carried solely by the underlying skeleton. The very first such machine was made by the German Dornier company in 1917. The Short design team at Rochester had calculated that thin sheets of duralumin, riveted to a basis of spars and stringers to keep them from buckling, would make for a very light and efficient airframe besides one having a smooth and more precise exterior shape than was common at the time. Like the Dornier, the Silver Streak was attractive and successful, yet at the start of the 1920s it did not appear to occur to anybody that this was a superior way of making an aircraft.

Britain therefore plodded ahead for 15 years with a series of aircraft, both civil and military, that were conservative in the extreme. The British airliners, which in the 1920s were almost all built to meet the needs of Imperial Airways alone, were a grand expression of the sailing ship translated into a new medium. The first was the de Havilland 66 Hercules, powered by three 450 hp Bristol Jupiter engines, a classic nine-cylinder air-cooled radial that was made under licence in 14 countries before 1930. This 14-seat machine was used mainly on routes outside Europe, to Alexandria and to Cairo and

367

copper and traces of other metals, that became available during the first world war. In 1919 these led to the J.13, later called the F.13, which although small marked a landmark in civil aircraft construction. Powered by a 185 horsepower engine, it carried a pilot and four passengers and did not have a markedly better performance than its wood and fabric biplane rivals. But in appearance it was totally different and much more modern. The low-mounted cantilever wing was quite

368 Breguet Avion Salon of Messageries Aériennes at Le Bourget, Paris, 6 October 1919

369 Breguet XIV flying the first service of Air Maroc, 1 September 1919

370

371

372

in 1927 onward to Basra and in 1929 to Karachi. European routes were served chiefly by the Armstrong Whitworth Argosy with three Armstrong Siddeley Jaguar engines, a three-finned biplane tail and 20 seats. Both types seated their passengers in a cabin which was marvellous in comparison with what had gone before, for it was big and unobstructed and housed a row of wicker chairs along each side from which the unbroken row of celluloid windows gave a fine view of a mighty engine, a thrashing wooden propeller and a vast expanse of silver-doped fabric heaving and crinkling gently as the great liner wallowed at 95 mph through the air pockets.

This British formula for air travel persisted into the mid-1930s, by which time the great biplanes of Imperial Airways looked decidedly old-fashioned. However, it offered the ability to carry useful payloads with considerable economy, reliability and safety at a time when none of these assets was common in aviation. But although Roy Fedden at Bristol built up a worldwide business with his Jupiter engine, there were no foreign customers for the majestic British airliners. Most of the business was won by the man who designed the best German fighting scouts in 1914-18, the Dutchman Anthony Fokker. His chief designer was Reinhold Platz.

After the war Fokker returned to his native land, set up a factory and began to design civil transports. From 1920 to 1940 he produced a series of designs that were sold, built under licence or simply copied in a score of countries. In almost every case he used Platz's cantilever

373

wooden wing, with a good deep section giving strength and rigidity as well as excellent lift at low speeds, at the expense of slightly higher than average drag at high speeds which tended to make his earlier transports somewhat slower than the 100 mph that was a common cruising speed for rival designs. Unlike Junkers, who put his body always on top of the wing, Fokker put the wing on top of the body where the spars could pass across above the ceiling of the passenger cabin. Invariably he made the body, and the tail, from welded steel tubes covered with fabric. The wing skin was plywood, bent round the curved profile and secured by glue and pins.

His first airliner, which was also the first aircraft to be designed for KLM, was the four-seat F.II of 1920, powered by the same 185 hp engine as the Junkers F.13 but cruising rather more slowly at 75 mph. Four years

370 ANT.2, the second design of Andrei N. Tupolev and the first Soviet all-metal aircraft, 1924

371 Short Silver Streak, 1920

372 Junkers F.13 in Luft Hansa service about 1927

373 Junkers J.1 all-metal aircraft, 1915

later, by which time there was a Fokker works in the United States, he produced the classic F.VII ten-seater, with a 360 hp engine and cruising at 84 mph. From this he derived the F.VII/3m, which was possibly the best known and most widely used airliner of the whole 1920s. As the designation suggests, it had three engines instead of one; the most famous F.VII/3m, the 'Southern Cross' of Sir Charles Kingsford–Smith, had 220 hp Wright Whirlwinds, but several other types of engine could be used. This classic design, with a high wing, an engine in

able foundations for the future. This was the US Air Mail, which was first organized by the US Post Office in May 1918 between New York and Washington and was soon extended right across the nation to San Francisco. After six years the central sectors of this great route were equipped in a primitive but effective way for flying by night, with large bonfires at intervals of about 20 to 30 miles and powerful beacon lights at the frequent airfields.

By 1926 the Federal government had taken over

374

375

376

374 De Havilland 66 Hercules of Imperial Airways flying with port engine stopped, 1926

375 Armstrong Whitworth Argosy of Imperial Airways with supply vans at Croydon Airport, 1929

376 Fokker F.II after first KLM service to Croydon, September 1920

the nose, one under each wing, and a big box-like fuselage, was copied by many other constructors including the American car magnate Henry Ford whose Ford Trimotor–which differed from the Fokker transports in having all-metal construction with a corrugated skin–is still to be seen on active service in several places.

American designers did little of note in the early 1920s, apart from Glenn Curtiss whose record-breaking seaplanes have already been described. United States airlines in the early 1920s were non-existent. Cars, buses and trains handled virtually all the passenger traffic, and there was no transcontinental air service of any sort until July 1929 when an air/rail service was opened in which passengers flew by day and travelled in rail Pullman cars by night.

While US airlines remained no more than ideas in their promoters' brains, there was one American development that involved much arduous pioneer flying and laid valu-

responsibility for the US mail routes, and established airfields, radio systems and the other supporting services needed. On the other hand, by the same year the actual operation of flying the mail had passed to private enterprise, and this was the beginning of what is today the biggest and busiest network of air routes in the world. Each route was opened to competitive bidders and awarded on a contract basis at a price of an agreed number of cents per ton of mail flown from end to end of the route. By 1928 there were 33 contracts, covering more than 14,000 route-miles. This mileage climbed to over 30,000 miles in 1930, exceeded 60,000 miles in 1947 and is today well over 100,000. One of the biggest single influences in promoting the 'take-off' of commercial aviation in the United States was the dramatic flight of Charles Lindbergh. Another was the swift improvement in the available aircraft. The first mail services were operated with wartime types, notably the excellent

377

378

380

379

de Havilland DH.4a. In 1927 Boeing, already a renowned aircraft constructor, put in a bid for the vital mail route from Chicago to San Francisco that staggered everyone. Most observers predicted the company would, in the idiom of the time, 'lose its shirt', because the rate offered was half that of the next lowest bidder. In the event Boeing Air Transport, which was formed as a subsidiary to run the route, made money; it did so because Boeing had designed a new mailplane far more efficient than anything seen previously. A key to its performance was the Pratt & Whitney Wasp engine designed in 1925 by a fine team that broke away from the Wright company. Although intended initially for Navy fighters the Wasp soon opened up broader horizons for the designers of transports.

377 Fokker F.VIIA of KLM about to leave Schiphol for Djakarta on first long-distance charter flight, 1927

378 Fokker Trimotor, with Wright J-5 engines, in service with Pan American, about 1928

379 Interior of KLM Fokker F.VIIA

380 First sustained air mail service: Curtiss JN-4 (150 hp Hispano engine) leaving Washington Polo Grounds, 15 May 1918

In Europe the only firm to rival Fokker as a supplier of commercial aircraft was Junkers, despite the handicap of being located in a defeated Germany. From the F.13 already described Junkers developed a succession of improved commercial aircraft, all constructed entirely of duralumin and characterized by having a low-mounted cantilever wing, which was as yet far from common. Some had a single engine, such as the W.34 which in 1929 gained a world height record of 41,790 ft on the power of a German-built Bristol Jupiter of 485 hp.

Many had three engines, and the final member of this family, the 17-passenger Ju 52/3M of 1932, combined good speed and range with the ability to use confined airfields. It was the main workhorse of Deutsche Lufthansa, the national German airline that during the 1930s grew swiftly to become by far the biggest and most prosperous airline in Europe if not in the world. More than 2,800 Ju 52/3Ms were built, most of them for the second world war, and in 1946-47 a fleet of them operated services within Britain for the young giant BEA.

381

382

383

384

385

386

387

One of the few drawbacks of the Junkers transports was their corrugated skin. The corrugations ran fore-and-aft, but the airflow was often in slightly different directions and the drag of the grooves was much worse than Junkers believed. Moreover, although the corrugations stiffened the skin in one direction they rendered it unsuitable for bearing loads perpendicular to the corrugations. Even during the war another German designer, Dr Adolf Rohrbach, had believed that a preferable answer would be to use a smooth skin of light alloy, such as duralumin, riveted carefully to an underlying skeleton of the same material so that the skin could help to carry many of the chief loads. For example, a metal-skinned fuselage would be much stiffer both in plain bending and in torsion (twisting) than one covered with fabric, and metal wing skins could handle powerful buckling compressive stresses on top and equally great tensile stretching loads underneath, and thus enable a monoplane to fly safely with a wing that was not excessively thick yet needed no external bracing struts and wires. By 1923 Rohrbach had refined his ideas and hit on the general title of 'stressed skin', a name which did not occur to Dornier or Short.

Although Rohrbach's own stressed-skin aircraft, most of them large flying-boats, did not find many customers, this was not because of the way they were built. With his brilliant structural designer H. A. Wagner he created a system of designing and building aeroplanes that not merely pointed the way to the future but gradually became the almost universally accepted method. In worldwide use by 1936, the light-alloy stressed-skin principle was used for well over 95 per cent of the vast armadas of combat aircraft constructed in the second world war, and it is the method adopted in practically all of the advanced high-performance aircraft of today.

By 1927 several American design teams had conducted extensive experiments with light-alloy stressed-skin structures. One team was located at the Seattle works of the Boeing Airplane company, which had already gained renown with its excellent mailplanes. In May 1930 Boeing flew the Monomail, a beautiful low-wing monoplane with a 'cleaner' exterior than any previous commercial aircraft thanks to its stressed-skin construction and retractable undercarriage. In the following year a twin-engined bomber followed and from this the company developed the Boeing 247. This is regarded by many as the first modern airliner, in the sense that it at last signalled the demise of the fabric-covered biplane and ushered in the new age of the smooth, unbraced monoplane. The 247 had a layout that was to remain right up to the present day, with the wing mounted low, so

388

that its spars passed under the floor of the passenger cabin, and carrying the two Wasp engines in neat nacelles merging at the rear into the wing. The main landing gears could be retracted up into these engine nacelles to reduce drag, and in the improved 247D of 1934 the propellers were of the variable pitch type, the blades being set to fine pitch to allow maximum power at low speeds for take-off and then being adjusted to coarse pitch in cruising flight to give higher aircraft speed with the engines throttled back.

Introduction of the 247 revolutionized the image of United Air Lines, the giant carrier formed in 1934 from Boeing Air Transport, National Air Transport and Varney Air Lines. The new ten-seater could fly coast-to-coast in a schedule of about 20 hours, it could perform the feat that had so long been desired in a 'twin' of climbing on either engine after failure of the other, and in its 247D form it introduced such advanced features as trim tabs on the control surfaces (which could be adjusted from the cockpit so that the aircraft would fly

381 Eddie Hubbard and William E. Boeing after flying the first international air mail from Vancouver, BC to Seattle, 3 March 1919

382 Boeing 40A of Boeing Air Transport opening the first US transcontinental air mail, 1 July 1927

383 Curtiss Falcon of National Air Transport, flying express mail, calls at Wichita, Kansas, 1929

384 Junkers G.31 all-metal trimotor transport, 1929

385 Junkers G.31 cockpit

386 Dr Rohrbach with pilot Steindorf and Dr Merkel, Director of Luft Hansa, with Romar stressed-skin flying-boat, 1928

387 Junkers Ju 52/3M of Lufthansa (now written as one word) loading for night flight, 1935

388 Boeing Monomail stressed-skin monoplane, 1930

perfectly without the controls being touched), full de-icing equipment (removing a hazard that had caused the loss of dozens of commercial aircraft) and an automatic pilot, a gyroscopically controlled wonder that took all the strain out of long-distance flying and even improved its accuracy. The autopilot, developed since 1912 by American Elmer Sperry, was complemented by the artificial horizon and the turn-and-bank indicator, directional gyro and more sensitive altimeters accurate to within about ten feet with less lag in the case of air-

389

390

craft changing altitude.

It was the American Daniel Guggenheim Fund for the Promotion of Aeronautics that in 1928 financed a very significant programme aimed at perfecting the goal of blind flying. At that time a pilot caught in low cloud and fog was almost as good as dead. With the Guggenheim money, a fine instrument craftsman named Paul Kollsman and a brilliant Army pilot, Lieutenant Jimmy Doolittle, the improved instruments were developed so surely that on 24 September 1929 Doolittle took off in a thick fog (with a hood pulled over his cockpit to cut off what little view remained), flew along radio beams for a quarter of an hour, returned to where he had taken off at Mitchell Field, New York, and brought the aircraft in to a passable landing. In Britain the same sort of thing was being done with slightly less advanced cockpit equipment, the outstanding pilot being W. E. P. 'Pat' Johnson who likewise flew complete missions with a hood over his cockpit.

With the immense technical improvement in air-frames, engines and instruments the airlines by 1935 were looking ahead to a new era in which their range, speed, regularity and safety would improve dramatically and make commercial aviation a far more effective and important transport medium, and possibly even a sound business for a private company to be in. Most of the European flag carriers were national corporations, but the airlines that were springing up all over the United States were without exception private firms. This giant nation, which had no sustained airline operation of any

sort until April 1927, when Colonial Airlines began passenger services between New York and Boston, was by 1935 showing every sign of becoming the world leader in mercantile aviation.

This opened up a new market for America's alert and well directed aircraft manufacturing firms. While the British virtually ignored the new streamlined, stressed-skin construction, even in the Schneider seaplanes, the US design teams became totally committed to it. As a direct result they quickly became not only technological leaders but they put their country in the position of undisputed supplier of commercial aircraft to almost every country in the world.

In Britain, the board of Imperial Airways had first met in 1924 to find that the little airlines from which Imperial had been formed had managed to win the lion's share of the traffic on all their routes between Croydon and Europe. Imperial could have forged ahead to build up a European network to every capital and won a position of total dominance, simultaneously providing a huge market for British aircraft manufacturers and helping the latter become the natural source of supply to world airlines. Instead services to Europe languished. Imperial thought of commercial aviation only in terms of politics and the British Empire. With painful halts and reverses, and using airliners never flying sectors longer than 370 miles, a route was gradually constructed to Egypt and thence to Cape Town in the far south and to the Persian Gulf and later India in the East. To fly these routes meant frequent changes from one aircraft

389 Ford T supplying air pressure-differential for ground test of US Army Sperry gyro instruments, about 1920

390 Boeing 247, the first cantilever monoplane airliner incorporating a generation of technical improvements, in service with United Air Lines, 1933

170

391

392

393

394

395

to another, and with long sectors spent in trains and ships. The first services involved a train from Paris to Marseilles and a ship from thence to Port Said; as late as 1934 passengers had to take a train from Paris to Brindisi, and the journey from Croydon to Cape Town was made up of 33 separate journeys in seven types of vehicle.

Despite this, Imperial built up a reputation based on the British tradition of conservatism, reliability and safety. Their work in pioneering routes through almost unknown and often hostile territory surpassed that of any other airline. Despite their reliance on a strange mixture of landplanes and flying-boats, all constructed only for Imperial and built in very small numbers indeed, the operating record was satisfactory. By 1930 it was clear the airline was concerned only to carry passengers and mail (air freight was virtually non-existent) with regularity; the notion that an airline's major saleable asset is speed was ignored. In that year Handley Page were commissioned to build a fleet of eight aircraft that epitomized the British way of life. Like giant silver galleons, they measured 130 ft across the upper wing and almost 90 ft from the nose (where the British captain was at last allowed an enclosed cabin) to the curious tail with three sets of fins and rudders linking biplane tailplanes and elevators. Four of the supremely reliable 550 hp Jupiter engines, driving four-blade propellers of carved wood, pulled each majestic machine along at a stately 100 mph. One critic quipped that the type had 'built-in headwinds'. Imperial's answer was to point to the opulent interior, soundproofed by three layers of material, in which could travel 24 passengers in the HP.42 'Hannibal' version for Eastern routes or 38 passengers in the HP.45 'Heracles' appointed for use in Europe. Similar thinking lay behind three great flying-boats and two land airliners supplied by Short Brothers.

France had likewise relied on very conservative machines, such as the flying-boats by the Breguet and Lioré et Olivier companies with which Air Orient opened a service to French Indo-China in 1931, but when Air France was formed in 1933 it saw the writing on the wall and soon ordered fleets of more streamlined monoplanes. Most of the French companies that had pioneered the aviation industry were still in existence, but the industry became fragmentary and ineffective and finally was pulled together in nationalized and private groups in 1936. Dewoitine, Farman and Potez were all builders of successful airliners. Italy's Savoia-Marchetti company, initially using licence-built Jupiter engines, built up a reputation with a series of three-engined low-wing monoplanes of outstanding performance which later

391 Sir Alan Cobham in a DH.50 surveying the route from Cairo to Capetown for Imperial Airways, 1925

392 Croydon, London's airport, 1932

393 Le Bourget, Paris's airport, 1930

394 Tempelhof, Berlin's airport, 1929

395 Antoine de Ste Exupéry with Latécoère surveying routes at Cap Juby, about 1926

171

396

399

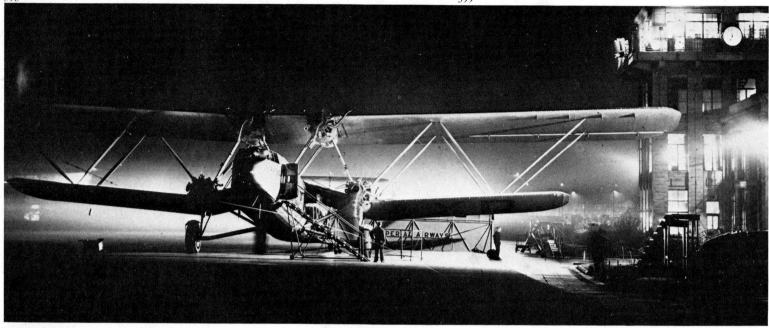

397

398

400

396 Refuelling Armstrong
Whitworth Atalanta
Andromeda of Imperial
Airways at Moshi,
Tanganyika, about 1932

397 Handley Page 45
Horatius of Imperial Airways at Croydon, about
1933

398 Short Scylla of
Imperial Airways, land-
plane version of the Kent
class boats, 1934

were to show themselves in their true colours as bombers. Together with the products of such firms as Caproni and Piaggio the speedy Savoias did much to enhance Italian prestige.

Ten European nations made airliners, and a dozen more made simpler aircraft. A prerequisite to a successful airliner construction industry has always been the possession of dynamic national operating companies, and between the wars none of the European airlines was more thrusting than Deutsche Lufthansa. The airline map of Europe soon seemed to be centred on Berlin, from which a score of busy routes radiated out to almost every capital. Chief among the German builders of transport aircraft was Junkers, whose output continued to be characterized by cantilever monoplanes with corrugated metal skins, although with the Ju 60 of 1933 and Ju 86 of 1936 they accepted the superiority of the smooth stressed-skin airframe. By the mid-1930s Heinkel was famed for his very clean and fast Lufthansa transports, and in 1937 Focke-Wulf sprang into prominence by building the Fw 200 Condor which Lufthansa flew non-stop from Berlin to New York in 1938. This fine four-engined machine quickly achieved export sales and was probably the best of all European airliners in 1939.

In the Soviet Union progress might have been slow had it not been for one man, Andrei N. Tupolev, who in 1928 became a designer at the Central Aero-Hydro-dynamic Institute in Moscow. He gave his initials to a

succession of airliners and bombers up to the second world war; then his great design bureau changed its designations to a series of numbers prefixed by Tu. Tupolev deliberately adhered to the old fabric-covered construction before the second world war, but some of these machines were among the world's largest, the eight-engined ANT-20 of 206 ft span being biggest of all. In 1932 the original Soviet operator, Dobrolet, was taken over by Aeroflot, the vast national civil aviation organization which has since been the largest single airline in the world.

In the United States the seeds sown by Rohrbach flowered into maturity so that the new era of the monoplane was accompanied by the far superior metal stressed-skin construction. But of at least equal importance to the future of American commercial aviation was the operating environment. The existence of strong, experienced and competitive privately owned air carriers soon showed incidental benefits of very real and far-reaching import. While the carrier existed solely to serve the customer public, the manufacturer had to serve the carrier. In contrast, the British civil scene was so bound up with the government that the national airline and the manufacturers tended to think they existed to serve the government, with disastrous results for both. The lack of connection between demand and supply was later to cause the British taxpayer to finance a succession of civil aircraft that were neither competitive nor needed. Since 1930 it has been practically impossible for such a thing to happen in the United States.

In that year four young carriers, Transcontinental Air

403

404

401

402

Transport, Western Air, Maddux and Standard, merged to form Transcontinental and Western Air (today called Trans World Airlines but still known by the same initials). TWA asked the Douglas company, which had hitherto existed chiefly on small military orders, to build a completely new 12-passenger transport tailored to the big airline's requirements. Arthur E. Raymond was the engineer entrusted with the task. Instead of straight away bending over his drawing board, Raymond went on a coast-to-coast flight on a 'Tin Goose', the Ford

405

Trimotor which was TWA's main existing equipment. He found himself being offered cotton wool to stuff into his ears: 'The thing vibrated so much it shook the eye glasses right off your nose. In order to talk with the guy across the aisle, you had to shout at the top of your lungs ... My feet nearly froze. The leather-upholstered, wicker-back chairs were about as comfortable as lawn furniture.' And after all this: 'When the plane landed on a puddle-splotched runway, a spray of mud, sucked in by the cabin air vents, splattered everybody.' This put Raymond in the right frame of mind. He knew he had to do far more than just design an efficient carrier of loads.

The result was the DC-1, DC meaning 'Douglas commercial'. Everybody at the Los Angeles factory felt a sense of pride as it took the air on 1 July 1933, but not even Donald Douglas himself dared to think of it as one of the most significant aircraft of all time. Its importance turned out to be incalculable. The last barrier to a resounding success was removed in the summer of 1932 when Raymond decided to throw out the third engine

399 De Havilland Leopard Moth used by J. R. D. Tata to fly his airline's first service in India, 15 October 1932

400 Galley of Short Scylla

401 Breguet Saigon flying-boat of Air France, 1936

402 Focke-Wulf Fw 200 Condor of Lufthansa, 1937

403 Wibault 283T of Air France, about 1937

404 Junkers Ju 86 of Lufthansa, with Jumo diesel engines; in rear, Ju 52/3M and He 111

405 ANT-20 *Maxim Gorki* of Aeroflot, largest aircraft in the world in 1934

406

408

407

409

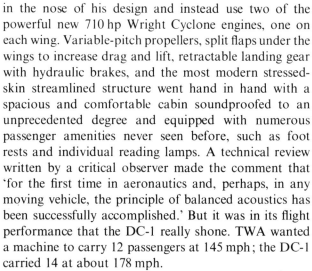

in the nose of his design and instead use two of the powerful new 710 hp Wright Cyclone engines, one on each wing. Variable-pitch propellers, split flaps under the wings to increase drag and lift, retractable landing gear with hydraulic brakes, and the most modern stressed-skin streamlined structure went hand in hand with a spacious and comfortable cabin soundproofed to an unprecedented degree and equipped with numerous passenger amenities never seen before, such as foot rests and individual reading lamps. A technical review written by a critical observer made the comment that 'for the first time in aeronautics and, perhaps, in any moving vehicle, the principle of balanced acoustics has been successfully accomplished.' But it was in its flight performance that the DC-1 really shone. TWA wanted a machine to carry 12 passengers at 145 mph; the DC-1 carried 14 at about 178 mph.

A month after it flew TWA ordered 20 of an improved version, the DC-2, and five months later bought another 20. Other airlines, including several in Europe and elsewhere outside the United States, took the sales to 75 by mid-1934. Almost everywhere the new Douglas set the air transport world by the ears. While manufacturers strove to copy it, operators either felt they must buy it or lose traffic to rivals. Only in Britain was there a dissident voice. C. G. Grey, outspoken editor of *The Aeroplane*, tried to equate aircraft of modern design with danger, and wrote that what the world really wanted was 'aircraft that land slowly and won't crash and burn up'. He appeared not to notice that the improved technology of the DC-2 was the greatest step towards safer flying that could be made, nor that its landing speed of 58 mph was slower than that of the most-used liner of the 1920s, the F.VII/3m. When KLM Royal Dutch Airlines entered one in the great race to Melbourne in October 1934, a London newspaper considered it to be 'an audacious assumption that such a ship could expect to compete with the fastest planes and designs (*sic*) on the Continent.' However the sight of the gleaming DC-2

on the grass field at Mildenhall shook British designers to the core. They were even more shaken when the KLM crew, passengers and mail were taken to Melbourne in three days 18 hours, second only to the Comet racer (which of course carried no payload) and outright winner of the handicap section. Next to finish was a Boeing 247D.

From the DC-2 Raymond's team created the bigger and more powerful DC-3, carrying 21 passengers at 195 mph. By 1936 this was well on the way to becoming the standard transport aircraft of the world. Not including the Li-2 version made in the Soviet Union, 500 had been delivered by Pearl Harbor (7 December 1941), and during the second world war various military versions served in every conceivable transport role on every front, bearing roughly 70 per cent of the total Allied air traffic throughout the war. When the last DC-3 was built in 1946 the total production amounted to 803 civil airliners and 10,123 of the military versions, a grand total not even approached by any other transport aircraft before or since. Several hundred DC-3s, of both civil and military versions, remain in use at the end of the third quarter of the century. To some degree their ability to do so is fortuitous. In the 1930s metal fatigue was not normally considered in aircraft design and few aircraft logged as much as 1,000 hours. John K. Northrop and the Douglas team happened to devise a multi-cellular wing construction, with numerous light-alloy sheet spars. This wing has excellent fatigue life and many of the DC-3 family have flown more than 60,000 hours, which even today is a remarkable figure. In contrast, post-war British airliners, such as the Dove and Viking, had wings with poor fatigue lives (less than 10,000 hours) that had to be re-sparred or scrapped while the old DC-3 carried on flying.

In 1934 the American Lockheed company, which had produced notable single-engined machines including the Vega and the very fast Orion airliner used by Swissair, risked much of its capital in a trim eight-seater with two Pratt & Whitney Wasp Junior engines. When this

406 Swissair's newest and finest equipment in 1936: two Douglas DC-2s and two DC-3s at Zurich-Dübendorf

407 Swissair's Curtiss-Wright Condor, 1931

408 Swissair's fast American machine of 1933, the Lockheed Orion

409 Swissair's Ju 86, 1936

410 De Havilland 89 Dragon Rapide, a biplane still found throughout the world

411 British flyer Jean Batten with her Percival Gull after her record-breaking flight from Lympne, England to Auckland, New Zealand in 1936

410

411

made money they followed with the Lockheed 12 and then the Lockheed 14, an outstandingly advanced machine fitted with Fowler wing flaps that extended the area of the wing for take-off and then gave great drag when further depressed for landing at relatively low speed. The Lockheed 14 was the first civil aircraft to have constant-speed propellers, in which a centrifugal governor regulates the pitch of the blades according to the desired engine power and air speed. Fastest airliner in the world before the second world war, the 14 was supplied to British Airways, formed by a merger of smaller lines late in 1935; one of these aircraft took Prime Minister Chamberlain to meet Hitler at Munich.

The Lockheed 14 rivalled in modernity anything in Germany, but the same could not be said of the land-plane equipment of Imperial Airways. In 1935 the proud flag carrier had announced the Empire Air Mail scheme (described earlier in this book), whereby all mail on Commonwealth routes would be carried by air without surcharge. To do the work Imperial took the exceedingly

412

413

414

415

412 Competitors at RAF Mildenhall before the great race to Melbourne in 1934; in the foreground, two de Havilland Comets

413 The incomparable Douglas DC-3 of 1935, here seen in service with Alitalia 25 years later

414 Lockheed 12, with two Wasp Junior engines, March 1938

415 Lockheed 14 ten-passenger transport, capable of cruising at 190 mph, in service with KLM, 1938

bold decision to use flying-boats, and a fine fleet of 28 'Empire class' boats was ordered off the drawing board from Short Brothers (see Chapter 9).

But the future lay with the landplane, in particular with the landplane having a circular-section fuselage pressurized to maintain the interior at a comfortable level even in cruising flight at 20,000 ft or more, where fuel economy is better and bad weather is rarely encountered. Pioneer pressure cabins were flown in Germany and by the Lockheed company, but it was Boeing which first produced a pressurized commercial transport. This was the Boeing 307 Stratoliner, a big four-engined airliner derived from the B-17 Fortress bomber and first flown in December 1938. Entering service with TWA and PanAm in 1940, the TWA machines were impressed for war service and completed 7,500,000 miles in 44,800 hours without trouble when they were returned to the airline in 1944.

Another big Boeing with a fine war record was the Model 314 flying-boat. Pan American, the chief flag carrier of the United States, began operations in October 1927 with a Fokker F.VII but soon turned to amphibians and flying-boats constructed by Igor Sikorsky's firm, a division of United Aircraft, in Connecticut. In October 1931 Mrs Herbert Hoover, then the First Lady in the White House, named the four-engined S-40 *American Clipper*, thus establishing a class of PanAm names that endures to this day. The route network spread across the Caribbean, throughout Latin America and then, using the superb S-42 flying-boat of 1934, to Hawaii, Manila and New Zealand. In 1935 the bigger and more powerful Martin 130 *China Clipper* took the air, and the greatest of all flying-boats in commercial service, the Boeing 314, followed in PanAm service in 1939 on both the Atlantic and Pacific. It was a Boeing 314 that flew that first scheduled passenger service across the Atlantic on 28 June 1939, although Imperial's experimental and mail services using the Empire boat began two years earlier. Powered by 1,500 hp Wright Cyclone GR-2600 engines, the great Boeing clippers carried 40 passengers no less than 3,000 miles. Three were built for BOAC. But like

416

416 Boeing 307 Stratoliner, four-engined airliner with pressurized cabin, 1939

417 First passengers to cross the Atlantic by airline flew by Boeing 314 *Dixie Clipper* of PanAm from Port Washington, NY, to Lisbon on 28 June 1939

418 People's Aviation day at Berlin-Tempelhof, 1 April 1934

419 Tupolev's ANT.25, of the type which flew from Moscow to California, at the Paris Salon of 1938

417

418

the British boats, they could not long survive in competition with the landplane, and the last had gone by the end of 1948.

Altogether the two decades between the wars saw not only the birth of civil aviation in practically every country in the world but also its development to the point where it ceased to be an erratic and dangerous undertaking and could take its place alongside older transport systems. But even in 1939 airliners were limited in their ability. They carried small loads, they could not fly very far and they wallowed through the bumpy air and clouds quite close to the Earth so that air sickness was taken for granted on a long flight (long in time rather than distance). To fly from New York to Los Angeles, for example, meant a succession of exhausting four to six hour flights spread over two or three days, with a total journey time not very much faster than the crack streamlined trains. Air transport was still small business.

419

13 The rise of air power

420

420 General Mitchell's men sink the 'unsinkable' German dreadnought *Ostfriesland*, in US hands, by exploding bombs close below the waterline, July 1921

421 DH.9A of No. 8 Squadron, RAF, over Baghdad, 1926

After the Armistice of 11 November 1918 air forces were slashed ten and twentyfold and aircraft manufacturers that had blossomed from California to Moscow suddenly found themselves out of business. Most of the young air services found they had to fight not only for independence as a separate arm but for their very lives.

Nowhere was the strife more acrimonious than in the United States. Here it centred around Brigadier General 'Billy' Mitchell, a strategist endowed with long range vision. He could see that the development of the military aircraft was not going to remain static, despite the wish of most Americans to forget everything to do with warfare. Already he saw the bomber as an offensive instrument of unrivalled range and striking power that could influence diplomacy and every conceivable kind of armed conflict. In the future he could see the swift development of the bomber as the dominant weapon—far surpassing the battleship, the heaviest of artillery or any other offensive firepower. Had he been able to argue his case in an impartial atmosphere its essential logic might have carried the day, and Mitchell would have realized his ambition of seeing a United States Air Force created as a separate arm to manage this formidable power, nurture its growth and keep abreast of its complicated technology. But he was an officer in the US Army, and his fellow generals were from the infantry, cavalry and other branches with long traditions. Soon Mitchell was the centre of a storm of controversy which history remembers best as a dramatic occasion in 1921 when Mitchell's bombers reinforced his argument by sinking

the most well-protected of the former German battleships in US hands. The admirals had denied such a thing was possible; once it was done they furiously proclaimed that it would have been impossible had the ships been manned and fighting back. Increasingly the forces of tradition clamoured for Mitchell's scalp, and despite the fact that he was absolutely right in all he said, and a passionate patriot, he was court-martialled and dismissed in disgrace.

In Britain his counterpart was Hugh Trenchard, who almost single-handed masterminded the creation of the Royal Air Force on 1 April 1918 and then commanded it with great distinction. Unlike Mitchell he had the massive advantage of a *fait accompli*, but until well into the 1920s he had to devote much of his time to political argument and intrigue to preserve his infant force from being cut to pieces and shared between the angry and greedy Army and Navy.

Yet the Royal Air Force survived, complete with its new rank names, its distinctive grey-blue uniforms and an *esprit de corps* that may even have been heightened by the surrounding adversity. It was the subject of keen and sustained interest by foreign powers, and these soon saw that the RAF was the most useful of all the services to the far-flung British Empire. In many parts of this vast commonwealth the local rule of His Majesty was hotly disputed. Along hundreds of thousands of miles of frontiers, roadways, mountain passes and desert tracks robust, lawless and well-armed tribesmen were intent upon harassing the thinly spread forces of law and order. The Army and Navy found it hard to do anything effective against these guerilla campaigns, but the handful of RAF aircrew were effective beyond belief.

Gradually the RAF assumed almost the entire responsibility for policing the wild places. Generally the mere local presence of an aircraft sufficed to keep the

421

422

peace. When there was a serious outbreak of raiding and tribal warfare the RAF devised an effective and relatively humane deterrent. Leaflets in the local language would be dropped from the air, warning the miscreants to evacuate their places of habitation on the following day, when a bombing attack would take place. Throughout the 1920s *Pax Britannica* was sustained by a handful of flimsy aircraft, at the cost of a nominal sum and the loss of a very occasional aircraft due to engine failure or a lucky hit with a rifle bullet.

This sustained and arduous peace-keeping role overseas led to the RAF having a continuous need for multipurpose machines carrying guns, bombs, radio, first-aid and survival kits, emergency rations, at least one camera and many other items, yet not needing a particularly high flight performance. Obviously the highest possible reliability was needed, and long range and endurance were as useful as the ability to operate from small and unprepared landing grounds with little or no servicing facilities, but the one thing that made the task of the designers easier was that it was unlikely the aircraft would ever encounter enemy fighters. In this role the faithful DH.9A soldiered on from 1918 until 1931; indeed, new 'nine-acks' were still emerging from the Stag Lane factory in north London in 1928.

Another requirement of the Empire policing duty was for aerial troop carriers. This class of machine was supplied by Vickers, whose Vernon of 1921 and Victoria of 1922 were big biplanes derived directly from standard RAF heavy bombers yet which did their task admirably

for many years. The Vernon pioneered the mail route from Cairo to Baghdad until it was taken over by Imperial Airways in 1926. The bigger Victoria, which could carry 22 troops, bore the main burden of the first major air lift in history. The insurrection of the 'Mad Mullah' in Afghanistan so endangered life in Kabul, the capital, that between December 1928 and February 1929 the eight Victorias of 70 Sqn, with a few smaller machines, brought to safety 586 civilians and 24,193 lb of luggage. Wapitis escorted the big machines through the hazardous Khyber Pass and on to Peshawar and safety.

The idea of specialized fighters and bombers for major wars was never far from the mind of Chief of the Air Staff

422 Westland Wapitis of No. 60 Squadron, RAF, about 1932

423 Vickers Vernons of the RAF's No. 45 Squadron flying the Cairo-Baghdad mail route, 1924

423

Trenchard and his successors, but money remained very tight. Whereas in 1918 the British industry had reached a rate of output of 30,000 aircraft a year, by 1920 an order for a single machine was important business. Even Frederick Handley Page, whose giant bombers and airliners were by 1920 so famous that 'Handley Page' appeared in the Oxford English Dictionary as 'a large aeroplane', called personally at the offices of the magazine *Flight* to ask for more time to pay a bill of ten shillings for an advertisement. But despite the lean environment,

425

424

426

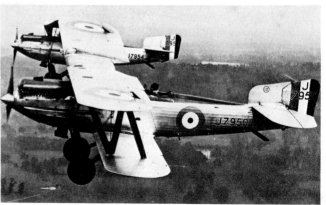

427

424 Vickers Victoria III troop carrier of 70 Squadron over Hinaidi, Iraq, 1928

425 Gloster Grebe fighters slung beneath the airship *R.33*, 1926

426 Armstrong Whitworth Siskin fighters of No. 43 Squadron, RAF, 1930

427 Two Fairey Fox day bombers of No. 12 Squadron, RAF, 1927

technical progress in the 1920s was rapid, partly because there was a great deal of development crying out to be done and partly because it was still of such a nature that a few gifted individuals could make massive contributions.

New equipment, designed after 1918, began to reach the RAF in 1924. The first fighters to be bought were both powered by the 325-420 hp Armstrong Siddeley Jaguar, one of the world's first two-row air-cooled radials and later, in 1927, the first engine to enter service with a supercharger to compress the induced air and thus help to maintain power output even in the thin air at high altitude. Designed by Maj. F. M. Green on the basis of an earlier engine, the Raf 8, conceived at Farnborough during the war, the Jaguar saw widespread service in the RAF, Fleet Air Arm and Imperial Airways until after 1930. The two fighters were the Armstrong Whitworth Siskin designed by John Lloyd, and the Gloster Grebe designed by Harry Folland (who had in 1916 designed the SE.5, one of the finest British fighting scouts of the war). The Siskin was a sesquiplane rather than a biplane because the upper wing had almost three times the area of the lower plane.

First of the British postwar heavy bombers was the Vickers Virginia, an angular biplane considerably bigger than the Vimy which it replaced. Powered in various versions by water-cooled Napier Lion or air-cooled Bristol Jupiter engines, the Virginia epitomized a classic type of machine known as a heavy night bomber. Broadly the notion was that a huge fabric-covered bi-

plane could be made to lift a heavy load of bombs from a short field of soft grass but would thereafter fly so sluggishly that daylight operations would be suicidal. The Virginia at night was detectable by the characteristic rasping growl of the big two-blade wooden screws, which reverberated for miles. The last Virginia was not delivered until December 1932, by which time the whole machine was hopelessly obsolete despite the introduction of an all-metal structure, an autopilot and more powerful Lion engines.

In contrast the RAF's idea of a day bomber was a small machine differing from a fighter only in having a second cockpit for an observer, and small bomb racks under the wings. Its first postwar day bomber, the Fairey Fawn (1924), was a distinctly unpretty creation which, in comparison with the earlier DH.9A, had precisely the same top speed (114 mph), carried the same armament and had a considerably lower ceiling (the altitude at which rate of climb at full power falls to 100 ft/min). A year later Richard Fairey invited Sir Hugh Trenchard to his test airfield at Northolt and showed him another two-seat day bomber, the Fox. Where the Fawn was big the Fox was small. Where the Fawn was bulging the Fox was slim. Where the Fawn was knobbly and angular the Fox was streamlined and pointed. Whereas the Fawn strained to exceed 100 mph the Fox readily exceeded 155 mph, and was thus handsomely faster than any RAF fighter!

Trenchard was so impressed he ordered a squadron of Foxes on the spot. 'Tell me, Mr Fairey,' he asked, 'how did you manage to build this wonderful aircraft after the Fawn?' Fairey could have given many answers. One contributory factor was that on a trip to the United States in 1923 he had seen the Curtiss D-12 engine and the streamlined Curtiss racers in which it was fitted, and he had imported the American power plant and got his chief designer, Marcel Lobelle, to create the Fox round it. But a more important underlying factor was that in creating the Fox Lobelle had had a free hand. He had not had to meet voluminous official specifications, nor satisfy the whims of officials. For example, an Air Ministry Safety Committee had insisted that the fuel should not be housed in the fuselage of the Fawn but in external tanks mounted on top of the upper wing. In the Fox there was no such nonsense, and in innumerable other points of detail design the Fairey engineers were able to choose not the officially approved method but the best method – which was often not the same thing at all. Until well into the second world war this dichotomy, the sleek private venture contrasting with the ungainly and often mediocre aircraft that resulted from official specifications, persisted – and not only in Britain – as a visible indictment of the methods of procuring military machines. Only with the coming of the jet age did the technology of the combat aircraft become so advanced and expensive as to preclude the private venture and, at the same time, to demand the closest and most sustained collaboration between customer and manufacturer in order that the new design should not be obsolescent before it was built.

In the United States Navy the problem was not quite so evident, and when that service expanded and re-equipped in 1926-27 (partly because of the commissioning of the two giant carriers, USS *Saratoga* and *Lexington*) the brand new Pratt & Whitney Wasp engine substantially improved the performance of the Curtiss Hawk and Boeing F2B, both trim single-seat fighters that were in no way inferior to anything in the US Army Air Corps. It was just at this time, after a Congressional investigation had examined the disastrous state of America's fighting forces and aircraft industry and declared the nation 'not higher than a third-rate air power', that the loud campaign of Billy Mitchell and the more restrained one of Admiral Moffett began to have an effect. Slowly the sleeping giant began to stir, and two committees decided that not only should there be US air power but also that there should be a strong industry to build the hardware. An incidental decision,

428

spurred largely by the performance, light weight and reliability of the Wasp, was that future American combat machines would almost exclusively have air-cooled engines – a belief not echoed in Britain.

Imperceptibly around 1930 the US aircraft industry began to become first competitive with the leaders in Western Europe and then, in certain fundamental respects, to draw ahead. The bedrock on which this progress was made was the assurance of business – if there can be any assurance at all in the aircraft business – as a result of the growing airline industry, the growing use of private aircraft and the growing might of US air power based on commercial products. On this basis American management gradually built up companies that were the strongest in the world in terms of qualified design and production engineers, expensive research equipment and modern manufacturing plant. Until long after the second world war it was common for British aircraft factories to be a hodge-podge of scattered buildings, many of them scarcely fit for human habitation and separated by long walks in the rain. The few British managers who visited the United States found more and more of their opposite numbers in vast windowless, air-conditioned, custom-built plants up to a mile in length, housing incredible research, development and production strength under one roof.

After 1930 America's technically oriented philosophy increasingly paid off. The light and reliable Wasp engine enabled the Army in 1929 to replace its 145 mph water-cooled Curtiss Hawk pursuit ship (fighter) by the 175 mph

428 A pursuit squadron of the US Army Air Corps, newly equipped in 1931 with the Boeing P-12E, with Wasp engine

429

430

formula. The high wing and even the parasol configuration (in which the aircraft is suspended below the wing) were particularly favoured, but it was difficult for France to make a major impact because of the profusion of manufacturing firms which tended to spread design and production strength too thinly. The Aéronautique Navale, for operation from both ships and shore bases, was created as a self-contained force within the French Navy in 1925, and in 1933 the prolonged battle for an independent air force separate from the army was won by the creation of the Armée de l'Air. But the supply of combat aircraft of competitive design was a cause for mounting concern. Finally in 1936 the industry was violently shaken up and most of the firms nationalized into five huge state groups named Nord, Centre, Ouest, Sud-Ouest and Sud-Est according to geographical location. But a few firms that were considered to have done well were allowed to remain in private hands. Notable among these were Dewoitine, whose D.520 was the only competitive French fighter in 1940 (though available in pitifully small numbers); Potez, supplier of the versatile Model 63 twin-engined fighter bomber; Morane-Saulnier, whose MS.406 was the only French fighter in 1940 that stood any chance in combat and was also available in quantity; Breguet, a proud name whose Br 690 twin-engined fighter was produced just in time to have a small effect in wartime; and Marcel Bloch, who like Dewoitine and Potez made transports for Air France and had also produced a fine modern fighter. But in the main September 1939 found the Armée de l'Air and Aéronavale lacking in modern equipment.

431

432

Boeing P-12, which in 1933 gave way to the same firm's P-26 monoplane. Most of the generals of the second world war Army Air Force had once served as squadron pilots flying these well liked, stubby, wire-braced monoplanes with dark green bodies, yellow wings and gay unit insignia. They graduated in 1938 to the stressed-skin Curtiss P-36 and this in turn yielded to the infinitely more formidable P-38 Lightning, P-47 Thunderbolt and P-51 Mustang of the second world war. In the matter of bombers the lumbering Keystone Panther biplane was rendered obsolete in 1932 by the Boeing B-9, a stressed-skin cantilever monoplane which itself yielded to the Martin B-10, a staggeringly advanced machine for 1932-33 that could outpace Air Corps fighters by more than 90 mph. Then in 1935 a new era dawned with the flight of the first B-17 'Flying Fortress'.

French military aircraft of the interwar years were robust, angular and generally undistinguished. Unlike the British and Americans, the Gallic engineers had no aversion to the monoplane and after 1918 most of their fighters and many bombers eschewed the old biplane

429 Boeing P-26A (built in 1935) over Hawaii, 1939

430 US Army Air Corps Martin B-10A, one of the most modern bombers of 1933

431 Boeing YB-9A monoplane bomber (*at right:* prototype P-26; *in rear:* Curtiss Hawk biplanes)

432 Potez 63 twin-engined fighter of the Armée de l'Air, 1939

433 Dewoitine D.520 fighter of the Armée de l'Air, 1940

433

434

435

436

Holland's Fokker and Koolhoven companies produced fine fighters and bombers, most of them powered by Bristol Jupiter, Mercury, Pegasus and Hercules engines, until the land was overwhelmed in May 1940. Belgium's Fairey and SABCA works tried to do likewise, and in Sweden a careful blend of licence-production of foreign aircraft and engines not only resulted in a strong air power but also provided national skills that since 1937 have been put to wonderful use. This independent nation, with a population much less than that of New York or London, has designed and built a remarkable series of fighter and attack aircraft which have proved the equal of any produced elsewhere; and they have never had an unsuccessful programme.

Poland, Czechoslovakia and many other nations built their own military aircraft, and still do, but attention must now be turned to the three powerful countries that in the second world war took on the rest of the world.

In 1914-18 Italy created a formidable air force, but when Mussolini took over in 1923, his great air minister, General Italo Balbo, had to build up a fresh Regia Aeronautica almost from scratch. As already related, this force made notable record flights, establishing world records for speed, altitude, distance, duration and other parameters. Balbo himself led the most famous of all formation flights when in 1933 a flotilla of 24 Savoia-Marchetti twin-hulled flying-boats flew to an exhibition in Chicago and back. The same manufacturer's SM.79 gained world records as a very advanced three-engined airliner and then in 1937 blazed into action in the Spanish Civil War as a bomber. Only the Fiat biplane fighters looked inadequate in 1939.

Japanese aviation was scarcely known in the West, and not very impressive, until a trim fighter-like monoplane named *Kamikaze* (Divine Wind) flew in record time from Tokyo to London in April 1937. A little over two years later a twin-engined machine flew round the world, but Western intelligence continued to underestimate the quality and quantity of the equipment of the Imperial Army and Navy air forces until December 1941.

In Germany the prohibition of the Versailles Treaty was circumvented by the building of various ostensibly civil machines which really – and increasingly obviously – were fighters and bombers. When the Luftwaffe was officially formed in 1935 there existed a strong industry which was expanded with awesome speed to become by 1937 by far the most powerful in Europe. Its first products were often not quite the equal of RAF equipment, but impressive results in the Spanish Civil War were combined with enormous numerical superiority to create a force that Reichsmarshall Hermann Goering

considered invincible. The chief German fighter was the Messerschmitt Me 109 and the main bomber the Heinkel 111. In speed, reliability, fire-power and military load they were noticeably better than the motley collection of machines that opposed them in Spain. They enjoyed a run of unbroken success until, almost unbelievably, they more than met their match over England in the autumn of 1940.

A lethargic Britain in 1936 had at last begun to put some muscle and sinew on its thin military skeleton,

437

438

434 Morane-Saulnier MS.406 fighter of the Armée de l'Air, 1939

435 Breguet Br 690 twin-engined fighter prototype, 1939

436 Fokker D.23 fighter of 1939 with push-pull engines

437 The Japanese Mitsubishi *Kamikaze* at Croydon, London, 1937 (*rear*: a Ju 52/3M of Lufthansa)

438 Heinkel He 51s of the Jagdstaffel Richthofen, the Luftwaffe's first fighter squadron, at Döberitz, August 1935

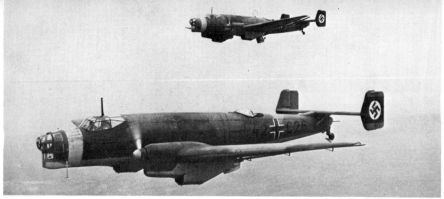

439

440

441

and military budgets doubled and quadrupled to pay not only for new aircraft but also for new factories far bigger than the old ones. A 'shadow industry' was created from general engineering and motor car firms to duplicate the tooling, techniques and products of the Bristol engine firm and of certain airframe builders. In three vital years the rate of delivery of combat aircraft, and of aircrew for them, was multiplied approximately eightfold, and the character of the machines changed out of all recognition. In 1935 there was not one modern stressed-skin monoplane in either the RAF or Fleet Air Arm; there were a handful of monoplanes of old-fashioned fabric-covered types but more than 95 per cent of the operational strength was in biplanes. It is not generally known how nearly the big rearmament scheme was based on biplanes. For example Vickers built a biplane to meet an Air Ministry specification for a general-purpose bomber and could easily have got orders for it. But as a private venture they built a modern monoplane to meet the same specification (it was notable for its 'geodetic' metal basketwork structure, devised by Barnes Wallis, which was later used in the very important Wellington bomber). The monoplane, named Wellesley, so out-performed the biplane that Vickers got the Air Ministry to think in terms of monoplanes for the future, and the Wellesley was ordered in quantity in September 1935.

In September 1939 the only modern British combat aircraft were the Hurricane and Spitfire fighters, the Blenheim, Battle and Wellington bombers and the Sunderland ocean patrol flying-boat. Most of these crucial machines were partly or completely the result of private initiative. The Hurricane was a private venture by the Hawker Aircraft company and the first monoplane in a classic series of fighters by a design team led by Sir Sydney Camm. Although of traditional construction, and initially made with fabric-covered wings, it had an adequate performance for the early part of the war and could absorb great punishment, fly home and be swiftly repaired. Above all, it was available in large numbers in 1939 as the result of the company's initiative in starting to build 1,000 long before they had an order. The smaller and faster Spitfire was again a completely private venture, created by a team led by Reginald Mitchell because he was dissatisfied with the aircraft he had designed to the official specification. Probably the most famous military aircraft of all time, this beautiful stressed-skin machine thus came about by mere chance, yet without it the RAF would have had nothing to match German fighters until the first squadron of Typhoons (a much more pugnacious successor to the Hurricane)

439 The Luftwaffe's first big bomber, the Junkers Ju 86D of 1937

440 The potent Messerschmitt Me 109E, on active service in France, 1940

441 Bombs (stowed nose-up) falling on the Soviet Union from a Heinkel He 111, 1942

became operational late in 1941.

The Blenheim, a light twin-engined bomber, arose through the urgent wish of the newspaper magnate Lord Rothermere to see Britain build a modern monoplane comparable with the American airliners he had seen at Mildenhall in 1934 before the race to Melbourne. Bristol made him the 'Britain First', which was tested at Martlesham Heath and found to reach 307 mph, compared with 225 mph for the fastest RAF fighter – hence the rushed production of the Blenheim bomber version. The Fairey Battle was a light bomber looking like a much enlarged Hurricane and powered with the same Rolls-Royce Merlin 1,000 hp engine. It was built to an official specification, and was very soon found to be deficient in speed, firepower and general potency. The fine Wellington, already mentioned in connection with geodetic construction, began the war with two 1,000 hp Bristol Pegasus engines and soon progressed to the 1,500 hp Bristol Hercules sleeve-valve engine. The Wellington could get home with major portions of the airframe shot away and, like the Hurricane, soon be airworthy again. The Sunderland was a splendid four-engined ocean patrol flying-boat derived from the Empire boats of Imperial Airways.

In the Luftwaffe the most important fighter by far was Willi Messerschmitt's Me 109. In 1934 Messerschmitt was discounted as a designer, and the Luftwaffe were quite uninterested in his new fighter until he made them watch it perform. As he did not have to meet an official specification he stuck his neck right out and made it as

184

442

manoeuvre on a pocket handkerchief. Messerschmitt's frightening, rakish machine with its rather cramped enclosed cockpit seemed wrong in every way. Yet within a year Udet thought it the best fighter in the world, as it probably was. Blooded in Spain, it hacked down hundreds of inferior foes before finding tougher opposition over Britain. Even then improved 109 versions kept it in the thick of the fray right up to 1945 and then in still later versions built in Czechoslovakia, Israel and Spain. More than 34,000 Me 109 fighters were built, a

443

446

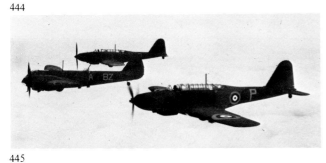

444

447

445

clever as possible. A stressed-skin monoplane, the 109 was small, angular and of extremely advanced design. Its wing was about half as big as usual, and slats were fitted along the leading edge to help it give more lift at low speed or in tight manoeuvres. General Udet, the 1914–18 ace who became a leader of the new Nazi force, said: 'That will never make a fighter!,' because to him a fighter was a biplane with an open cockpit, able to

total believed to exceed that for all other aircraft in history.

Less lasting was the Junkers Ju 87 'Stuka' (an abbreviation of Sturzkampffflugzeug, or dive bomber). The idea behind it was that a fairly small bomber could drop a heavy load accurately by diving almost vertically on to the target and pulling out of the dive just after releasing its bombs. The reasonable accuracy obtained

448

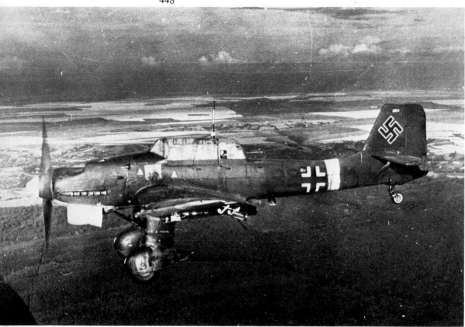

449

450

451

British Expeditionary Force. By June the AASF was shattered. A few of the battered Battles and early Hurricanes (with fixed-pitch wooden propellers that were a national disgrace) escaped to England; most of the men and equipment did not. But then instead of pursuing the shattered and demoralized Allied forces across the Channel, Hitler gave the RAF time to catch its breath, bring into use a dozen new fighter squadrons and gird itself for the Battle of Britain that was sure to come.

The most epic air battle of all time began on 8 August 1940. On the previous day the RAF had 32 squadrons of Hurricanes (2,309 aircraft on strength) and 19 of Spitfires (1,400 aircraft on strength), with an average effective force each day amounting to 2,100 aircraft. German combat strength in the West exceeded 6,500 aircraft, of which 3,500 were fighters and bombers sent against England. As only a small part of the RAF strength could intercept each raid, the odds were often long. Moreover, had not the Air Officer Commanding

was coupled with shattering psychological effect that was heightened by fitting sirens to the fixed landing gear. The Ju 87 demolished opposition in Spain, Poland and the Low Countries, but over Britain it was a sitting duck. Much more enduring were the conventional twin-engined bombers that made up the bulk of the Luftwaffe striking force: at first the Heinkel He 111 (one of the so-called civil airliners of the mid-1930s) and the slim Dornier Do 17 'Flying Pencil' and, later, the Junkers Ju 88 which became one of the most potent and versatile machines of the war.

The second world war was not a war of personal aces but of immense numbers of aircraft and aircrew which both suffered an attrition rate that strained the resources of great nations. In 1935 the British government announced that the RAF had a front-line strength of '580 aeroplanes' (a gross overestimate). During the years 1940-45 this number of aircraft, each many times more costly than the average of 1935, were often written off in a week. Trenchard had said that a war would be won by the side that could best make good its losses, and throughout the war millions of men and women performed herculean tasks not only in making combat aircraft but also in remaking them, modifying them, repairing them and putting them back into service.

When the real war blazed forth on 10 May 1940 the Luftwaffe had little reason to doubt its invincibility. It met indifferent French, Belgian and Dutch aircraft and shot them down. It met the RAF also, the Advanced Air Striking Force that had gone to France with the

Fighter Command, Air Chief Marshal Dowding, been a man of uncommon foresight and courage most of his resources would have been frittered away in France earlier in the year.

Dowding had another incalculable asset. In 1934 experiments conducted by a team led by Robert Watson-Watt had shown that radio waves could be detected after they had been reflected from distant metallic objects such as aircraft. By 1938 radiolocation (later called radar, for 'radio direction and ranging') sets were in production that could detect aircraft at a distance of more than 60 miles and give an accurate indication of bearing, range and direction of travel. By the summer of 1940 the initial deployment was almost complete–an invisible shield of radio waves from Scotland, down the East Coast, round the Dover Strait and along the South Coast. Controllers on the ground could 'vector' fighter forces to intercept enemy aircraft they could not yet see, and

448 Short Sunderland ocean patrol flying-boat of RAF Coastal Command, 1944

449 Junkers Ju 87B 'Stuka' dive bomber of the Luftwaffe, about 1940

450 Dornier Do 17Z bomber of the Luftwaffe, 1940

451 Junkers Ju 88S high-speed bomber of the Luftwaffe, 1942

continue to give directions with great accuracy throughout the battle. Radar probably made Dowding's forces equal to about three times as many aircraft without such help. The Battle of Britain was a long-drawn-out gruelling test of pilots and of a complete defensive system, but radar meant that no pilot flew unless he was almost certain to fight. This was a technological advance bigger even than the change to monoplanes.

The Battle of Britain involved many types of aircraft at all altitudes. Both sides suffered from exhaustion, although the German numerical strength was at all times considerably greater than that of Fighter Command. It is often incorrectly asserted that the battle was won by a very slender margin: in fact, at its close Fighter Command had not been eliminated but was roughly as strong as at the start. The crippling defeats inflicted on huge aerial armadas, comprising He 111 and Do 17 bombers escorted by Me 109 and Me 110 (twin-engined) fighters, on several days in September made Goering pause and decide he was not going to win this way.

The Luftwaffe turned to night bombing, and in the blitz all through the winter of 1940-41 the Heinkels and less numerous Dornier and Junkers bombers unleashed indiscriminate destruction over London and other British cities in a random attempt to destroy not so much British property—which was mainly private houses—as the British will. At first the night attacks were hard to counter, although the occasional bomber would be brought down by gunfire from the ground. But with painful slowness the British scientists and engineers put radar into the defending aircraft. The key to this development was the magnetron valve, a carefully machined block of copper which, when cooled with water and subjected to a heavy current, emitted powerful radiation from a series of small cavities. This radiation was of an extremely short wavelength so that a dish-like scanner not much bigger than a large dinner plate could focus it into a pencil beam pointing ahead of a fighter like an invisible headlight. The beam could be made to oscillate to search for a target and then to give the fighter's observer a visual 'blip' on the face of a cathode ray tube which, if he was skilled and persistent, would allow him to direct the pilot towards the enemy until the bomber's glowing exhaust pipes or black silhouette could be seen clearly enough for it to be shot down.

Despite remarkable feats of miniaturization, the AI (airborne interception) radar could be carried only by a fighter much bigger than the single-engined single-seaters that had fought the daylight battle. By sheer good fortune the RAF had the perfect carriers. The Bristol Beaufighter, powered by two 1,500 hp Hercules engines, had flown three weeks before the war and proved to have the size and power needed. It also had the formidable armament of four 20 mm cannon and six machine-guns, all firing forward, with drums of 20 mm ammunition being changed by the observer sitting aft of the wing, and it was fast enough to catch any German aircraft likely to come to England at night. By May 1941 over 200 had been delivered and their increasing numbers, and the increasing reliability of their vital radar and the skill of the crews, caused the Germans to give up mass attacks on Britain entirely. Until June 1944 the island

suffered only sporadic sneak raids by isolated crews and hit-and-run attacks on coastal towns by speedy fighter bombers. Among the latter were to be counted the radial-engined Focke-Wulf 190, a clever and compact fighter of very advanced design which was a nasty surprise to Mk 5 Spitfires engaged on 'daylight sweeps' over Northern France in 1941.

The RAF soon had an even more effective night fighter, and it was not planned as a fighter at all. The Mosquito was one of the most versatile war-winning

452

453

452 Lockheed Aircraft Service shop overhauling Twin Wasp engines of the US Army at the rate of one an hour, 1944

453 One of the first Bristol Beaufighters to reach the RAF, winter 1940

aircraft of its age, and like the Beaufighter was a complete private venture carried through in the teeth of considerable official disbelief and disinterest. Late in 1938, when the Air Ministry were still not wholly sold on a light bomber as fast as the 270 mph Blenheim 1, de

Havilland Aircraft proposed a bomber of rather smaller size, powered by two Merlins and capable of a speed at least 100 mph faster. It was to need no defensive armament, and to complete the revolutionary picture its construction was to be almost wholly of wood. Despite being dropped from the official programme entirely in the summer of 1940 the first 'Mozzie' flew as early as November of that year. Its performance was so staggering it was soon in production for bombing, night fighting and reconnaissance, and before long there was scarcely

454

455

a single military job not being performed by these incredible machines. One of the specialities of the Mosquito bombers was the low-level attack on a single building, such as Amiens prison or the Gestapo HQ in the centre of Oslo. A contrasting role was the high-altitude strategic bomber with a bulged bomb bay capable of carrying a 4,000 lb 'blockbuster' to Berlin, while yet another vital duty was pathfinding, as presently

described. Equipped with successively improved forms of AI radar the Mosquito night fighters destroyed hundreds of German aircraft all over Western Europe, while the most widely used version of all was a multi-role fighter bomber seen in every theatre of war. As a civil transport they maintained a BOAC service to Stockholm despite the fact that agents warned the Luftwaffe of every take-off from Sweden. In Coastal Command the Mk 18 version attacked ships with a six-pounder gun and rockets, special high flying versions had pointed and extended wings, the pressurized photo-reconnaissance machines set world records that were beaten only by jet aircraft, the Royal Navy had special torpedo and target-towing models and yet further versions were made in Canada and Australia.

But by far the biggest British effort, in terms of both hardware and aircrew, from 1940 until the end of the war was devoted to the 'heavies' of Bomber Command. The RAF had first ordered four-engined bombers in 1938, and by the spring of 1942 it expected to have 1,500 of the giant Short Stirlings (four 1,500 hp Bristol Hercules) and 500 Handley Page Halifaxes (four 1,300 hp Rolls-Royce Merlins), as well as 1,500 of the almost as large Avro Manchesters (two 1,760 hp Rolls-Royce Vultures). In the event the Stirling was not a great success, the Halifax rather better and the Manchester a total failure because of its engines, and the great heavy bombers did not really get into their stride until late in 1942. What was quite unforeseen was that the Lancaster, a hastily contrived version of the Manchester with four Merlin or Hercules engines, would prove to be by far the best of the lot. In the end over 15,000 four-engined bombers were delivered from UK plants to the RAF, almost half of them Lancasters. The supremely effective 'Lanc', lighter than its rivals yet carrying a much heavier load further, excelled in three action-packed years over the most heavily defended territory on Earth.

In the course of 1941 and 1942 Bomber Command learned how to operate, and the surviving crews were made increasingly effective by new technology, almost all of it based on radar, and also by new techniques. On the night of 30 May 1942 the RAF scraped together 1,000 bombers to raid Cologne, but as was generally the case at that time, the attack comprised a loose scattered straggle of aircraft of which a few bombed accurately while most released their load miles off target and often over open country, despite their best efforts. Within a year the picture had changed dramatically. While day fighter pilots still operated much as had the scout pilots of 1914-18, the bomber crews began to operate in a totally new way that pointed the path that development would later take in civil aviation, shipping and many other activities in which human crews have to be supplemented by 'black boxes'.

One of the first black boxes was cryptically called H$_2$S. It was a radar carried in the bomber, its presence made obvious by the large streamlined blister on the underside of the fuselage covering the scanner aerial, which on a cathode-ray tube face in front of the navigator or signaller continuously painted a picture of the ground directly beneath. Each circular sweep of the scanner updated the picture as the aircraft moved. Water and

456

457

458

459

460

461

462

some types of land showed black, other land showed lighter (because it reflected more of the radar energy) and buildings and ships showed brightest of all. It was a valuable aid to the crew's navigation, and the picture when passing over a harbour or a big city at a confluence of rivers was so clear that a completely untrained person could have known where he was. As it was unaffected by thick cloud H_2S could be used for blind bombing if the required degree of accuracy was not very high.

thing previously dreamed of if they were not to collide. As it was, scores did collide (and many survived), while at least 300 were struck by bombs falling from above, usually before the bomb had fallen far enough to be detonated by such an impact.

How could this torrent of giant bombers be made to bomb with precision? The answer lay in the techniques of the Pathfinder Force whose elite crews showed the main force exactly where to bomb. One technique was as follows. Mosquitoes would come in at an exact height

463

A totally different aid was Oboe, derived from an experimental system used in 1941-42 to help high-flying aircraft hit the German capital ships *Gneisenau*, *Scharnhorst* and *Prinz Eugen* in French Atlantic ports. A ground station, known as the 'cat', sent out radar signals which were reflected from the bomber as it neared its target. While the cat staff accurately measured the bomber's position and speed, the pilot could hear a continuous note if he precisely held a gently curving path forming an arc of a circle centred on the cat station; if he strayed to either side he heard dashes or dots, and with much practice a pilot could hold the correct, very gently turning path within a few yards. Meanwhile the navigator listened to a complicated coded signal from a 'mouse' station. At the exact moment he would release the bombs. Eventually, by the end of 1942, skilled Oboe bombing without looking at the ground was more accurate than anything attainable with an optical bomb sight.

Unfortunately, apart from the danger of having to approach the target along a known path held very nearly straight for several minutes, Oboe had the drawback that each cat and mouse pair could handle only one aircraft at a time. Bomber Command knew the only way to reduce losses was to saturate the defences by so precisely timing the flight of every bomber that they could flood across the target at the rate of fifty a minute. Completely blacked out, with even the engine exhausts shrouded, the hundreds of giant bombers had to maintain their course and timing far more accurately than any-

somewhere near 30,000 ft under exact direction by Oboe and drop bright red markers spot on the target centre. These would burn for eight minutes. While the main force, coming in lower from the opposite direction, bombed the markers, a small proportion of these heavies would be Pathfinder aircraft which would lay down green back-up markers more often than once every eight minutes. Brief gaps in the bomber stream would then allow further Oboe Mosquitoes to put down further red markers, every one of which would be accurate to within a few yards. The main force would always aim on these if any were visible. There were countless variations and refinements that enabled the attack to be made through dense cloud, that prevented the force from bombing on fake German markers, that prevented the vital Mosquitoes from being misled by powerful spurious Oboe signals sent out locally, that took care of any conceivable disaster. On 5 March 1943 Essen was raided by 400 aircraft by the new technique. The results were literally shattering.

In the summer of 1942 these growing attacks were joined by daylight raids by the US Eighth Air Force (differently numbered Air Forces of the US Army served in different theatres). After Japanese carrier-based aircraft that took off before dawn on Sunday, 7 December 1941 had without warning struck the great naval base at Pearl Harbor, Hawaii and brought the United States into the war, catastrophe followed catastrophe for the Allied forces in the enormous south-west Pacific and south-east Asia theatre of war. These often

459 Hawker Siddeley Gnat trainer and Anglesey lighthouse, 1971

460 BAC (English Electric) Canberra B.6 bombers of the RAF, 1955

461 Hawker Siddeley Buccaneer S.2A of RAF Strike Command firing rockets, 1972

462 Hawker Siddeley Nimrod MR.1 of the RAF, 1970

463 Avro Lancaster I of No. 83 Squadron, RAF, 1942

stemmed from the fact that the Japanese had very large numbers of modern fighters and bombers which, though lightly built and carrying little gun power or armour, were fast and very manoeuvrable. Yet prodigious efforts gave the US Army Air Force and Navy much greater numbers of far better aircraft. Two carrier fighters, the Vought F4U Corsair and Grumman F6F Hellcat, gained total Allied air superiority over the Japanese by mid-1944, and mighty sea battles that were almost wholly a matter of air strikes took such toll of

465

By 1943 hundreds of these fine fighters were making round trips of more than 1,000 miles deep into Germany escorting the Boeing B-17 Fortresses and Consolidated B-24 Liberators of the Eighth Bomb Groups. Each of these bombers was a flying battleship, bristling with 0.5 in calibre machine-guns pointing in every direction and carrying from three to six tons of bombs high into the stratosphere on the power of four engines fitted with turbo-superchargers driven by turbines spun at immense speed by the white-hot exhaust gas. The sight of the daily armada of up to 1,000 Forts or Libs, each gleaming in polished metal except where it bore brightly coloured unit markings (not forgetting the flamboyant, and invariably female, 'nose art' that reached remarkable proportions), was an unforgettable sight, especially as the vast 200 mile long force climbed to levels where each engine left a thick white contrail. German fighters could see the force scores of miles away, and bloody combats ensued. Often 50 or more great bombers would go down, some in a ball of fire and others with painful

464

464 Japanese Kate torpedo bomber hit by anti-aircraft fire over Pearl Harbor, 7 December 1941

465 Vought F4U Corsair of the US Marine Corps salvoes rockets on Okinawa, 1945

466 Grumman F4F Wildcat fighters of the US Navy on Henderson Field, Guadalcanal, 1942

467 Grumman F6F Hellcat fighter of the US Navy returns to USS *Cabot*, 1944

468 Lockheed P-38F Lightning escort fighter of the US 8th Air Force, Britain, 1942

469 North American P-51H Mustang single-seat fighter-bomber, 1944; a very late wartime version of what many people consider to have been the best of all piston-engined fighters

470 Republic P-47N Thunderbolt fighter bomber, 1945

471 Consolidated B-24 Liberator of the US 8th Air Force stricken over Austria, 1944

466

467

the Japanese carriers that none was left by December. In that year the Hellcat was made at the rate of well over 500 per month, a figure exceeded only by the even bigger Republic P-47 Thunderbolt, which like the Navy fighters was powered by a 2,400 hp Pratt & Whitney Double Wasp engine.

Thunderbolts, weighing more than twice as much as a Spitfire, came to Europe in 1942 and built up the Eighth Fighter Command to a formidable strength, soon being joined by the unique twin-tail-boom Lockheed P-38 Lightning and the Rolls-Royce Merlin powered North American P-51 Mustang, possibly the best fighter of the entire war, possessed of outstanding speed and range.

192

468

469

470

471

472

473

472 Curtiss P-40N Warhawks of the US Army Air Force, 1944

473 Douglas SBD Dauntless bomber returns to its US Navy carrier at sunset, Pacific Ocean, June 1943

474 Boeing B-17F Fortress formation over Africa, 1 March 1944

475 Douglas C-47 (military DC-3) leaves for Europe on D-day towing British-built Horsa glider, both with 'invasion stripes'

474

475

slowness as feathered engines forced them to drop below and behind.

The Eastern Front, which flared up in the summer of 1941, was the only theatre where the Luftwaffe was not on the defensive by the end of 1942. Courageous Russian crews fought with skill and daring in aircraft that, despite the supply of rather second-rate British and US fighters and bombers, were usually not quite the equal of the best German machines. Apart from measures intended to keep an air force flying in extreme sub-zero temperature, the Russians contributed only one major new technique, and this was most effective: use of heavy calibre rockets fired against ground targets. By mid-1943 a standard rocket motor of quite different design was being made by the hundred thousand in Britain, usually carrying a 60 pound high-explosive head. Mosquitoes, Beaufighters, and even Fairey Swordfish biplanes of the Fleet Air Arm did good trade with these against ships and trains, and after D-day Rommel's armour in northern France was caught in the Falaise gap by rocket-firing Typhoons and almost annihilated.

D day, 6 June 1944, saw the extensive deployment of airborne forces, using ideas pioneered in Germany in which crack infantry dropped by parachute or landed in gliders or powered transport aircraft and held airfields or bridges as key positions ready for an advancing land force. By far the most important transport was the Douglas Dakota, the military DC-3, of which 4,900 were delivered in 1944 alone. The assault gliders were mainly British, the 25-seat wooden Airspeed Horsa being used hundreds at a time in the Rhine crossing and at Arnhem, and the tank-carrying General Aircraft Hamilcar glider suddenly bringing armour to unexpected places. Special versions of the powerful Stirling and Halifax were the usual tugs, and a stirring sight it was to see the great aircraft lined up scores at a time, each bearing on the fuselage and wings the special invasion markings of a huge white band crossed by two black bands.

The second world war was the pinnacle of aircraft development in terms of numbers of manufacturers, numbers of types of aircraft and numbers built of each

194

type. The belligerent powers constructed well over half a million aircraft of more than 400 different types. They included many weird and wonderful designs. The German Dornier 214 would have been a giant flying-boat bigger by far than any previous flying machine, an impregnable fortress too big to alight on land. The Messerschmitt 321 was a glider so big it needed three powered aircraft to tow it – until a special tug was constructed by joining together two Heinkel 111 bombers with a fifth engine in the middle. Britain made fighters capable of nudging 500 mph and 'fleet shadowers' designed to fly as slowly as possible while they spent a whole day lurking in the clouds over hostile ships. America made fighters that flew tail-first, transports faster than fighters and a wooden flying-boat with a span of 320 ft, a dimension never approached before or since.

In the year 1944, the climax of the war, aircraft production reached incredible levels. In the United States alone almost 96,000 combat machines were delivered, a high proportion of them big and expensive aircraft packed with hydraulics, electrics, oxygen, self-sealing fuel systems, armament, radar, armour, de-icing, autopilot and seemingly countless other devices all necessary for their purpose yet imposing a heavy burden on the manufacturing industry, on the aircrew and ground staff training programmes and all who had to keep everything functioning perfectly, repair it after battle damage and use it properly in action. The British and Russian industries, both with a female labour content exceeding 50 per cent, performed prodigies of skill and endurance with a working week frequently amounting to 90 hours. Sometimes, as when special filters were needed to stop the Typhoons' complicated Napier Sabre engines from being worn out by the sand of Normandy airstrips, men worked three days and nights without a break.

In Germany desperate plant managers, faced with a written threat of Dachau if production did not increase, gathered tools from shattered factories, organized fresh production in countless sheds, forest tents, disused mine shafts and other dispersed places and then, when other transport failed, used boys with bicycles to bring baskets of finished parts to the assembly area, wheeling the machines where rubble and craters made riding impossible. Somehow, production actually went up, often by startling amounts; but the Luftwaffe had lost its best aircrews, its airfields were blasted and, worst of all, fuel was critically short.

Yet despite these overwhelming difficulties, the Luftwaffe came near to prolonging the war. Whereas the Allies entered 1945 using advanced versions of the aircraft with which they began the war, the Germans were feverishly trying to build aircraft so much later in concept they seemed to belong to another world – and, in a sense, they did. Radical innovations in propulsion, in aerodynamics and in weapon technique were swiftly bringing in the age of the jet and the guided missile.

This change was the most profound and revolutionary development in aviation since the Wright brothers' first powered flights. The advent of the streamlined stressed-skin monoplane gave a method of construction that could permit aircraft to fly safely at speeds greatly in

476

excess of those previously achieved. The fastest Allied machines of 1939-45 were the Mk 19 photo-reconnaissance Spitfire and the P-47M Thunderbolt with water injection, both of which could reach about 465 mph. But it had long been evident that increasing aircraft speed much beyond this level was going to take many years and demand a totally new sort of propulsion system. There were fundamental reasons why piston engines of the traditional type could not be made to give the enormously greater power needed, and for equally fundamental reasons a conventional propeller could not give thrust at speeds much in excess of 500 mph. It was the jet that swept these barriers away so that, allied with new aircraft shapes, the speed and all-round performance of aircraft was enabled to rise more rapidly than it ever had before.

The birth of the jet did not take place at any one place or time, nor can it be ascribed to any one individual. There had been numerous patents for jet engines of various kinds since 1791, and in 1911 and 1917 inventors

477

described in general terms exactly how a modern turbojet functions. But their patents were useless because, even if anybody had been so seemingly lunatic as to try to build such an engine, the basic technology did not exist. To be useful, a turbojet called for an air compressor that, for a given size and weight, handled dozens to hundreds of times as much air as any in existence. It called for com-

476 Douglas A-20 Havoc bomber of the US 9th Air Force loses its tail to flak over France, 1944

477 North American B-25 Mitchells bombing and strafing Japanese warships, 1944

195

bustion chambers that, for a given size and weight, completely and efficiently burned liquid fuel dozens of times faster than any previously built. Perhaps most impossible of all, it demanded turbine rotor blades capable of withstanding enormous mechanical loads over long periods while heated to a temperature above the melting point of many metals in common bulk use. To bring about such a completely new range of human abilities demands years of painstaking research and testing, which in turn calls for a lot of money, faith and determination.

Several of the pioneers of the jet had faith in the idea, but lacked the determination to overcome official lethargy. One of the major figures in early jet history was the Englishman A. A. Griffith, one of the most gifted researchers at the Royal Aircraft Establishment at Farnborough. In 1925 he devised a new conceptual treatment of cascades, the term for a long series of identical aerofoils or small wings placed one above the other with gaps between them. This is almost the same thing as the row of blades around a turbine wheel, and by 1927 Griffith was working on calculations for a gas turbine. Turbines driven by hot gas from fuel burned inside the engine – as distinct from a steam turbine, where the fuel is burned externally to heat a water boiler – had been running since the turn of the century, mainly at the Swiss firm of Brown Boveri. But Griffith was one of the first to see that such an engine might one day be able to replace the piston engine as the source of power for aircraft propellers. Eventually, after years of official lack of interest, he saw his work culminate in a

479

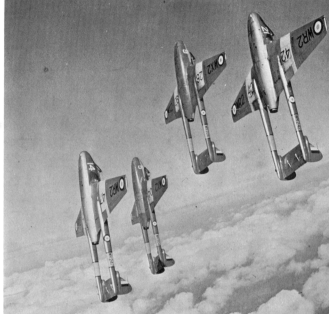

480

no hope of exceeding one quarter of this speed, yet his work was only just in time to save severe Allied embarrassment in 1944. His vital contribution was to use a gas turbine not to drive a propeller but simply to produce a flow of hot gas. He calculated that the exhaust from the turbine could, if allowed to expand and accelerate back to the atmosphere through a suitable nozzle, provide a propulsive thrust that could drive an aircraft along. His calculations suggested that such a device would suffer from none of the fundamental restrictions of the piston engine and propeller; and he even had vague dreams about using such a method to propel aircraft faster than sound.

Whittle graduated from Cranwell in 1928, leaving various theses and articles on jet propulsion. Had he been killed in the years that followed with a fighter squadron, or instructing pupils or test-flying seaplanes, his idea would have been forgotten until it burst unpleasantly upon the Allies in 1944. But Whittle continued his work, and once was granted a polite audience by Air Ministry officials who, although they showed no interest, at least did not forbid him to continue his investigations. Eventually after heartbreaking years of courteous refusals he managed to borrow enough money to set up a little company, Power Jets, and even to construct an experimental engine which ran near Rugby in April 1937. The Air Ministry had not expected this at all, and although Whittle still had far more enemies than friends he was awarded a contract for an experimental unit and then a second contract for an engine to fly a small

478

478 Sir Frank Whittle (*centre*) accompanied by British Ambassador Sir Oliver Franks (*right*) presents his W.1X turbojet to Dr Alexander Metmore of the Smithsonian Institution, 1949

479 Bell XP-59A Airacomet, powered by two Whittle-type GE engines, October 1942

480 De Havilland Vampire single-seater relegated to training, 1955

powerful turboprop engine at the end of the second world war.

While Griffith toiled in an official laboratory there grew up another pioneer who not only hit on an idea even more valuable than Griffith's but also possessed the determination to see it through to the bitter end. While a Flight Cadet at the RAF College, Cranwell, in 1926, Frank Whittle became engrossed in the problems of aircraft propulsion. He desperately searched for some way of overcoming the fundamental barrier, previously referred to, suffered by the piston engine and propeller at about 500 mph. He did this while looking out of the window at fabric-covered biplanes that had research aircraft. This, the Gloster E.28/39, was flown at Cranwell on 15 May 1941.

By this time the Whittle engine was a priceless national asset, the twin-engined Gloster Meteor fighter was being hurriedly designed, de Havilland were designing both a jet fighter and its engine and a range of Whittle turbojets was being developed by Power Jets, Rover and Rolls-Royce. Moreover, General H. H. 'Hap' Arnold, Chief of Staff of the US Army Air Force, imported a Whittle engine and the drawings into the United States and

481

quickly got Bell to create a twin-jet fighter, the XP-59 Airacomet, which flew on 1 October 1942. In 1943 both the Meteor and the de Havilland Vampire began their flight development, and on 9 January 1944 the very advanced Lockheed XP-80 Shooting Star began its trials in California a mere 143 days after the start of design.

From the green grass of England and the red desert of the Mojave fighter pilots and technicians were putting into the air a new sort of aircraft which, although it had no propeller, contained an engine of potentially enormous power that would with further development open up a new realm of flight performance. Fuelled with kerosene, which reeked across the airfield as penetratingly as the castor oil of thirty years earlier, the new engines ran like sewing machines without the slightest roughness or vibration of the kind fighter pilots had long been used to. Opened up for take-off, they sent the pulse racing with their surging thrust which, unlike that of previous aircraft, did not die away but kept the pilot's seat pressed firmly into his back as the air speed indicator recorded 100, 200, 300 and then 400 mph. By 1945 amazing work by Rolls-Royce enabled the basically unchanged Meteor to keep thrusting in its pilot's back until the ASI read 500 and then 600 mph, and the dense sea-level air was roaring past so fast that the transparent cockpit canopy became softened by the heat and had to be replaced by a metal one.

But while war was on world records were a dream. The immediate concern was that it was all too obvious that most of the earliest jets had flown from neither English swards nor American desert but from airstrips among the dark conifers of the German forests. Just as Whittle was not the only pioneer of the jet among the Allies, so was Hans von Ohain not the only pioneer in Germany; but, like Whittle, he achieved a notable 'first'. Although his first turbojet, built by the Heinkel company, ran a month later than Whittle's, a modified version of it had flown the He 178, the first jet aircraft in the world, as early as 27 August 1939. But Heinkel achieved scant

official support in this work, and it was the big jet programme of the Junkers company, soon paralleled by the rival firm of BMW (Bavarian Motor Works), that by 1943 led to two engines being ready for large scale production. The Junkers Jumo 004 and the BMW 003 were both crude but effective engines of the axial flow type, which although more difficult to develop and make than the Allied centrifugal engines, offered better long term prospects in greater efficiency and lower frontal area. By 1944 both engines were building up to a truly amazing rate of production. Despite shattered factories and an extraordinary and barely controllable dispersal of production, the combined deliveries of the two engines reached 1,000 a month by the summer of 1944 and continued to climb. This was many times greater than the Allied figure, for unlike the Allies the Germans regarded jets as overwhelmingly, desperately important, and a faint hope for final victory.

Again unlike the Allies, the German designers worked flat out creating astonishingly advanced new aircraft and even pilotless guided missiles with turbojet and rocket propulsion. By 1944 several small guided missiles were in service with the Luftwaffe, and one of these sank the giant battleship *Roma* after her Italian crew had decided to throw in their lot with the Allies. In June 1944 the highly unpleasant 'V-1', which officially was designated the Fi 103, began its bombardment of southern England from launching ramps in northern France and later, when these were overrun, from aerial launching over the North Sea from He 111 bombers. Much smaller than a fighter, these pilotless carriers of a formidable war-

482

head were driven at 350 mph by a pulsejet, a very simple jet engine with springy flap valves over the air intake which caused the fuel to burn in a succession of explosions. The resulting throbbing vibration could be heard for 20 miles, day or night; then it would suddenly stop, to be followed after a few seconds by a tremendous explosion.

483

484   485

483 Cannon-armed Me 410 flashes past a B-17G of the US 8th Air Force, 1944

484 One of the staggering new German creations of World War Two, the Ju 287 jet bomber, flying in 1944

485 Prototype of the Me 262 twin-jet fighter with Jumo piston engine in the nose 1942

486 Messerschmitt Me 163B rocket intercepter, with take-off trolley, 1944

487 Canadair CF-104 Starfighter, 1961

488 Dassault Mirage G8 with wings at 23°, 1971

489 Dassault Mirage F1 intercepter fighters, 1971

490 Dassault Mirage G8 with wings at 70°, 1971

491 Saab Draken J35F with Falcon air-to-air missiles, 1970

492 LTV Corsair II carrier-based strike aircraft of the US Navy, 1970

493 General Dynamics F-111A swing-wing bomber, 1966

494 Northrop T-38 Talon supersonic trainer, 1965

486

Only the fastest fighters could catch the 'Doodlebugs'; the Tempest, Mustang and Griffon-engined Spitfires could do it, and in July 1944 the twin-jet Meteor became the first jet in action when it began its own run of success against the flying bombs, starting by tipping one over with a wing tip after the Meteor's guns had jammed.

Over the Continent the Messerschmitt Me 163, an odd bat-like tailless fighter, had been an object of interest and some awe to American bomber crews who had watched it shoot almost vertically up at them on the power of its rocket engine, fire its guns in a pass too fast to be followed and then descend. But a more formidable opponent was the Me 262, a fine fighter powered by two Jumo 004 engines and carrying the devastating armament of four 30 mm cannon. But for Hitler's insistence that it should be turned into a bomber it might have been in use even earlier than the Meteor, and although the first squadron became operational one month later than the first RAF jet the number available was far greater. By the end of the war almost 1,300 had been built, and they would have been even more effective had the Luftwaffe had experienced pilots, fuel or proper air-fields. Further, the Arado 234 jet bomber was in squadron use late in 1944, factories were fast getting into production with the Heinkel 162 jet fighter at a rate planned to exceed 1,500 per month, using semi-skilled labour and non-strategic materials, and scores of new aircraft of other types were in production or advanced development.

When peace returned to a shattered Europe, Allied intelligence teams found in laboratories, caves, barns and huts all over Germany evidence of the most amazing aeronautical development. There were giant turbojet, turbofan and turboprop engines, transonic fighters with swept wings, research aircraft that were all wing, or that had delta (triangular) wings, and even one prototype almost completed with variable sweep wings that could be spread out sideways for take-off and landing and folded sharply back for supersonic flight. New methods of construction, new accessory systems and instruments, and new far-reaching thought could be seen everywhere. An exhibition of some of these advances was put on at London's Science Museum. Many of the senior officers and governmental officials scoffed at it, saying: 'Why bother, haven't we won the war?'

Once the European war had been won plans were made to rush mighty forces to the Far East to defeat the Japanese who, though on the retreat for a year, resisted every yard with fanatical determination. It was a war of islands, aircraft carriers and mainly small aircraft, although in 1944 the US 21st Air Force had been formed to deploy the Boeing B-29 Superfortress, by far the most complicated, most powerful and most costly aircraft ever designed. Weighing more than twice as much as the original Fortress, it was an entirely new bomber with pressurized crew compartments to allow it to fly for ten hours at over 30,000 ft, remotely controlled gun turrets armed with 20 mm cannon and 0.5 in guns, a speed as high as a Battle of Britain Spitfire and a bomb load and range never before attained. Japan had previously been immune from attack except by a daring raid by a small force led from an aircraft carrier in 1942

487

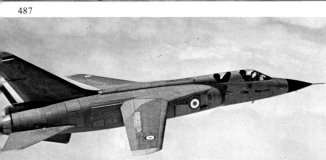

488

489

490

491

492

493

494

495

496

497

498

by General Jimmy Doolittle, but now the B-29 raids, mainly from Okinawa, seriously disrupted war production and drastically reduced the supply of weapons to the combat areas. Japanese naval air units in the Philippines voluntarily undertook Kamikaze suicide missions, loading up their precious remaining aircraft with fuel and bombs, donning special silk headgear and then carefully diving on to an Allied vessel. The chief types of aircraft used were the familiar Mitsubishi fighter popularly called the Zero by the Allies, the Nakajima Tenzan (Heavenly Mountain) torpedo bomber and the Yokosuka Susei (Comet) attack bomber, all single-engined. A potentially formidable specially designed suicide vehicle was the Jinrai (Thunderclap), popularly dubbed the Baka (Idiot), which dived with rocket propulsion at 620 mph. But on 6 August and 9 August 1945 B-29s dropped atom bombs of different types on Hiroshima and Nagasaki, bringing the war to a swift conclusion on 15 August.

Japan yielded no staggering technological advances similar to those found in Germany, although elementary jet aircraft based on the rocket Me 163 and twin-jet Me 262 were under development. Rather was it the manner in which the war was concluded that gave humanity to pause. Henceforth a single bomber had the power to destroy a large city in the space of a few seconds. Perhaps the terrifying new bombs could also be carried by long range rockets. Suddenly the problem of defending a country against air attacks was multiplied a millionfold.

499

495 The classic Mitsubishi 'Zero' Navy fighter, 1942

496 Typical Japanese bomber: a twin-engined 'Sally' over the Pacific, 1943

497 Boeing B-29 Superfortress, late 1944

498 Martin PBM Mariners of the US Navy return to Rio de Janeiro after guarding a convoy in the South Atlantic, 1945

499 65 hp Piper L-4 Grasshopper, used by the US Army as a 'flying Jeep', taking off from an English country lane

14 Air transport becomes a giant

Unlike British companies, the US airlines at the end of the second world war were mature privately owned organizations that had to make money or go broke. They were thus vitally interested in their equipment, and four of them – American, TWA, United and PanAm – have for thirty years been world leaders in specifying exactly what they are going to need five or more years ahead. The British corporations did not learn to do the same until it was too late. Although British industry, initially with virtually no customer input at all, did succeed in creating two absolute world-beaters, these were the exceptions that prove the rule of American domination.

In 1945, while the DC-3 was still an extremely efficient vehicle for short ranges and available by the thousand all over the world, American Airlines teamed with Convair to produce a replacement. The result was the CV-240 of 1947, an extremely modern and much more capacious aircraft powered by two 2,400 hp Pratt & Whitney Double Wasp engines and fitted with a nose-

piston engines and turboprops.

In the medium to long range bracket the dominant manufacturer was Douglas. In 1942 they had gone into production with a fine four-engined transport known as the DC-4 (although all the first models were military C-54 versions) and this showed exactly what could be done with four 1200 hp Twin Wasp engines. The same engines were used in the British Short Sandringham, derived from the Empire boat and the only postwar flying-boat to see wide use. While the Sandringham carried 21 to 37 passengers at 180 mph for 1,800 miles. the landplane DC-4 carried 44 to 58 passengers at 245 mph over a slightly longer range and was marginally cheaper to buy. As airfields were available near every city while flying-boat bases were not, the DC-4 outsold the Sandringham many times over. When Douglas built the DC-6 in 1948 they were on the road to dominating the whole trunk-route market. Powered by Double Wasp engines, this enlarged, pressurized successor to the DC-4 could carry 70 passengers at 280 mph, and it soon

500

wheel landing gear, high-lift wing flaps, a large pressurized fuselage and a form of simple jet propulsion from the engine exhausts that boosted cruising speed from 270 to 280 mph (indeed, the Convair-Liner, as it was called, could cruise at 300 mph if need be). In 1948 this was an extraordinary performance, and when KLM Royal Dutch Airlines flew their first service into London Heathrow a sensation was caused on the scale of that at Mildenhall in 1934. From the 240 came the bigger 340 and 440, and many of these are still in use with both

appeared in a still further 'stretched' version, the DC-6B.

The DC-6B was by 1952 the biggest-selling long range airliner in history, and the yardstick against which the operating economy of all large civil aircraft was being judged. By this time the whole business of operating airliners had become more clearly understood with the American definition of such basic factors as the 'direct operating cost' (expressed in terms of cents per seat-mile or per ton-mile), of 'balanced field length' (a measure of

500 Convair CV-240 of KLM, fastest airliner in Europe in 1948

501

502

503

the size of runway needed for year-round safe operation) and of how to schedule flight operations and plan overhaul and maintenance for minimum overall cost. The airliner was no longer a fragile and temperamental creation but a tough workaday vehicle that could be relied upon to maintain tight schedules in virtually every kind of weather day and night. Traffic was growing fast, at the rate of about 12 to 15 per cent a year, equivalent to a doubling every five years. With the DC-6B it at last became certain beyond all doubt that civil airlines could make money year after year as a matter of course, with no government subsidy or hidden financial aid.

Britain, throughout the second world war, concentrated on combat aircraft and left the manufacture of transports to the Americans. This was Britain's choice, although in later years some in Britain suggested that there had been some kind of agreement with the United States which had explicitly forbidden the development of British transport aircraft. This was not so: indeed, during the war British industry produced so many indifferent bombers that the island became cluttered with even less outstanding transport conversions. Conscious of the limitations of these conversions, the Brabazon Committee held long deliberations in London in 1943 and 1944 to draw up a list of specifications for civil aircraft in an effort to ensure British leadership in the postwar years.

During the last years of peace British manufacturers had at last begun to design competitive airliners, most of them based on the new Bristol series of sleeve-valve

radial engines. Fairey planned the FC.1 with four of the slim 1,000 hp Taurus; Short Brothers scaled up the Empire flying-boat and turned it into the outstanding Model 14/38 with four 1,500 hp Hercules, a landplane which could have been a world-beater. Both aircraft were being built against government orders when the war began. But the Brabazon committee ignored them, and suggested a list of totally new projects. Ignoring also the American competition, and the needs of the world market, it called for an odd range of aircraft that in

501 Short Sandringham flying-boat of New Zealand's Tasman Empire Air Lines, 1948

502 Douglas DC-4 of Air France, late 1940s; later used for Postale de Nuit services

503 Douglas DC-6B of Alitalia, 1953

general had only one thing in common: they were designed to carry such a small payload that they could hardly have made a profit. Indeed the whole history of British civil aviation up to 1950 was bedevilled by the fact that it was regarded as a government enterprise rather than as a commercial business.

Top priority was given to the first machine on the list, a huge and ponderous landplane to be built by the Bristol company to carry passengers and mails non-stop across the North Atlantic. The Brabazon was slowly and pains-

United States, not because of any lack of technical ability but because of a lack of communication between the planners and the users.

On the world scene, however, civil aviation in the postwar decade was on the way to becoming a giant business. On 900 airports throughout the world fine new transports resplendent in the colourful livery of more than 200 scheduled carriers bore witness to the fact that the giant was completely international. The airliner was busy in Britain and Western Europe where unpre-

504

takingly created over five years and at last flown on a very successful maiden flight in September 1949, ten years and a day after the start of the war. By this time work was well advanced on the rather faster Brabazon 2 with more powerful turboprop engines, but after millions more had been spent on the improved machine the whole project was stopped in 1952. The Brabazon was completely uncompetitive and unwanted by any airline. This typical saga of British planning was repeated on a slightly bigger scale by the Saunders-Roe Princess, a vast flying-boat even heavier and more capacious than the Brabazon (see Chapter 9).

Britain also produced many smaller airliners, and began to build its two great nationalized corporations, BOAC and BEA, on a hodge-podge of aircraft that were mainly foreign. BOAC used the last of its Short and Boeing flying-boats, Liberators, DC-3s and a motley collection of British machines including Yorks (derived from the Lancaster bomber), Lancastrians (converted Lancasters), Warwicks (converted bombers), Haltons (converted Halifaxes) and, eventually and on a very small scale, Tudors (the great hope of British civil aviation, this type was derived from the Lancaster and Lincoln bombers but was quite unable to compete with the US opposition). BEA relied almost wholly on the DC-3, but used German Ju 52/3M 'Jupiters' on routes within Britain, until in 1947 it built up a fleet of Vikings (based on the Wellington bomber) which could do most of the things the much older DC-3 could do. Across the board, Britain was totally outclassed in civil aviation by the

dictable weather combined with short intercity distances and a dense network of rail and road routes to hold back the growth of internal airlines. It was also busy in the shimmering desert, the frozen wastes, the steaming jungle and emerging nations everywhere, where other means of transport were simply not available. It was during the 1950s that supposedly backward peoples began to travel by air as often as Europeans, surrounded by sacks, bicycles, pigs, guns, market produce, missionaries and an indescribable variety of other items needed to sustain human life.

In Britain de Havilland, which in 1935 had become the only British company with much overseas business in transport aircraft, sold useful numbers of Dove and Heron light transports to serve in tough outback and upcountry regions. But de Havilland's main preoccupation was with bigger fish. One of the Brabazon Committee's recommendations had been for a 'jet propelled mailplane'. The committee had not looked on jets as ordinary aircraft that could do ordinary transport jobs a bit more quickly than before, but as something exotic carrying hardly any load. The DH.106 Comet began life as a tailless three-engined machine and could easily have ended up as an ineffective vehicle of the kind the committee had envisaged. But in 1947 the design team at Hatfield came to their senses and turned it into a useful passenger carrier with a long pressurized body and tail, and powered by four of their own 5,000lb-thrust engines buried inside the roots of the almost unswept wing. The first Comet flew from Hatfield in July 1949.

504 Lockheed Constellation and Super Constellation, in service with Air France, 1957

At the great air show of the Society of British Aircraft Constructors at Farnborough in 1949 the Comet was on display. So was the Handley Page Hermes 4, an ordinary piston-engined British airliner that at last looked as good as the opposition. So was the beautiful high-wing Airspeed Ambassador, about to become the mainliner of BEA as the Elizabethan class. So were the Viscount and Apollo, both powered by four pencil-slim turboprops. Either of the latter would have been a showstopper in its own right. Suddenly it was the turn of the Americans to feel the Mildenhall feeling. For years they had heard about British gas-turbine airliners. Now they could watch them, feel them, hear and smell them, and a few could even ride in them. For the first time ever, American vice-presidents sensed dangerous competition.

The Comet was so futuristic it was difficult to regard it as a threat to the DC-6B, or to the equally well established Constellation and Super Constellation from Lockheed. Although roughly as big as these machines it seated only 36 passengers, or about half as many as the airlines were coming to expect from trunk-route equipment. Not everyone noticed that by flying twice as fast it could carry at least as many people in a day. Dozens of airlines were agreeably surprised to find that de Havilland claimed a range of 2,140 miles and a cruising speed of 490 mph, but most regarded the beauteous Comet as an unknown quantity and therefore to be avoided.

One or two airlines, such as Canadian Pacific and the French line UAT, actually placed orders as they saw how swift and sure was the progress towards commercial jet aviation. But all the giants of the airline world took their cue from the Americans, who argued: 'The Comet is too small and quite uneconomic. It is premature. Buy our new versions of the well-tried Douglas and Lockheed transports with the efficient Turbo-Compound engine. Then you will stay in the forefront and make money, while the Comet operators lose their shirt. In 1955 we will be ready to convert your equipment to turboprop power, putting you in the 400 mph class; and we should by then be able to take orders for a real jet airliner, bigger and faster than the Comet, that will make you glad you never bought the loss-making British plane.' To the Americans' profound relief this argument was almost universally believed; airlines even outdid themselves inventing reasons why the Comet was not as attractive to them as straight-winged, propeller aircraft stemming from designs of 15 years before.

Air transport operators, naturally cautious, had never been so conservative in their lives. But as 1951 progressed, and de Havilland flew production Comets for BOAC and then an improved version with Rolls-Royce Avon axial engines, one airline after another felt compelled to buy a few Comets to safeguard its position. It was a time of frantic rearmament in Britain, and British industry had run down to such an extent it was hard pressed to make military aircraft, let alone civil ones as well. And it was soon obvious de Havilland were running a race to produce more Comets of more improved versions sooner. If they had miraculously been able to conjure up 200 of the Avon-powered Mk 2 versions by the end of 1952, two years before the first

was actually to be ready, there is no doubt all would have been sold very quickly. Scheduled services to Johannesburg with the Comet 1 began on 2 May 1952, and the world's airlines gradually realized a vital fact none had been quite prepared for. Comet travel did not just mean getting there in less than half the time. It also meant a totally new sort of travel, almost silently suspended under a dark-blue vault of heaven at 40,000 ft, far above any clouds or weather and with the most splendid terrestrial panoramas slowly moving past far

505

506

505 Vickers-Armstrongs Viking of BEA, 1949

506 Departure of de Havilland Comet of BOAC from London-Heathrow for Johannesburg to fly the world's first jet service, 2 May 1952

below. Giant cities, mountain ranges and broad seas were cut down to a new perspective, and after a 500 mph near-glide down to one's destination from 200 miles out the traveller emerged fresher than after the shortest of flights in any previous transport. One airline president who had previously expressed no interest in the Comet

507

508

said when placing his order: 'After this, nobody will ever again be content with propeller aircraft.'

Then an almost unbelievable thing happened. Early in 1954, when de Havilland were on the high road to a smashing worldwide success with the far bigger and more powerful Comet 3, bought off the shelf by the main US flag carrier PanAm, two of the original Mk 1 machines mysteriously vanished into the Mediterranean, both a few minutes out of Rome. Comets were grounded, the whole programme was disrupted, Britain stood shocked in a way never previously experienced by the mere occurrence of trouble with a commercial product. After a brilliant and gruelling salvage job by the Navy and 'the most fantastic piece of engineering detective work ever performed' by the structural experts at Farnborough, it was shown that one of the two aircraft had blown open in the thin upper air as the result of the sudden ripping of a tiny crack in the skin that must have been slowly growing for months. Exactly the same thing happened when a Comet was pressurized and depressurized in a huge water tank (to prevent it from blowing to pieces, as it would if filled with air), exactly simulating the treatment encountered on each flight. By the autumn of 1954 the cure was known to be a straightforward modification of the various apertures cut in the fuselage for radio aerials and cabin windows, changing them all to a rounded shape and reinforcing them with extra layers of metal skin. It could have been done quite cheaply on each Comet in a matter of two or three weeks. But the magnitude of the disaster prevented Britons

from seeing what to do, and for four years de Havilland worked on the wholly new Comet 4 while abandoning all hope of continuing with earlier versions (most of the Comet 2 fleet already building were modified and sold to the RAF where they returned a flawless performance over many years). Four years later an American airliner encountered a problem of equal magnitude: it persistently shed its wings in flight. Although the cure was more complicated than that needed by the Comets the maker, Lockheed, rushed through a field modification programme in a matter of weeks, persuaded the airlines they had a product better than before and turned disaster into a triumph in good business relations.

When the Comet 4 finally picked up the threads in October 1958 it found itself operating BOAC services across the North Atlantic, a gruelling route for which the aircraft was never designed. This was because, just one month later, PanAm began rival services with the Boeing 707, much bigger, more powerful and faster than any Comet and capable of immense 'stretch' over subsequent years. When Boeing committed $20 million of stockholders' money to the 707 in 1952 they readily conceded the first round, or perhaps the first two rounds, in the jet sales battle to de Havilland. But by 1958 the incredible four-year hiatus in Britain had given the Americans virtually the whole market, because the 707 and the very similar Douglas DC-8 were indeed the more advanced and more efficient jet transports the Americans had always rather hopefully promised. They were possible because Pratt & Whitney had de-

206

veloped the J57, an extremely advanced high-compression turbojet in the 10,000 lb thrust class, for the US Air Force and Navy. Its fuel economy and high power made it ideally suited to the great new 'Big Jets'. When these were planned many airlines, while finding them almost irresistible, considered them frightening in their size, speed, capacity and cost. It was thought airline crews would never be able to fly them, that runways would be too short, that aprons would break under their weight and that terminal buildings would never cope with upwards of 150 passengers arriving at once.

But the great swept-wing machines proved to be the wholly admirable transport vehicles their builders had said they would be. Whereas a British 'expert' described the airlines' wholesale switch to jet equipment as 'an industry gone mad', it was soon evident that the jet was to be the industry's salvation. At one stroke it quadrupled the traffic a given number of aircraft could handle in a day, cut the costs by cutting the time, transformed the whole image of what airliners looked like, and made airlines profitable. And traffic jumped as never before. On the North Atlantic the jets were carrying well over 99 per cent. With amazing swiftness brightly painted new DC-7s and Super Constellations were taken off the world trunk routes and replaced by the 707 and DC-8. To the chagrin of Britain the same fate awaited the splendid Bristol Britannia, the world's first long range turboprop liner, that would have scored a resounding success if its makers could have got it into service four years earlier.

Britain had had a promising big jet, the Vickers V.1000, being built in 1953 for the RAF, with the VC7 planned as a civil version. When the Americans began to sell the 707 and DC-8 in the winter of 1955-56 the British government cancelled the whole Vickers programme, persuading itself the RAF could use the Britannia just as well. Then, when there was no longer any doubt the whole future of civil aviation over all but the shortest stages lay with the jet, BOAC frantically tried to get an all-British jet. For some months de Havilland worked feverishly and then ground to a halt. Vickers took on the job, and today BOAC has in the rear-engined VC10 a superb vehicle which, had it been started much earlier, might have captured a significant share of the huge world market. Unfortunately, as if the story of British jetliners were not bad enough, BOAC, who were largely to blame for the absence of a rival to the American big jets, publicly criticized the VC10 and demanded government compensation for having to use it. The fact that the cost per seat-mile or per ton-mile of the British aircraft is slightly higher than that of the American designs arises solely from the demand of BOAC that it should use shorter runways, which inevitably penalizes any aircraft in cruising flight because it demands a bigger wing and bigger engines resulting in increased drag and fuel consumption. As anyone could have predicted, by the time the VC10 was in service the main runways at civil airports throughout the world had been extended to cater for the omnipotent 707 and DC-8.

In their original form these two classic aircraft each had a gross weight of about 2,300,000 lb and could carry 120-140 passengers over sectors of some 2,500 miles at

509

510

511

575 mph on the power of four JT3C (civil J57) turbojets of 13,000 lb thrust each. The engines were heavy, noisy and smoky, and their efficiency was reduced by large and heavy propelling nozzles which broke up the jet into segments or separate streams to reduce noise on take-off. But such was the development possible with these machines that by 1967 both were in service at weights up to 350,000 lb, carrying up to 250 passengers at very much reduced costs. Pratt & Whitney added large stages of fan blading at the front of the JT3C to produce the JT3D turbofan, almost like a multi-bladed, closely cowled turboprop giving a thrust of 18,000 lb for about the same fuel consumption as before.

Until 1960 aircraft had a choice of the turbojet, simple and effective up to very high speeds but rather wasteful of fuel and noisy, and the turboprop fitted with a reduction gear driving a propeller and giving more efficient, quieter propulsion up to about 450 mph. The

509 BAC (Bristol) Britannia long-range turboprop transport (this example is used by the RAF), 1959

510 Douglas DC-7C long-range compound-engine transport, with Alitalia, 1956

511 BAC (Vickers-Armstrongs) VC10, East African Airways, 1968

turbofan is today an intermediate type of engine that has to a considerable degree supplanted both the earlier kinds. Today's turbofan 707 and DC-8 can not only fly the North Atlantic non-stop but they even operate non-stop services between European capitals and the US Pacific coast.

More than three quarters of air passenger journeys are on sectors of less than 1,000 miles. Today this is very definitely 'short haul', although such a journey would have been quite beyond the capability of almost every

of approximately 600. Of these, well over one in every ten have been bought by industrial companies and other 'executive' users. The use of aircraft for legitimate business transport, as distinct from mere sporting or other use by manufacturing firms, began to grow in the United States during the second world war. Today, despite the fact one can fly anywhere on Earth by scheduled airline or charter company within 18 hours or so, more than 2,000 business companies find it pays to have their own aircraft, equipped for all-weather instrument flying, and often a full-time professional pilot. Many of these business aircraft are piston-engined, but an increasing proportion are turbojet and turboprop powered, the largest examples being special versions of well-known jetliners able to cross continents and oceans at 550 mph or more. Approximately 1,000 are specially designed baby twin-jets which duplicate in miniature the comfort and performance of the big jetliners.

One of the most successful of these aircraft is French, and to France also goes the credit for creating something which today is universally accepted yet when first suggested in the early 1950s seemed nonsense: the avowedly short haul jetliner. Compared with piston engines or turboprops, jets need longer runways and burn more fuel, and this form of propulsion seemed unsuitable over short sectors of much less than 1,000 miles, especially as such services are flown at relatively low altitudes (where jets are especially thirsty) and the higher speed of the jet cannot save more than a minute or two on each trip. Despite these supposed objections the French nationalized group known as Sud-Est

512

513

514

512 BAC (Vickers-Armstrongs) Viscount 813 turboprop of South African Airways over Cape Town

513 Fokker F.27 Friendship turboprop of Sabena (Belgian World Airlines) flying Common Market Commuter service, 1972

514 Super VC10 of BOAC making automatic landing, 1966

515 Dassault Mirage IIIE fighter bomber of the Spanish Air Force, 1971

516 North American OV-10A Bronco

517 North American B-1A supersonic strategic bomber (model)

518 Boeing B-52F Stratofortress bombers in Vietnam, 1970

airliner before the DC-3. For many years after the war the DC-3 carried the bulk of the traffic in more than 120 countries, but swift development was pushing it off the main routes by 1950 in the richer nations. One new short-hauler was the Convair-Liner already described. In 1953 even this was unexpectedly eclipsed by the British Viscount, which very nearly failed to go into production when BEA bought the Ambassador instead. It was only the decision of Vickers to lend the prototype to BEA for passenger service in the summer of 1950 that made the airline see what a winner the aircraft would be. Passenger reaction was unprecedented. Never before had travellers had such a smooth, quiet, swift and pleasant trip, while sitting beside the big elliptical windows giving a panoramic view. Vickers sold BEA an enlarged 44-53 passenger Viscount, with more powerful Rolls-Royce Dart turboprops. Soon it was clear that, for the first time in history, here was a civil airliner better than anything comparable from America. American airlines bought it by the score and eventually a small batch for the Peoples' Republic of China in 1964 brought the total to 444 aircraft. It is doubtful that any other single type of aircraft has done so much to show every kind of aircraft operator that tiny red-hot turbine blades, even if they drive a propeller, are a better source of power than oscillating pistons.

By 1955 the Dart was in demand for many other transport aircraft. One of these, the Dutch Fokker Friendship, has now overtaken the Viscount as the most successful non-American type of airliner with total sales

208

515

516

517

518

519

520

521

(South-East), which is today part of the giant Aéro-spatiale combine, flew the first Caravelle in 1955. It incorporated the complete nose and flight deck of the Comet, but had a more slender wing and a pair of Rolls-Royce Avon engines mounted in what was then a quite new way: hung on each side of the rear fuselage. It looked beautiful, and was very pleasant to ride in, but nobody really believed that Sud would sell more than a handful. After a slow start the French were perfectly set to cash in on what the Comet had discovered: the enormous passenger appeal of the jet.

Today the last Caravelles have emerged from the Toulouse assembly shop, preceded by nearly 300 earlier models. They probably speeded the short haul jet by as much as two years, although the Soviet Tu-104, derived from the Tu-16 bomber, was developed to a schedule even earlier than the Caravelle, and for use in a land where there is no airline competition. The great design bureau of Constructor-General Andrei Tupolev has an amazing record of achievement in almost every facet of large aircraft design. The Tu-104, the first modern Russian transport to burst on the West in a surprise visit to London in April 1956, was succeeded by the smaller Tu-124, the rear-engined Tu-134 and the very big and versatile Tu-154 trijet. In Britain de Havilland produced special short haul versions of the Comet carrying less fuel but more passengers, and then created the Trident series of trijets for BEA which between 1960 and 1970 more than doubled in range/payload capability despite their continued use of three quite small Rolls-Royce Spey engines. With the VC10, the Trident has pioneered the difficult technology needed for totally blind automatic landing with dense fog right down to ground level (the difficulty lies in making the system work safely even after some part has gone wrong). In 1961 British Aircraft Corporation, formed by Vickers, English Electric and Bristol, and taking in the Hunting company, turned the Hunting H.107 into the BAC One-Eleven which in terms of cash value is today Britain's most successful civil aircraft. Even so the One-Eleven programme is small compared with those of American transport aircraft.

When the One-Eleven first flew, in 1963, it was the only really modern short haul airliner in the world. Compared with the pioneer French Caravelle it had a smaller wing, bigger and more roomy fuselage, later and more efficient engines and other fundamental advances. Although Boeing were building their much bigger 727 trijet no American firm was building a rival to the One-Eleven and for a surprisingly long time it looked as if the world-wide success of the Viscount could be repeated – even though on this occasion the Americans were not handicapped through lack of an engine. Then in 1965 Douglas, later to become McDonnell Douglas, flew the very similar DC-9, using two of the 727 engines. The Americans have a giant home market, good and dynamic management and an outlook which plans for success (whereas in Britain the public attitude towards aviation is fear of losing money). By the end of 1965 the DC-9 was carrying passengers on scheduled services and a vast production network had been set up embracing hundreds of firms throughout the United States and even

522

523

including Canada and Italy. Today 700 of these aircraft have been sold despite the fact that at an even later date Boeing came in with the 737 and sold over 300 of these. Since the start of the DC-9 programme the Americans have sold over 1,000 short haul twinjets compared with approximately 70 of the British One-Eleven.

The reasons for the American success and the comparative British failure are extremely complex and are interwoven with product performance, delivery date, past trade associations, the enormous political and financial power of the United States and the ability of the contracting parties to arrange suitable terms (involving not only interest rates on borrowed money but also the training of crews, special customer options and the disposal of the customer's old aircraft that are being replaced). In such matters BAC are second to none, but the very fact they are British and not American is a grave handicap.

On the other hand the Dutch, with smaller resources and hardly any home market, have followed the world-wide success of the F.27 Friendship with the F.28 Fellowship which is essentially a slightly smaller One-

519 Douglas DC-3 of American Airlines, 1936

520 De Havilland Comet on early test flight, summer 1949

521 Prototype Boeing 727 (yellow), later to become the world's most successful jetliner, at Bogotá, Colombia, 1962

522 Dassault Mercure short-haul transport, 1971

523 Aérospatiale Caravelle 11 R of Sterling (Danish charter operator), 1970

524 Tupolev Tu-104A of Aeroflot, 1957

524

Eleven for secondary routes. Likewise the Japanese have made some 200 of the efficient YS-11 powered by two late-model Dart turboprops, and the VFW-Fokker 614, the first postwar transport from Federal Germany, appears well on the way to securing a valuable market at the bottom end of the spectrum, carrying 40 people out of short fields on the power of turbofan engines in unique pods well above the wing.

Altogether the business of building advanced aircraft of all kinds is no job for the fainthearted, and in Britain the government view is that the past shows a disastrous record of projects that never had much chance of success. In fact the blame rests mainly on the customers who specified the wrong aircraft or the right aircraft at the wrong time. But even when BAC took immense pains over a period of three years to plan an airliner tailored to the world market – the Three-Eleven, a much bigger successor to the One-Eleven – the British government refused to put up half the launching cost of about £130 million. The problem of launch cost is more acute in the world of aviation than in any other business in the world, and it calls for a high quality of government and company management.

In the whole history of aviation the biggest launch cost of all has been that of Concorde. The idea of a civil airliner flying faster than sound was clearly appreciated by 1955, and extensive project studies were put in hand by seven manufacturers in the United States and Britain. The former aimed at very advanced machines cruising at up to Mach 3 (three times the local speed of sound or 2000 mph), but the main British work was directed to the Mach 2.2 aircraft that represent the structural temperature limit for light alloys. By 1960 Sud Aviation (now called Aérospatiale) had begun to study a Mach 2.2 successor to the Caravelle, and the British government suddenly decided it would be a good idea if the two countries joined forces in the first big collaborative technological programme. The politicians had one eye firmly on British entry into the Common Market, but although this was not to be for another decade the engineers of the two countries succeeded in scaling up

525

526

525 Tupolev Tu-134A of Aviogenex (Yugoslavia), 1969

526 Tupolev Tu-154 of Aeroflot, newly assembled at Kuibyshev, 1971

527 Ilyushin Il-18 turboprops of Aeroflot and an Li-2 (Soviet-built DC-3) at Petropavlovsk-Kamchatsky, 1967

527

528

531

532

supposed rampaging technologists the original Boeing SST programme was terminated in 1970. But a rival to the Concorde exists in the Soviet Tu-144, exceedingly similar in design but matched to shorter route sectors. Development of the 144 has proceeded slightly more quickly, and therefore more cheaply, than that of the Concorde; and if past experience is a guide, it will be offered for sale at a much lower price than the more versatile Anglo-French aircraft.

Increasing capacity is the other major development

the French project and scaling down the British one until they met in a 100-seater capable of flying 2,500 miles. By 1963 the design had grown again, the range had been extended to span the vital North Atlantic, and the result was the 130-seat, 4,500 mile range Concorde, capable of cruising at 1,400 mph. By 1970 a total of 74 production line positions had been reserved by 16 airlines, but the eventual production total by 1990 could reach a four-figure quantity.

Compared with a subsonic airliner an SST (supersonic transport) has more efficient engines but considerably greater aerodynamic drag, and thus tends to have less room inside and to burn more fuel. The Concorde has engines twice as powerful as those of the 707, and to carry half the payload (25,000 lb against 50,000) a rather shorter distance it needs slightly more fuel. At about $30 million it is also at least three times as expensive to buy. On the other hand it has the inestimable quality of flying faster—no less than $2\frac{1}{2}$ times as fast—and, as speed is of profound importance to almost all transport and

529

530

especially to airline passenger travel, this is an advantage of enormous magnitude.

Although the SST in 1972 still appeared slightly exotic, so did the Comet in 1949. Long haul traffic will be very largely supersonic in the closing decade of the century. Almost certainly some of the future supersonic equipment will be American, although in a remarkable head-on collision between supposed conservationists and

533

528 BAC One-Eleven of Tarom (Romania), 1970

529 Fokker VFW F-28 Fellowship, test flying before delivery to the President of Argentina, 1971

530 YS-11 turboprops in final assembly at Nihon Aeroplane Manufacturing Company, Komaki, Japan, 1968

531 Boeing 727 of Lufthansa, 1966

532 McDonnell Douglas DC-9 of Atlantis, West Germany, 1971

533 Roll-out of BAC/ Aérospatiale Concorde 02, Bristol, 1971

in civil transports of the past decade, and this route has been spearheaded by the Boeing 747. Based on technology acquired in an unsuccessful bid to provide the US Air Force with its huge C-5A freighter, Boeing, teamed with Pratt & Whitney engines, knew by 1965 exactly how to make the vital step into the next generation. The 747 is characterized by exceptional size, and in particular by the biggest body ever offered to the airlines, and by completely new turbofan engines handling so great an airflow – 18 times as great as the engines of the original

economic growth of air transport. Following the 747 have come the two very nearly as big American trijets, the McDonnell Douglas DC-10 and Lockheed 1011 TriStar, both matched to a very wide spread of duties and propelled by a tail engine and one on each wing (and able to fly on any one). In Europe, after almost a decade of intergovernmental discussions and committees the Airbus A 300B was in 1972 nearing completion at Toulouse with major participation by France and West Germany, with wings designed and built in Britain and

534

535

Comet – as to be almost ducted turboprops. These JT9D engines, each rated at 43,500 lb thrust, were in 1970 by far the most powerful and most efficient jets in airline service. They were the foundation on which Boeing built a vehicle capable of using existing airports yet of carrying up to 500 people faster than any previous transport over the greatest ranges needed by the airlines. So great is the capacity of the 747 that airlines can make money with every seat empty merely by filling the cargo holds under the floor.

Such vehicles are vital to the continued swift and

534 Boeing 737-200 of New Zealand National Airways

535 TWA's terminal at Kennedy Airport, New York, with Boeing 707s and four 747s

with American engines built mainly in Europe. This aircraft demonstrates that almost 300 people can safely be carried on two engines, whereas 30 years ago it was common to carry 30 passengers on four. All these aircraft rest on engines in the 50,000 lb thrust class.

Future even more powerful engines will be quieter than today's 50,000-pounders, which in turn are from 10 to 100 times quieter, in terms of sound annoyance, than the much smaller engines of the earlier jetliners. Noise in the neighbourhood of busy airports was a severe problem in the days of piston engines, and with the basically military designs of engine used in the first jetliners it became even worse. Since 1967 the money spent each week on making transport aircraft more socially acceptable in terms of reduced noise and visible smoke has been multiplied dozens of times.

In addition to attention to the engine, tomorrow's aircraft will need much shorter runways and climb and descend more steeply. Generalized under the headings of RTOL and QSTOL (respectively, aircraft able to perform restricted and quiet/short take-off and landing) these future vehicles will replace today's 100 to 200 seat airliners with ones able to operate from small runways near 10,000 cities instead of today's 1,500 cities, and to do so while causing less than one-thousandth as much aural annoyance. Most of these machines will have very high-ratio fan engines with variable-pitch and reversible blades like those of today's propellers. They will have cunning high-lift wings able to claw at the air at speeds no higher than 100 knots during a climb-out sustained

536

at a very steep angle; they will also make little noise during an almost frighteningly steep approach. The 90 PNdB (perceived noise decibels) contour is likely to be contained within an area only a little larger than the short 2,000-ft runway that these aircraft will use. This is considerably quieter than city traffic and it means in practice that by 1985 a growing proportion of transport aircraft will be noticed only visually. And to most of the world's population such vehicles are an agreeable sight.

Millions still go every year to air shows. In the United States there are hundreds ranging from local county productions to the giant National Air Races which attract vast crowds to watch a series of carefully planned competitive events highlighted by a transcontinental or closed-circuit multi-lap duel between the fastest piston-engined machines in the world. In 1971 the first and second places were gained by British Sea Fury fighters of the immediate post-1945 period, one painted in D-day 'invasion markings' and both privately owned by men in non-aeronautical professions. Similar races are held in many countries, and at irregular intervals there are intercontinental events such as the race from London to New Zealand in 1953, the race between the top of the Post Office Tower in London and the top of the Empire State building in New York in 1969 and a dash from England to Canada's Pacific Coast in 1971. In Europe there are two world-famous trade shows, the Paris Salon Aéronautique, held on odd-numbered years, and the British Farnborough show on even ones. The British show used to be a pure shop window for UK and Commonwealth products but now anything is admitted that contains British parts (and few advanced aircraft do not). In contrast Paris has always been a supremely international occasion, and is in most respects the greatest aeronautical show on Earth. It is distinguished by the massive participation of the Soviet Union – which springs surprises such as the totally unknown Ilyushin 76 giant jet transport that flew in to the 1971 show. One day at Paris is devoted solely to light private aircraft, sports machines and gliders.

536 McDonnell Douglas DC-10 of American Airlines, 1971

537 Lockheed L-1011 TriStar of Eastern Airlines, 1972

537

Gliders are a big worldwide industry ranging from simple primary trainers to extremely advanced competitive sailplanes calling for the most advanced aerodynamic and structural design. Many would consider the modern world championship sailplane the most beautiful category of flying machine there has ever been. The pilot almost lies on his back under a long transparent canopy, where he needs special protection from scorching sunlight as he makes the atmosphere's thermal currents lift him for hour after hour on his incredibly long and slender

wings–approaching the span of a Concorde–as he strives to go faster or further than his rivals. Sailplanes have been flown with skill and determination to a height greater than 46,000 ft and for a distance of almost 720 miles. Among the great sailplane nations must be listed Federal Germany, Switzerland, Poland, Czechoslovakia, the United States, France, Austria and Britain.

After the second world war there was a sudden boom in small private machines (in 1946 the American firm of Piper made 6,320 of one model alone, the J-3 Cub)

538

539

540

and numerous lightplane makers began, or resumed, operations in Europe. Gradually over the years the world market has grown, the design and sophistication of the average private owner machine has become more advanced and the successful companies have become fewer in number. It follows that the companies that have stayed in the business can reap bigger rewards, and such US giants as Piper, Beech and Cessna each sell a four-figure total of new aircraft each year, representing a turnover of tens of millions of dollars. Nearly all modern light aircraft are powered by either one or two American flat-four or flat-six piston engines, so called because they have four or six cylinders lying horizontally on opposite sides of the crankshaft, rated at from 100 to 450 hp. A growing number have turboprops in the 300 to 1,000 hp class and now the latest private machines have turbofan engines taking them into the 400 to 500 mph class.

Roughly 70 per cent of the world market for light aircraft, and at least 95 per cent of the market for engines, is held by the United States. Other countries with substantial lightplane industries are France, Germany, Czechoslovakia, Italy, Poland, Japan and Sweden, as well as several in Latin America. An odd omission from the list is Britain, where attempts to build light and executive aircraft on any scale have tended to result in bankruptcy, while lightplanes from other countries are imported by the hundred. But some of the British aircraft, notably the Beagle Pup and Bulldog single-engined four-seaters, the fine twin-turboprop Jetstream and the extremely successful Islander and Trislander light transports, have survived despite their original producers going into receivership.

The spirit of the lone enthusiast, of the pioneer aviator who is designer, builder, chief test pilot, owner and operator, is still strongly in evidence around the world. Many people—of all ages, occupations and of both sexes—who have decided to realize the dream of creating their own aircraft have joined the International Experimental Aircraft Association, an organization dedicated to helping the world's population educate itself in air matters and in particular to produce 'home-builts' that are all their creators hope them to be. The EAA has over 60,000 members in at least 53 countries.

541

542

543

546 Canadair CL-215
water-bombing a forest
fire, 1972

547 An unconventional
'homebuilt': the pusher
Teal, by Edgar J. Lesher,
a professor at the University
of Michigan

548 Boeing 747 'Jumbo' of
Air India, 1971

549 McDonnell Douglas
DC-8-61 jetliner, 1965

545

546

organized in Chapters, and at any given time its members are building 8,000 or more aircraft to their own or another member's design. Their creations are often beautiful to the eye, superlatively finished and delightful to fly.

Unlike the original *Pou-du-Ciel* described earlier, today's EAA creations are thoroughly safe. All home-builts are, of course, certificated by their own national licensing authority, and most EAA Chapters have highly qualified designee inspectors to help avoid certification problems. EAA's great annual 'fly-in' at Oshkosh, Wisconsin, United States, has become the largest aviation event in the world, attended by some half a million.

In complete contrast there is a big world market for utility aircraft intended for lifting heavy loads, spraying or dusting crops and even extinguishing forest fires. The agricultural realm is the last haven of the biplane, and in the past decade many hundreds of powerful biplanes have been built in the United States and Soviet Union for agricultural and utility purposes. Most of these machines, however, are stoutly built monoplanes and an increasing proportion have turbine engines. A typical machine in this class would be a humpbacked single-seater able to carry a ton and a half of liquid or powdered chemicals and made so strongly that the pilot could expect to walk away from a crash (because much of this work is very hazardous). A unique fire extinguisher designed purely for forestry patrol is the Canadair CL-215, a big amphibian which can repeatedly land on any nearby stretch of water, scoop up six tons of it in seconds and then dump it on a fire.

Yet another contrast is the man-powered aircraft. Many have sought to build aircraft driven by muscle power, and in 1960 a prize of £5,000 (later doubled) for accomplishing a controlled figure-8 without losing height attracted a flurry of contenders. In 1964 the Puffin, built at Hatfield, England, began successful tests but did not win the prize. Several other man-powered machines have now flown, all the successful ones having a wing of almost 100 ft span yet an empty weight of barely 100 lb. The prize may yet be won.

547

548

549

550

551

553

552

554

15 Aircraft in the missile age

Throughout the summer of 1945 Allied intelligence teams crawled through the mud and rubble of Germany unearthing the secrets of fantastic aeronautical research. The American team was large, well-equipped and voracious, and it speedily swallowed up experimental hardware, research equipment, engineers and professors and once-secret papers. But the British team was tiny, ill-equipped and hamstrung by officialdom, and the amazing disclosures it did bring back merely made British experts, from Air Marshals to chief designers, laugh scornfully. The RAF had the two best jet fighters in the world, it was thought. The Gloster Meteor, the first jet ever to see action, had been much improved and later in 1945 gained a startling world speed record at 606 mph. The smaller de Havilland Vampire, with a stubby wooden central nacelle ending with a jet nozzle just behind the wing and a twin-finned tail carried on slender booms, was outstandingly cheap, reliable and effective. Both were thoroughly well developed and practical, and were being bought by air forces all over the world. In any case the Labour government elected in 1945 cut aeronautical research drastically, and cancelled a programme for a supersonic aircraft, giving as the reason that it 'had not the heart to ask pilots to fly it'. The politicians decided there would probably be no need for an air force until about 1957—a date conjured out of the blue—and laid deep plans for very advanced aircraft to be ready then. Meanwhile it exported batches of the latest Rolls-Royce turbojets, including engines not even chosen for any RAF aircraft, to the Soviet Union.

British engines were world beaters. For a decade after the war thousands of them were made under licence in almost every powerful industrial nation, even including the United States. They were put into the fighter prototypes that mushroomed up in a resurgent France, they were the foundation of jet development in every other part of Western Europe, and the Swedes even found they could take the German piston engine out of their latest fighter and bolt a Vampire jet engine on instead. In the United States a British engine had launched the Lockheed F-80 Shooting Star, which by the end of the war was in volume production with an American Whittle-derived engine and even beat the Meteor's speed record. Republic, creators of the famed Thunderbolt, were in production with the excellent F-84 Thunderjet. When fighting began in Korea in 1950 these were the main fighter bombers, together with the F-82 Twin Mustang (two Mustang bodies sharing one wing) and the US Navy's wartime Corsair and the outstandingly useful Douglas Skyraider, a big piston-engined strike machine which proved so versatile it is still used in 1972.

555

556

550 Ansett DC-9-30 and Cessna 206 air taxi, Coolangatta, Australia, 1970

551 Hawker Siddeley 748 turboprop airliner, 1967

552 Hawker Siddeley HS.125 (Beechcraft Hawker 125) executive jet, 1970

553 Beech King Air turboprop executive aircraft, 1968

554 Hawker Siddeley Trident 3B of BEA, 1970

555 Lockheed F-80C Shooting Stars of the 26th Fighter Intercepter Squadron, USAF, over Okinawa, 1953

556 Republic F-84E Thunderjet firing 5 in rockets at Eglin Air Force Base, Florida, May 1951

North American, builders of the Mustang, were left behind by Lockheed and Republic with their new jets. By 1947 they saw what a blessing this had been. Thanks to their careful perusal of the transonic information from Germany, on 1 October of that year they were able to fly the first F-86 Sabre. Its wings and tail were rakishly swept back at 35°, and even though it temporarily lacked sufficient engine thrust it was obviously going to be the classic fighter of its time. By 1948 it was in squadron service, Air Force pilots had fired its guns and

Sabre, and accelerate away on the level, but the Sabre was stronger (Migs sometimes broke during violent manoeuvres) and had a great technical advantage in an advanced radar-laying gunsight.

By this time both North American and the Mig team were busy with later aircraft. The Sabre itself was developed into a version whose advance was strictly technical. The F-86D was distinguished externally only by having a different nose; instead of a big open snout that seemed to gulp air like a goldfish, the D model had a

557

558

dropped bombs from it, and one of them had easily taken the world speed record to 671 mph. And the citizens of Los Angeles gradually came to realize that the explosive bangs they had been hearing were audible proof that the Sabre could exceed the speed of sound in a dive. Soon Sabres were pouring off the assembly line in other parts of the United States, Canada, Italy, Australia and Japan, and including subsequent naval versions the total production amounted to almost 10,000, far exceeding the production of any other jet outside the Soviet Union.

Inside the Soviet Union the Rolls-Royce production process was duplicated with amazing speed – especially considering that the Russians did not buy a licence – while the design bureau of Mikoyan and Guryevich urgently planned a fighter to combine the 5,000 lb thrust of the refined and reliable engine with the aerodynamic data on swept wings obtained from Germany. The result was the Mig-15, one of the most significant aircraft in history, which took the air as early as 2 July 1947 and was thus the first fully swept piloted aircraft to fly. It was a winner from the start, despite its simplicity, rudimentary equipment and rather old-fashioned armament of three large-calibre cannon of prewar design. By 1948 the Mig-15 was coming into very large scale production, and pilots of Shooting Stars over Korea three years later were nonplussed to find the sky increasingly full of shiny silver arrowheads that could outpace them by 100 mph. But when Sabres reached Korea the tables were turned. The much lighter Mig could easily outclimb the

557 Bomb-laden Douglas Skyraiders and (*left*) Vought Corsairs about to spread their wings and leave USS *Princeton* during the Korean war

558 North American F-82E Twin Mustang, 1950

559 North American F-86E Sabres pass Mt Fujiyama, August 1951

560 Mig-15UTI, tandem-seat trainer version of the Mig-15, 1951

561 Watches synchronized for a squadron of missile-armed Mig-19s (aircraft with high tailplanes are Mig-15UTIs), 1960

562 Mig-17, all-weather radar-equipped version, East German Air Force, 1959

563 Grumman F9F Panther jets and Vought F4U Corsairs aboard USS *Essex* returning from Korea to San Diego, 28 June 1951

559

560

561

562

fat black radome beneath which the air intake appeared like a mouth. Behind the radome was radar interception and fire-control gear of greater complexity than anything previously put into a production aircraft, and its purpose was to enable a single-seat fighter to operate at night or in bad weather and successfully intercept and destroy enemy aircraft never seen by its pilot. After years of harrassing development, in the course of which hundreds of D models were lying about waiting for their electronic packages to be installed and connected up like a telephone exchange, the whole system was at last cleared for squadron use. Two further advances were that the engine had an afterburner, a swollen jet pipe in which extra fuel was burned to give increased thrust, and instead of guns the F-86D was armed with a large box of rockets which at the appropriate moment was extended below the aircraft, salvoed at the enemy and retracted back inside again without the pilot lifting a finger.

Mikoyan and Guryevich were offered no computerized systems of this kind but they were still able to improve on the Mig-15. Indeed, they embarked on a path of fighter development that has brought their bureau great eminence, the Soviet Union vast overseas sales and Western defence staffs ceaseless headaches. First came the Mig-17 of 1952, a faster and more refined Mig-15; then in 1953 the first Mig-19 took the air and showed beyond doubt that the Mig-15 and 17 had not been a flash in the pan. The new fighter was bigger, sleeker, had even more acutely swept surfaces and was powered by a pair of Soviet axial engines giving more than twice the thrust of the now obsolescent British unit. From the start it was intended to exceed the speed of sound in level flight, and this was convincingly accomplished. Ultimately the Mig-19 was supplied to at least 17 air forces, and formed a link in a chain of outstanding fighter successes from 1947 until the present. The Mig-15, 17 and 19 were each manufactured on a greater scale than any other jet fighters in history.

During these developments Britain maintained its cheeseparing and insular policy, was unable to send any modern aircraft to Korea, and got on with painfully slow ordering of prototypes which were to test some of the supposedly revolutionary new shapes of the future fighters and bombers – shapes already in squadron service elsewhere. The eminent teams that had produced the Hurricane and Spitfire did not even attempt to introduce sweepback, but created jet fighters 100 mph slower than their rivals because that was what the government ordered. Finally, in 1952 the situation had become so disastrous that taxpayers in Canada and the United States paid for 430 Sabres to be built in Canada and

563

223

564

565

finally triggering its sudden extension into a receptacle socket. In Britain a quite different scheme was adopted. The tanker was equipped with from one to three hose reels from each of which a long and flexible hose could be freely unrolled with a large funnel-like drogue on the end. Responsibility for contact rested solely with the recipient who would fly his aircraft so as to steer into the drogue a rigid forward-pointing probe pipe. When securely locked home, the probe and drogue automatically made a fuel-tight coupling which could be

supplied free to the RAF for Fighter Command and the 2nd Tactical Air Force in Germany.

The profound influence exerted on war by the nuclear bomb was already being reflected in the design of bombers. The earliest nuclear bombs were fat and cumbersome, and the first H-bombs could be carried only by a very big bomber; but the provision of high performance jet bombers able to carry nuclear weapons had been since 1946 the first priority in the United States and Soviet Union. The US Air Force created Strategic Air Command, which grew to be the biggest armed force in all history in terms of its equipment capital cost—which by 1958 represented an aggregate investment exceeding $15,000 million—and annual operating budget, and incomparably the most formidable in terms of destructive power.

SAC's first equipment was the piston-engined B-29 Superfortress used against Japan and its much more powerful development the B-50. From these aircraft Boeing derived the civil Stratocruiser which in turn yielded the KC-97 tanker bought by SAC to the tune of 888 aircraft to refuel in flight the already long-ranged bombers and enable them in theory to penetrate to the furthest fastnesses of Soviet territory. The technique used was developed by Boeing and involved a crewman in the tanker aiming a long rigid but telescopic pipe at the recipient aircraft flying just below and behind and

broken by the recipient pulling off to the rear. The British probe/drogue method was adopted by the US Navy and also by many other forces including the strategic bomber units of the Soviet Union.

In 1950, the year in which the US government freely lent Britain a force of B-29 bombers to make up for the lack of any modern British bomber, SAC began to take delivery of the Convair B-36. While the B-29 dwarfed everything in the RAF when it arrived, the B-36 dwarfed the B-29. While Britain took from 1943 to 1949 building a single Brabazon airliner with nothing inside it, the Convair plant at Fort Worth in the same period built the even bigger B-36, developed its fantastically complex systems and equipment—which included a small railway to carry crew members along the tunnel linking the front and rear pressurized cabins—and tooled to produced it at a high rate until 385 were in use. It was in many ways the most impressive bomber ever built. The wing measured 230 ft from tip to tip, and deep inside it were six 3,500 hp Pratt & Whitney engines driving huge pusher propellers behind the trailing edge. By 1950 the B-36D version was urged along at 435 mph by the addition of four General Electric turbojets in pods hung under the outer wings, well over 100 ft from the lofty flight deck where, it was said, the captain always hung a calendar to mark the passage of the days and nights. After the coming of the H-bomb

564 Boeing KC-97G air refuelling tanker and freighter, 1952

565 Convair B-36D strategic bomber, 1952

aircraft flew singly. A special jet fighter was designed to be launched from the giant bomber to protect it, afterwards hooking on again. In other trials the B-36 carried reconnaissance fighters deep into enemy territory and then carried them home.

But technology soon swept away these battleships of the skies. As early as 1943, when the B-36 was a mere project for bombing Germany should Britain fall, the US Air Force had signed contracts with five manufacturers for totally different designs of jet bomber. Most were fairly conventional, although Northrop made an amazing machine that consisted of a huge 172 ft wing and nothing else (inside the wing were the crew, fuel, bombs and eight jet engines).

The last of the above-mentioned five prototypes to fly was the XB-47 Stratojet from Boeing. Unlike all their rivals Boeing had used the swept-wing data from Germany. Boldly they had risked millions of dollars building a huge bomber of a totally new kind. Although almost as heavy as the B-36 it had a crew of only three; the slender wing was swept at 35° and carried six turbojets in streamlined pods hung in a new way below and ahead of the wing; the main landing gears folded into the fuselage, one in front of the cavernous bomb bay and one behind it; rockets could be used to boost the take-off, and a mighty parachute deployed to help slow the streamlined giant after landing. The B-47 was an unbelievable success. Possibly for the first time in the history of aircraft design its measured drag was 25 per cent less than the estimate. It carried a bigger bomb load further than its rivals at a speed roughly 100 mph faster. Soon it was the backbone of SAC, displacing the B-29, the B-50 and even the B-36, and in 1957 when SAC accepted the last off the line it was No. 2040.

By this time Britain did at last have a modern bomber, but the counterpart of the B-47, the Vickers Valiant, was available in a quantity approximately 2,000 fewer. The Valiant was a fine four-engined machine that dropped live H-bombs at Christmas Island, fission bombs at Maralinga and ordinary high explosive against the Egyptians before suddenly developing metal fatigue in 1964 and being scrapped. In any case, it was only an interim machine pending the availability of the more advanced Avro Vulcan, with a huge delta (triangular shaped) wing, and the Handley Page Victor, with a more conventional wing described as crescent shaped. The Vulcan and Victor were boldly planned in 1946 to a challenging specification calling for a bomber able to carry a heavier load of bombs than any existing RAF machine, for at least as great a range at twice the speed and twice the over-target height. The demand was met, but it took almost ten years of development. Moreover, both types were persisted with because cautious procurement authorities could not at the outset decide which was best. The result was that a small and uneconomic quantity was made of each and the RAF had to bear the costs of introducing and maintaining two types of aircraft for the same job.

Problems of penetration of defended airspace dominated the design of strike aircraft by 1955. As guided missiles became more widespread and reliable the bomber's traditional mission became suicidal, and the future appeared to lie either in greater speed and height or else in crossing the hostile region at the lowest possible altitude in order to stay as far as possible beneath the enemy's invisible radar waves. One of the first aircraft explicitly designed to penetrate at treetop height was the Royal Navy's Hawker Siddeley Buccaneer, a quite small two-seater looking rather like a fighter but able to carry weapons both externally and in a capacious internal weapons bay. Its key lay in its immense structural strength and stiffness, fitting it to the gruelling task

566 Boeing B-47E Stratojet strategic bomber, 1953

567 Vickers-Armstrongs Valiant B.1 bomber, 1955

566

567

568   569

of flying at the speed of sound through the thick and
turbulent air just above the Earth's surface. But this
was in no sense a strategic aircraft and so the Vulcan
and Victor were, as far as economically possible,
modified to permit them to attack at low level. Both
were also equipped to cárry the Blue Steel missile which
could be released about 200 miles short of the target and
left to navigate by itself at supersonic speed to deliver a
warhead having a yield equivalent to at least a megaton
of conventional explosive. The Victor was also converted
to serve as a strategic reconnaissance aircraft, packed
with advanced sensing devices, and also as a flight
refuelling tanker with three hose reels.

In 1954, long before either of these 'V-bombers' was
ready for service, the Vulcan team were given an even
greater challenge: a supersonic bomber. Known as the
Avro 730, it proceeded rapidly despite the formidable
magnitude of the task, but in 1957 the government
suddenly considered there was no future in piloted
combat aircraft and that future wars would be fought by
missiles, and the bomber was cancelled (although there
was no missile to replace it) and the remarkable
prophesy was uttered in the *White Paper on Defence 1957*
that the RAF would be 'unlikely to require' any further
fighters or bombers.

The United States did not subscribe to such a doctrine,
even though that country did have a wide range of well
developed guided missiles. The enormous SAC force of
B-47 bombers and their supporting tankers was by 1956
being backed up by two considerably more potent air-

craft, the Boeing B-52 bomber and KC-135 tanker. Many years of careful research enabled Boeing in 1948 to offer the US Air Force two versions of a huge bomber to replace the B-36, one of them a turboprop and the other a turbojet. The Air Force wanted the far more attractive jet, but it was not until 1952 that Pratt & Whitney could deliver the engine, the J57. This engine was a turning point in American military and civil aviation. It was not only all-American, previous Pratt & Whitney jets having been of British design, but it was also extremely advanced in concept, with very high compression achieved by using two compressors one behind the other turned by separate turbines. It gave 10,000 lb thrust, twice as much as most earlier engines. Yet so enormous was the B-52 that it had to have eight of these engines, in four double pods. To build the B-52 a great network of suppliers was set up throughout North America, in the way that is usual with every US aircraft programme of great magnitude, suppliers delivering not only rivets, instruments and landing gear but major parts of the airframe. Boeing then put everything together.

By 1956 the first SAC squadron had been equipped and the range and striking power of SAC jet bombers were both approximately doubled. Soon hundreds of the mighty machines were ranging the globe, attended by the KC-135 tankers derived from the civil 707 airliner (itself based on the J57 engine) and able to refuel the B-52 at twice the height and speed possible with the KC-97. Eventually later models of the B-52 appeared with new turbofan engines of much greater thrust and economy, a wing full of fuel (instead of containing separate tanks)

and nuclear weapons delivered by supersonic Hound Dog missiles, the bomber itself being protected by eight tons of electronics carried on board and a further complex array carried away as a decoy by small Quail robot aircraft released from the B-52 over enemy territory. Over Vietnam the B-52, now painted black, terrified jungle guerillas by dropping 84,000 lb of high explosive at a time. Now SAC has stiffened its remaining giants to fit them for low-level missions carrying a cluster of SRAM supersonic missiles.

The Soviet Union had no counterpart, but still built up a formidable long range force after 1945. It began with the mass production by the Tupolev bureau of the American B-29, two of which landed intact in Manchuria in 1944. Dissecting the complex bomber, analysing the materials and constructional techniques and duplicating the entire process took a bare 18 months, and the Tu-4 version was in full operational service before the end of 1947, three years before the original version joined the RAF. From the Tu-4 the Tupolev bureau not only learned a vast amount of modern engineering but also were able to extract gun turrets, fuel and hydraulic systems, landing gear and brake parts, flight deck equipment and numerous other items which they used in the Tu-16. This, the first strategic jet aircraft designed in Europe, was made possible by A. A. Mikulin's M-209 turbojet which ran in 1950 at 15,000 lb thrust, a remarkable figure for that time. By 1954 the engine was rated at 19,200 lb, and the twin-engined Tu-16 was as effective as the four-jet British Valiant and six-jet American B-47. Thousands of Tu-16s were built in many versions, some

570

571

carrying huge reconnaissance radars or long range missiles, and squadrons were supplied to Egypt and Indonesia.

By 1955 Tupolev had flown a much bigger and totally different bomber, the Tu-20. This was the ultimate expression of the propeller-driven aircraft, having four huge engines of 15,000 hp each, driving enormous eight-blade contra-rotating propellers of 18 ft 4½ in diameter. Wings and tail surfaces were swept back, and the monstrous machine possessed an unrivalled combination of load-carrying ability, speed and, above all, intercontinental range which was manifest by numerous world

570 Boeing B-52H Stratofortress being refuelled by Boeing KC-135 Stratotanker, 1962

571 Pratt & Whitney J57 turbojets, 1953

records set by the Tu-114 and 114D civil versions (which included flying a 6,200 mile circuit carrying a very heavy load at a speed of almost 460 mph). Known in the West as 'Bear' the giant bomber caused expenditure of over $4,000 million on defending missile and fighter systems. Even without its long range missiles in the form of pilotless fighters carrying huge warheads the Tu-20 could bomb the United States and return.

For tactical attack the most widely used Soviet machine in the 1950s and 60s was the Ilyushin 28, a light twin-engined machine using the same Rolls-Royce turbo-jet as the Mig-15 and likewise flown in 1947. Unusual in having a swept tail but straight wing, the Il-28 served in huge numbers with all Communist and friendly air forces, and was backed up in the light attack and night fighting roles by Yakovlev's Yak-25 family, a sort of scaled-down B-47 with two engines which had a close parallel in the transonic French Vautour. But none of these aircraft quite rivalled the all-round qualities of the British Canberra, a classic design with a life that may exceed that of all other aircraft in history. W. E. W. Petter directed the design in 1945, taking care to choose a big, broad wing to give good behaviour at great altitudes, and following the precept of the Mosquito in relying on speed rather than gun turrets for defence. English Electric completed the first Canberra in 1949. Here was a bomber that was not only as fast as the best fighters but could also out-turn and out-manoeuvre them. More than 20 different types of Canberra were subsequently built in Britain, large numbers were exported and the Canberra became the only British aircraft to be produced in quantity under licence in the United States, by Martin. Today advanced redesigned versions are used by the US Air Force as extremely high-flying reconnaissance machines capable of operating at heights in excess of 90,000 ft. Meanwhile the BAC factory near Preston, England, continues to deliver rebuilt Canberras to air forces all over the world, almost 30 years after the start of the programme.

This incredible longevity has been gained by the Canberra's combination of tractability, economy and undemanding nature, which has made it ideal for smaller

572

573

574

575

228

576

Until the emergence of the jet during the second world war man had faced a speed barrier in the neighbourhood of 500 mph. With the jet he was soon able to breach this barrier and add a further 200 mph, which seemed a substantial further advance; but the barrier imposed by the speed of sound in the atmosphere took longer to conquer. Britain, having set out to do so in 1943, gave up in 1946. But between 1947 and 1952 the Americans not only did it but planned to introduce completely supersonic machines into regular military service. And the re-

air forces. Yet by 1950 the US and Soviet air forces could see clearly that the route ahead inevitably led into the supersonic regime of flight in which everything becomes infinitely more difficult. Wings and tails have to be much thinner yet several times stronger and stiffer, frontal areas have to be reduced yet fuel capacity must increase (for a given flight range), and engines must be slimmer yet far more powerful. It was also known that the best supersonic shapes might be quite different from the traditional one, and by 1950 experimental aircraft were flying with wings of strange shapes including the triangular delta already mentioned.

First supersonic aircraft was the US Air Force Bell XS-1 (later re-styled X-1), which exceeded sonic speed on 14 October 1947 in the course of a long and gruelling test programme over Florida and then California. Later much improved versions of the rocket-propelled X-1 were built, and by 1948 a Navy team of test pilots was giving the Air Force programme severe competition with the Douglas Skyrocket. Unlike the X-1 series, which were carried aloft by a B-29 and released at 30,000 ft, the Skyrocket could take off from the ground, and ultimately one was driven to 1,327 mph (Mach 2·01) and reached a height exceeding 20 miles. The greatest Mach number reached by an X-1 (in 1953) was even higher: 2·42, equivalent to 1,650 mph. These aircraft laid the essential groundwork of flight data needed for a successful supersonic air power. Concurrently more than $3,000 million were spent on new facilities and supporting systems including huge machine tools for sculpturing metal, giant presses for forging and plate forming, longer and stronger airfield runways, better navigation aids and radar systems, new types of armament including rapid-fire cannon and both spin-stabilized and automatically guided rocket missiles, and a completely new range of powerplants and airborne accessory systems.

578

577

579

580

581

Force the F-102A Delta Dagger. This was the supersonic successor to the F-86D, and it combined supersonic speed (achieved after frantic redesign to change the shape) with completely automatic radar interception and fire control systems and guided missile armament. It entered service in the same year that the RAF received the first of its Gloster Javelin all-weather fighters which, though delta-winged like the F-102, did not have automatic fire-control gear, guided weapons (not until later, at least) or supersonic performance. By 1959 squadrons of US Air Defense Command were re-equipping with the F-106 Delta Dart, longer and slimmer than the F-102 and, with half as much thrust again, capable of tremendous speed, gaining a world speed record at 1,525 mph with full combat equipment. Modified versions of this aircraft still protect the United States against bomber attack in the 1970s. Britain's counterpart is that country's solitary supersonic military aircraft, the Lightning. Although the design was begun as long ago as 1947 this remains a potent and tractable all-weather fighter a quarter century later.

An especially versatile Century-series aircraft is the Republic F-105 Thunderchief, powered by the same huge 26,500 lb thrust Pratt & Whitney J75 engine as the F-106 and capable of very nearly the same speed. Described as 'the one-man air force', the F-105 can carry a large load of varied weapons and strike at point targets hidden deep in enemy territory even in bad weather or at night, using very advanced navigational and radar systems. If necessary it could deliver a nuclear weapon in an 'over the shoulder' toss, conducted without the pilot touching

582

583

580 North American F-100A Super Sabre before delivery to the US Air Force, 1954

581 Foredeck of USS *Ranger*, 16 May 1963, with four F-8C Crusader supersonic intercepters catapulted off and McDonnell Douglas F-4B Phantom about to follow

582 Lockheed F-104G Starfighters coming off the line in Germany, 1962

583 General Dynamics (Convair) F-102 Delta Dagger intercepters, 1957

markable thing, in retrospect, is the swiftness with which the giant task was accomplished.

The US Air Force introduced the North American F-100 Super Sabre–the first of the 'Century series' of supersonic fighters–as early as September 1954, at the same time as the RAF began to use the subsonic Swift and Hunter. More than 2,000 Super Sabres were built and many were still at work over the Vietnam jungle almost 20 years after the basic design was planned on the basis of Korean experience. Another Century-series machine stemming from Korea lessons was the amazing Lockheed F-104 Starfighter. Dubbed 'the missile with a man in it', this has so tiny a wing that it seems to consist of little more than a finely streamlined fuselage. It was planned as an air-superiority fighter to gain command of airspace, but in 1960, six years after the F-104 first flew, the F-104G version was chosen by Germany, Holland, Italy and Belgium as their standard tactical strike aircraft and over 1,000 were built by these nations (concurrently, Germany and Italy made the Italian Fiat G91 light strike fighter) as well as a further 380 in Canada and 180 in Japan. This world success is in contrast to the very brief and limited use of this 1,500 mph aircraft by the United States.

In June 1956 Convair began to deliver to the US Air

230

and strike bombers of both the Air Force and the Navy, a special version being planned for use from aircraft carriers.

Redesignated F-111, the first machine flew on schedule in December 1964, but the programme ran into intense difficulties due to weight-escalation, poor propulsive system performance and large increases in cost (and especially in cost per aircraft). One of the biggest advantages of the original scheme was that the same basic flight vehicle was intended to be produced in numerous

585

the controls, which throws the bomb high into the air to allow the F-105 to escape before the explosion.

To replace this fine and complicated machine the US Air Force contracted with General Dynamics in 1962 for the TFX–Tactical Fighter Experimental–which swiftly became one of the great aircraft of history and also the most controversial. In the TFX the US Air Force hoped to combine a whole series of new technological developments made since the Century-series were designed in 1951-53. Turbofan engines with advanced high-compression fans and compressors and greatly improved afterburners and nozzles promised increased thrust and efficiency and reduced fuel consumption. Major airframe parts made of titanium could be almost as strong as steel, almost as light as aluminium and very resistant to the high temperatures, often approaching a dull red heat, encountered in supersonic airframes as a result of air friction and power plant heat. Instead of a mere ejection seat, that shot the pilot out in a dire emergency, it was proposed to make the whole crew compartment, housing pilot and navigator, eject itself from a stricken TFX, float down by parachute and then serve as a survival shelter on land or sea. Most important of all, it was proposed to make the wings swing fore and aft on giant pivots on each side of the fuselage so that they could be spread out for take-off, landing and subsonic cruise or 'loiter' periods and acutely folded back at 72·5° for supersonic flight right down to ground level. So impressive did the TFX seem that it was soon decided that it could replace all the tactical fighters, intercepters

586

slightly different versions to serve many customers, and it was calculated that at least 1,700 would be bought by the US Air Force and Navy and several hundred more by allies. In the end the Navy fighter version had to be abandoned and the foreign sales did not go through, except for an Australian order that escalated in price to more than three times the original $A112 million for 24 aircraft that were due for delivery in 1966 and will not actually be delivered until 1973. The critical view of the American Congress and public is that the total run of some 540 aircraft is costing more than the budget for over 1,700; yet the fact remains the F-111 represents a

584 Hawker Siddeley (Gloster) Javelin Mk 9 of RAF, Malaya, 1960

585 Fairchild Hiller (Republic) F-105D Thunderchief in Vietnam, 1969

586 General Dynamics F-111A swing-wing bombers with KC-135 tanker, 1968

giant forward step in man's ability to make an aircraft change its shape in a gross way to fit it perfectly to different flight conditions.

This swing-wing or variable-geometry quality was worked on at great length in Britain long before the F-111, notably by Barnes Wallis, but no use was made of it. In contrast the Soviet Union immediately copied the F-111 and flew Mikoyan and Sukhoi supersonic fighters embodying the principle as early as 1966. Likewise the aggressive and supremely successful French Dassault

Mirage. When in 1960 de Gaulle created his Force de Frappe, the French counterpart of SAC, its first equipment was the Mirage IV supersonic bomber, twice as big and powerful as the fighter.

Since 1960 the Mirage family have had little competition and well over 1,600 have been ordered by air forces on every continent. The latest versions include the Mirage F with a conventional high-mounted wing and tailplane, the Milan with a retractable 'moustache' foreplane to improve behaviour with heavy loads or in

587

589

588

violent manoeuvre, and the G with variable sweep, all of which are being produced in quantity. The G was Dassault's answer to the proposal that he should collaborate on a swing-wing aircraft with Britain, a farce which the French torpedoed after 18 months in 1967.

It was in the mid-1950s that international collaboration had first become important as a possible way of overcoming the soaring cost of developing advanced aircraft. The 14 countries that then formed the North Atlantic Treaty Organization (NATO), formed in 1949, studied the problem with especial urgency as they watched the flood of formidable machines pouring from Soviet and other Warsaw Pact factories. In 1955 and again in 1957 NATO held a competition for a light-weight strike fighter. The French fought hard to win–going 'far beyond the bounds of propriety', in the words of the Italian General Pisani–but the eventual winner was the Italian Fiat G.91, virtually a scaled-down Sabre with British Bristol Orpheus engine. The French refused to use it, but it was built in numbers by Italy and Federal Germany and supplied to other NATO nations. At this time Britain was inclined to be as proud and nationalistically superior as the French, but times were to change.

To the British, collaboration has since 1962 appeared to be the only way to produce complicated and expensive aircraft. Some programmes have gone very well. One of the best, despite French criticism, is the Jaguar, which began life as simple subsonic trainer and strike aircraft projects at Breguet and BAC, and is now in production as an extremely compact, well equipped and versatile

587 Dassault Mirage IVA supersonic bomber, 1962

588 Fiat G.91 aerobatic team, Italian Air Force, 1967

589 Dassault Super Mystère B2, 1956

company swiftly produced a variable-sweep version of its Mirage. Dassault (the name by which Marcel Bloch was known in the French Resistance forces during the war) began postwar fighter production with the Ouragan and Mystère powered by British jets made in France and then graduated to the Super-Mystère 4B with a French Atar engine which was capable of sustained supersonic speed. In 1956 the first Mirage III ushered in the most successful European fighter of modern times. A small supersonic delta, with an advanced Atar engine and sometimes a booster rocket also, it can reach Mach 2 on the level, climb and manoeuvre like lightning and carry a tremendous assortment of guns, bombs, rockets and guided missiles weighing 8,820 lb, not including heavy external fuel tanks. This external load is 50 per cent greater than the laden weight of second world war fighters having a much greater wing span than the 26 ft

family of supersonic aircraft able to handle any tactical military or naval mission including training, strike (attack on surface targets) and air superiority (destruction of aerial targets). Each Jaguar has an offensive power greater than whole squadrons of second world war aircraft, and its twin engines can blast it out of a restricted field even when burdened by five tons of armament. Following it in development is the MRCA, or multi-role combat aircraft, which could have embraced many nations but has finally settled down with Britain, West

590

591

593

Germany and Italy. This will be little bigger than the Jaguar but will have a variable-sweep wing and more powerful engines and is intended to fulfil many roles well into the 1980s.

A remarkable exception to the collaborative trend is Sweden, which, alone and on a modest budget, has produced an unbroken succession of outstanding modern combat aircraft. In 1949 the fat Saab-29 Tunnen (Barrel) had swept wings; in 1952 the Saab-32 Lansen (Lance) was a transonic all-weather fighter and attack aircraft; in 1958 the Saab-35 Draken (Dragon) introduced a dramatic shape and Mach 2 performance; and today's Saab-37 Viggen (Thunderbolt) is a computerized multi-role aircraft, again of unique shape, flying at Mach 2 yet able to operate from main roads and forest clearings.

In the United States there has been a very distinct trend away from multi-role aircraft, despite the amazing

590 Panavia MRCA: artist's impression bearing markings of Britain, West Germany and Italy, 1972

591 BAC/Breguet Jaguar, RAF two-seat version, 1972

592 Saab AJ37 Viggen multi-role fighter, 1972

593 Saab 35F Draken intercepter landing on Swedish farm, 1972

592

233

success of the McDonnell Douglas F-4 Phantom which began life in 1954 as a fighter for the US Navy and by 1960 had shown itself capable of outperforming every Air Force fighter in practically every respect. This remarkable aircraft combines tremendous performance, the ability to carry a heavier load than any other fighter, unrivalled search radar equipment and excellent slow-speed qualities, and over 4,500 have been made for many countries including 170 for Britain with more powerful and more economical Rolls-Royce engines. This machine has had to make up for deficiencies in many others, but by 1974 the burden should be eased by two promising new fighters both aimed primarily at the air-superiority mission. One, the Grumman F-14 Tomcat, will fill the gap in the US Navy left by the F-111B, and it will be a swing-wing two-seater. The other will be the McDonnell Douglas F-15 for the Air Force, powered by twin Pratt & Whitney engines of very advanced design similar to those of the Tomcat but differing in being a single-seater with a wing that does not change its basic planform shape. The F-15 in particular is being tailored over-whelmingly to the urgent need to defeat enemy fighters, and the main reason for the urgency is the staggering progress made by the designers in the Soviet Union.

While Pavel Sukhoi created a series of very effective large single-engined strike fighters, roughly comparable to the American F-105, the Mikoyan bureau followed the Mig-19 with an extremely neat and small delta-winged fighter, the Mig-21. Capable of Mach 2, this has been produced in enormous quantity in many versions between 1955 and 1972 and is also in production in India.

595

596

594

597

Although most versions are fairly simple day fighters, not equipped to perform automatic radar-guided inter-ceptions nor strike surface targets, the cheapness and economy of these fighters is matched only by their great pilot appeal. In round terms a Mig-21 costs half as much as a French Mirage, which in turn costs half as much as an American Phantom. They rival the Mirage in being the best small, lightweight fighters of modern times, and they probably bring the total number of fighters made to Mikoyan designs to more than 70,000. Since 1964 this bureau has surprised the West a number of times, but the outstanding shock was caused by the Mig-23, a very big and formidable twin-engined fighter first flown in 1964. Capable of Mach 3·2, or more than 2,100 mph, the Mig-23 has gained a spate of world records, embarrassed the Pentagon by the lack of any US counterpart and embarrassed the Israelis by its use

594 Sukhoi Su-7B fighter bomber (*in background*: Mig-17s and -21s), 1970

595 Grumman F-14A Tomcat fighter, 1972

596 Artist's impression of McDonnell Douglas F-15 fighter

597 Mig-21PF intercepters. Soviet Union, about 1968

598 Mig-23, 1967

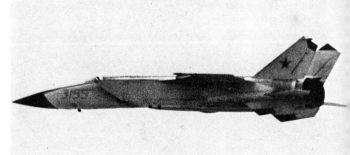

598

from Egyptian bases on missions which are completed before they can be intercepted. In its broad box-like body, almost unswept wing, long engine ducts with sharply inclined intake lips and outward-sloping twin fins the Mig-23 introduced features still only on the drawing board in other countries. Western designers are wonder-

599

600

ing what the Mig bureau have been doing since 1964.

The only military aircraft with a performance equal to the Mig-23 is the special family of Mach 3 machines created by Lockheed for the US Air Force primarily to undertake strategic reconnaissance missions. So-called 'overflights' by the clandestine Lockheed U-2, a very lightly built high-flying machine thought to cruise too high to be intercepted, were abruptly halted when one was shot down over Sverdlovsk on 1 May 1960, creating a diplomatic incident of unparalleled nature. By this time Lockheed were well advanced with the successor, an immensely long, rakish machine with two extremely powerful wing-mounted engines and intended to cross Communist territory at Mach 3 at more than 85,000 ft. In 1964 President Johnson revealed the first version, called the A-11. Although more than 10,000 people had been involved in its making, and it was probably the noisiest aircraft ever to have flown, not a word had leaked out to the US press. Later the A-11 was developed into an all-weather fighter, the F-12, and also a strategic reconnaissance machine of even greater potential, the SR-71.

In complete contrast to these black-painted monsters weighing almost 90 tons each, new classes of military aircraft have been produced since 1960 to handle more economically what are called 'brushfire wars' or 'limited wars' in which nuclear weapons are proscribed and the enemy is relatively primitive and ill-equipped. Mach 2 aircraft costing $2 million and carefully designed to fight major wars are uneconomic when used against scattered guerillas in the jungle, and urgent studies in the Pentagon in 1960 led to the conversion of jet trainers and even piston-engined machines for use in Vietnam and also to the LARA (light armed reconnaissance aircraft) specification that eventually resulted in the North American OV-10 Bronco. This STOL (short take-off and landing) machine has two 715 hp turboprops and an odd stubby wing and very high tail carried on twin booms. In the central nacelle is a mass of equipment enabling the machine to act as a fighter, bomber, reconnaissance aircraft, casualty-evacuation ambulance, transport, psychological warfare aircraft (dropping leaflets and making loud broadcasts) and target tug. It is just one manifestation of the need to create new types of flight vehicle for changing situations.

The traditional bomber is today almost dead. Strategic Air Command was equipped between 1960 and 1970 with the Convair B-58 Hustler, the first really big supersonic aircraft. This sharp-looking delta was powered by four afterburning engines and could sustain Mach 2 for over an hour; with air refuelling it was easy for a B-58

601

to cover 5,000 miles in well under five hours and world records were set in supersonic flights to Paris and Tokyo and in racing the Sun across the United States. The B-58 was followed by the B-70 Valkyrie, possibly the most awesome aircraft ever made. In this 300 ton tail-first delta designed in 1955-59 were incorporated major advances in materials, aerodynamics, structures and operative systems, all aimed at creating an aircraft capable of flying 6,000 miles in three hours. But its enormous cost, and the emergence of the reliable ICBM (intercontinental ballistic missile) as a surer delivery system, caused the Valkyrie to be limited to a two-aircraft programme. Even this limited procurement ran away with over $2,000 million, but it must be remembered that the B-70 was probably the first type of aircraft since the Wright brothers that could claim to be simultaneously the longest, the heaviest, the fastest, the most powerful and the costliest. The giant white-painted creation would have been much cheaper if it had been of solid gold. North American Rockwell, which built the Valkyries, are today well advanced with the B-1A, a Mach 2 swing-wing bomber for Strategic Air Command that will again combine new technologies in structures, aerodynamics and, especially, in propulsion, with four very clever reheat turbofan engines by General Electric. SAC have made a firm claim to the B-1A, but today the colossal funding needed for such a programme has to be voted by an increasingly critical Congress and the B-1A may never be built.

Manufacturers are having to finance their own develop-

599 Lockheed U-2A high-altitude aircraft, 1960

600 North American XB-70A Valkyrie, second take-off, October 1964

601 Northrop F-5 (made by Canadair as CF-5B), 1970

ments in the military field to an unprecedented degree. Northrop Corporation has spent more than $20 million of its own cash developing a successor to the F-5 Freedom Fighter, which itself was largely funded by the company in the early days. The F-5 is an attractive light twin-jet which has been very widely exported and built under licence in both single- and two-seat forms and is claimed to be notably cost/effective especially in limited-war situations. Its proposed successor, the P.530 Cobra, is tailored to the air-superiority rather than the ground-attack mission and Northrop would welcome an international programme to develop the aircraft. Canada, Australia, most European countries and Japan would be likely participants. Canada makes the F-5, Australia the Mirage and Japan has flown an advanced trainer that is a close relative of the Jaguar and could do a similar range of missions if properly developed.

Since the second world war the two classes of military aircraft that have increased most markedly in stature are the transport and the ASW (anti-submarine warfare) machine. Thirty years ago military transports were merely civil ones with air force equipment, but today the major air forces have bought logistic freighters that out-carry any other aircraft, STOL transports for use from short unprepared airstrips, jet transports that can also refuel combat aircraft in flight and even special transports bristling with guns and psycho-gear for use against guerillas. Two of the most significant transports have come from Lockheed Georgia Co. In 1954 the C-130 Hercules combined four turboprop engines, a big pressurized fuselage, an unobstructed cargo compartment, full-width rear doors for loading or parachute-dropping heavy stores, the speed of a Spitfire and the ability to use short airstrips. The combination was such that the Hercules is still in production well into the 1970s long after later 'successors' have been phased out. Lockheed's other contribution is the C-5A Galaxy, a less successful programme financially but nevertheless the world's biggest and most capacious aircraft and one that could later lead to a revolution in civil airfreight, carrying 150 tons of almost anything.

In the ASW field the two major families of the second world war—small aircraft used from carriers and big ones based on land—have both been enormously improved and extended to keep pace with the enhanced threat of nuclear vessels that cruise at 40 knots under the ocean and fire missiles that destroy cities. Latest of the carrier-based ASW machines is the Lockheed S-3A Viking, a four-seat aircraft powered by twin turbofans and packed with sensing devices for detecting modern submarines. The newest shore-based ocean patroller is the British Hawker Siddeley Nimrod, derived from the Comet airliner, in which a crew of 12 can spend 12 hours or more operating an even greater array of sensors and, if they find a 'contact', attacking with an assortment of weapons. Modern ASW aircraft can use radars, magnetic anomaly detectors measuring the way a submarine distorts the Earth's magnetic field and even devices that 'sniff' traces of contaminants in the atmosphere. They are typical modern military aircraft in that their systems and equipment are so extensive and complex that they cost more than the aircraft in which they are fitted. This is true even in the case of such basically clever aircraft as the jet-lift VTOLs to be described later. Thus the modern military aircraft is really a great collection of functioning systems all closely integrated like the systems of the human body. It is almost a secondary task to package these into an airframe providing the desired flight performance.

602

603

602 Antonov An-22 heavy freighter landing beyond a line of An-12s on manoeuvres, 1967

603 Lockheed C-5A Galaxy disgorging a string of Army vehicles, Fort Hood, Texas, 1971

604 Lockheed S-3A Viking anti-submarine aircraft, escorted by two-seat Cougar chase machine, Mojave desert, 1972

605 S-64E crane-lift helicopter, 1969

606 Sikorsky HH-53 (S-65) multi-role helicopter, 1968

607 Aérospatiale Alouette III, Swiss Air Force, 1971

604

606

605

607

609

608

610

16 VTOL

As already outlined, flying machines capable of lifting themselves vertically by the power of their engines took much longer to bring to fruition than those lifted by the motion of a fixed wing through the air. One of the most fundamental facts upon which rests the design of all heavier-than-air aircraft is that a given aerodynamic force, for either propulsion or lift, can be obtained by accelerating a small airflow violently or a large airflow gently. The sailplane and man-powered aircraft lift themselves by the latter method, and in consequence are quiet and efficient. The heavy, small-winged supersonic aircraft imparts a violent acceleration to a relatively small airflow, and is thus rather noisy and inefficient. To obtain lift without forward motion, and thus achieve VTOL (vertical take-off and landing), exactly the same principles apply.

In the early days of aviation it was only just possible to match the combination of wing span and airspeed to obtain the desired reaction from a fixed wing. Any form of vertical flight was exceedingly difficult to accomplish. Apart from Breguet's few seconds of success in 1907, nobody achieved it at all until the mid-1930s. By this time the latest fighters might just conceivably have been able to take off vertically if they had been raised into a vertical position standing on their tails, with the aircraft stripped of non-essentials. Powerful piston engines and large propellers could generate static thrust greater than the aircraft weight, but unless a contra-rotating double propeller were used the propeller would tend to drive the aircraft round in the opposite direction. But by 1946 this idea, far-fetched as it may seem, was being seriously considered by the US Navy, which unlike Britain decided to act on VTOL tail-standing proposals discovered in Germany. The idea was that the machine would use its propeller thrust to pull it vertically up to a height at which it could be tilted over forwards until it was flying fast enough for the wing to support it in the conventional way. An important factor was the promise of the emergence of the turboprop as a source of shaft-power much lighter and more compact than the piston engine, and paper studies showed that it should be possible to create VTOL fighters capable of being carried by every US Navy surface vessel and not just by aircraft carriers.

Convair and Lockheed built competing prototypes of such aircraft which both flew in 1954; the Convair began its trials in the vertical mode on 2 August 1954, and thus became the first fixed-wing aircraft in history to hover on the power of its engine and rise and descend without forward movement and without using a separate lifting rotor. Both these 'Pogo Stick' tail-sitters were powered by a 5,850 hp Allison double turboprop driving

611

612

508 Four ex-World War Two Mustangs before the 1,000-mile Mojave race, California, 1971

609 'Bomb burst' by Gnat trainers of RAF 'Red Arrows' acrobatic team, Farnborough, 1968

610 Aérospatiale Alouette III helicopter at the Hanover Air Show, 1968

611 Convair XFY-1 'Pogo Stick' in hovering mode, 1954

612 Lockheed XFV-1 ready for take-off, 1954

239

613

a 16 ft contra-rotating propeller, and the pilot's seat was pivoted to preserve a reasonably comfortable attitude during the vertical mode. Gross weight of both machines was about 15,000 lb, and the thrust of the propeller at full power was some 3,500 lb greater, not quite providing the 25 per cent reserve of power needed for effective vertical flight control. An important disadvantage of these machines was that, like all subsequent VTOL aircraft, in the vertical flight mode they did not immediately obey pilot commands. With conventional aircraft pilot control movement results in instant change in trajectory, but with these tail-sitters the VTOL mode was quite different. With the aircraft sinking there was no way of suddenly stopping the descent and then climbing. Opening up the engine power merely caused the rate of descent to diminish, and if enough power was applied the descent speed would eventually pass through the zero value and turn into an ascent. Thus landing demanded very fine judgement to avoid either crashing or perpetually over-controlling.

This was one of the reasons for abandoning the scheme in 1955, but by this time VTOL development in the United States was in full spate. While the tail-sitting turboprop, which was to pitch over forwards into ordinary translational flight and then tilt back into the vertical attitude for landing, proved itself inadequate in performance and dangerous to fly, an incredible profusion of strange vehicles buzzed and roared aloft throughout the United States. Some of them were like helicopters with rotors that tilted to become giant propellers; some had big wings carrying giant flaps that could deflect downwards the slipstream from enormous propellers; some had the whole wing, complete with engines and propellers, arranged to pivot as a single unit so that the propellers pointed to the sky; some were wingless devices lifted and thrust along by multiple propellers or fans; some had the propellers shrouded inside huge circular ducts arranged to tilt; and some were mere circular platforms on which the pilot stood as he buzzed around. Other companies explored clever ways of integrating propulsion and lift by means of deflector vanes, shutters, geared fans and ejector slits along the wings. None of this early VTOL breed led to a useful production vehicle, and it was almost as if the funds were being voted because this new sort of flying machine promised limitless fun.

True to the fundamental law that the most efficient VTOL rises on the thrust of a large rotor or propeller, none of these early machines was a jet. But in England Dr A. A. Griffith, one of the earliest pioneers of aircraft gas turbines and many other aviation ideas, noticed the

simple fact that by 1950 turbojet engines gave thrusts very much greater than their own weight. He had been installed by Lord Hives of Rolls-Royce in one of the world's first 'think tanks': a large country house near Derby where he and a small staff applied their brains to schemes that seemed futuristic if not impossible. By 1952 his assistant, Donald Eyre, was designing one of the strangest flying machines ever conceived. It was hardly an aircraft at all, but rather a pair of turbojets that flew without needing an airframe. Its basis was a space-frame of tubes carrying two Nene engines each rated at 5,000 lb thrust. Their jet pipes faced each other but, at the centre of the device, turned sharply downwards, the pipe of one being bifurcated to blast through half-size nozzles on each side of the jet nozzle of the other. This was done so that failure of either engine would merely cause the contraption to descend, without violent gyrations. It was obvious that for practical jet VTOL aircraft special precautions were going to be needed to keep them stable, controllable and safe even after engine failure.

Officially called the TMR, for thrust-measuring rig, the Rolls-Royce creation was immediately given the unofficial name of Flying Bedstead. It was gingerly tried out in 1953 with cables tethering it; free flight trials began on 3 August 1954, the day after the first Pogo Stick hovered in California. Most of the subsequent development was devoted to perfecting the system of control. When hovering motionless, ordinary aircraft controls are useless because they work only in a fast-moving airstream. So the Bedstead was equipped with long arms, pointing to the front and rear and on each side, carrying

614

downward-pointing nozzles fed with compressed air bled from the engines. The pilot's controls were connected to valves on these nozzles so that by allowing a jet of air to blast from one nozzle the whole device could be tilted to move in any direction. Swivelling the nozzles made the thing pirouette. By 1955 the ungainly contraption was being flown forwards, sideways and backwards at up to 30 mph.

Early in 1955 the American Bell company, which had built America's first jet and the world's first supersonic aircraft, began testing the world's first true jet VTOL aircraft, which had been quickly assembled using portions of other machines. On each side of the fuselage was a small turbojet which could be pivoted to point downwards in

613 Hiller VTOL platform for US Navy, February 1955

614 Rolls-Royce 'Flying Bedstead', 1954

the vertical mode and horizontally in conventional flight. A separate small gas turbine supplied the vital compressed air for the reaction control jets at the wing tips and tail.

With this unpretentious device Bell explored a vast amount of new territory. In 1957 the same company flew the X-14, in which two turbojets fixed horizontally in the fuselage discharged through jet pipes equipped with diverter valves to horizontal thrust nozzles and downward-pointing lift nozzles. In the same year the British Short firm flew the SC.1, a far more advanced machine with five of a totally new species of simple and light turbojet tailored to VTOL. One was mounted at the tail for forward thrust while the others formed a battery of lift engines arranged vertically on each side of the centre of gravity in the middle of the aircraft. Two SC.1 aircraft spent more than 12 years exploring the 'flat-rising' technique, the use of an autopilot and autostabilization in the VTOL mode and even vertical blind landings. Another arrival in 1957 was the Ryan X-13 Vertijet, a US Air Force delta powered by a British turbojet

616

which took over where the Pogo Sticks left off.

Between 1956 and 1959 experimental aircraft of the US forces and NASA investigated 17 distinct forms of VTOL. In addition to the forms already mentioned, some had jets that could be tilted or deflected, some had jet augmenter systems using air induced by batteries of lift nozzles, some had rows of tilting propellers or fans, and at least one had giant fans inside its wings which could be energized by opening doors in the wing and driving the fans by gas turbine exhaust. In France the Atar Volant, a pure jet engine pointed downwards and with a pilot's position on top, produced by the nationalized engine company SNECMA, led to the even stranger Coléoptère in which the final form of Atar Volant with

a streamlined fuselage incorporating a pilot cabin was surrounded by an annular wing to permit translation into horizontal flight. In Britain work had just begun on the concept of a vectored-thrust engine proposed by Wibault which, as described later, resulted in the remarkable Harrier tactical strike fighter.

By 1960 the world of aviation, and particularly the military part of it, was hardly able to think of anything but VTOL. To the generals and air marshals it meant a wonderful independence of airfields, which with their

617

huge and expensive runways were large and immobile targets that could be instantly put out of action by a cheap tactical missile as soon as such weapons were fully developed. To the admirals VTOL meant aircraft of every conceivable type, from supersonic fighters to big cargo transports, that could land on a small flat platform easily built on any surface vessel of destroyer size and upwards. Even the airline managements were interested because jet VTOL meant combining the utility of the city-centre helicopter with the established speed and carrying capacity of the jet airliner.

Within the NATO countries the arguments became polarized around two important specifications known as NBMR-3 and -4 (the initials signifying NATO Basic Military Requirement). NBMR-3 called for a strike-fighter aircraft capable of taking off with no ground run at all at light weights, and with a short ground run in overload condition carrying heavy external weapons, and of then flying various stipulated missions primarily concerned with the delivery of bombs against surface targets. NBMR-4 called for a similar V/STOL (vertical or short take-off and landing) performance in a transport aircraft capable of supporting the NBMR-3 squadrons when operating from dispersed and inaccessible bases to which fuel, food and ammunition could not be brought by conventional means. More than 20 companies entered the resulting competitions, and it looked as if the winners would be made in impressive quantities. Britain had the Hawker P.1127 already flying with the Pegasus vectored-thrust engine derived from the conception of Wibault,

615 Bell jet VTO research aircraft, 1955

616 Ryan X-13 Vertijet hovering, May 1957

617 Short SC.1, 1957

and in France Dassault swiftly produced an enlarged VTOL version of the Mirage III using the Rolls-Royce idea of a separate battery of lift jets.

In the event both competitions simply faded away. Several of the main nations let it be known that, if their own designs did not win, they were not interested. Everyone became increasingly alarmed by the costs as more realistic estimates began to seep through the rosy haze that surrounds most new ideas. It was also abundantly clear that the provision of jet lift involves severe penalties. As explained at the beginning of this chapter, an aerodynamic force is achieved most efficiently by gently accelerating a very large airflow. To lift an aircraft, nothing can beat a wing, preferably one of great span. Next best comes the rotor of a helicopter. Worst of all is the turbojet (a rocket would be even worse) because this handles the smallest airflow and so must impart the most violent acceleration. It follows that a hovering jet-lift aircraft burns fuel at a prodigious rate.

Out of the big NATO competitions came a great deal of new technical knowledge and several actual aircraft. One of the most remarkable was the Do 31 developed in 1960-70 by the German Dornier company in collaboration with Hawker Siddeley in Britain. It was the first jet-lift transport actually built, although many projects preceded it. West Germany has concentrated aircraft project design studies upon jet VTOL transports, convinced that such aircraft will eventually come to be of great importance in an overcrowded future world. After more than ten years of such studies a Federal government committee under Dr Karl Thalau in 1971

evaluated six refined proposals and selected the one which drew most closely upon Do 31 experience. This design, the Do 231, is proposed as a civil airliner seating up to 100 passengers and as a military transport with large rear freight doors which could be used for para-dropping. Lift would be provided by the Rolls-Royce RB.202 arranged in groups near the nose (two), tail (two) and wing tips (four each). The RB.202 is the first of a wholly new sort of aircraft power plant designed solely for short periods of lift. It is utterly unlike propulsion engines and gives enormous thrust from a small volume and weight, and with the whole design tailored from the start for minimum noise.

In Britain the RB.202 is the basis for the HS.141, the final end-product from a 13-year research and development programme by Hawker Siddeley at Hatfield. Essentially the HS.141 would be the optimized answer to the problem of adding jet lift to a 100-passenger transport cruising at 600 mph over inter-city routes. The very large sum needed to launch such an aircraft may well mean that the airline industry will need to progress in easier stages to the true VTOL vehicle able to operate from restricted airports close to city centres. British Aircraft Corporation may have a more saleable answer, which has close parallels with Aérospatiale in France and with a partnership between Boeing and Aeritalia, in a STOL airliner with a very effective high-lift wing and quiet geared-fan engines with variable-pitch blades that can give thrust in either direction to allow the aircraft to use short airstrips.

Noise has been a major problem holding back the commercial use of helicopters in built-up areas. Another has been high cost, and altogether the helicopter has not yet realized the bright hopes entertained by Bristol when they began to develop an airline version scaled up from the Bristol 173 twin-rotor machine in 1953, or the Belgian airline Sabena when they began a helicopter network of routes throughout the Low Countries in the same year, or New York Airways when they began metropolitan services with fine twin-turbine Boeing-Vertol 107s in 1962. The helicopter is handicapped by the fundamental inefficiency of its lifting system in translational flight, even though this same system is the most efficient of all means at present known of generating powered lift independent of forward motion. A further fundamental problem is the fact that the dynamic parts of a helicopter, from the engine right through the gearboxes, shafting, rotor hubs, bearings, hinges and blades, are all subject to ceaseless and severe oscillating stresses worse than anything normally encountered by fixed-wing aircraft. It has taken many decades to develop these parts to give thousands of hours of reliable service.

Today's helicopters range from one-man machines that can be picked up and carried by the user – indeed some are strapped to the wearer's back – to the monstrous V-12 by the Soviet bureau of Mikhail Mil which measures 220 ft across the tips of its side-by-side rotors each absorbing 13,000 hp. All except the very smallest and cheapest helicopters use gas turbine engines, because more power and less weight is exactly what all rotary-wing aircraft have always needed. In the small utility sizes the turbine engine has a secondary advantage in

618 Dornier Do 31 E1, 1968

619 EWR-Süd VJ 101C hovering with engines vertical, West Germany, 1964

618

619

620

620 Hawker Siddeley
Harrier GR.1 leaving
Manhattan for London in
a transatlantic race, 1969

621 Model of Hawker
Siddeley HS.141 V/STOL
airliner, 1970

622 Model of proposed
STOL transport in Boeing
wind tunnel, 1971

that it can be mounted close up beneath the main rotor hub where the dynamic parts can be kept in a light, compact group whilst simultaneously leaving the cabin and payload space completely unobstructed, and probably less prone to noise and vibration. First helicopter with this neat layout was the American Bell UH-1 family originally built for the US Army in 1955 and later developed in a profusion of versions, including a 'gunship' variant bristling with weapons and having a performance which approaches that of a Spitfire, which have been made by the thousand. Helicopters of this family, like many other designs, have been fitted with wings and jet engines to boost their speed to levels considerably above those of normal rotary-wing machines. As an indication of the possible improvement in speed, the Bell UH-1 family can normally reach a maximum speed of 127 mph but the winged and jet-boosted Model 533 has exceeded 316 mph in level flight.

Some of the most remarkable helicopters since 1960 have been built by Lockheed, whose designs have all featured a radically new main rotor of 'rigid' type devoid of the usual complicated bearings and hinges. The rigid rotor has opened up a new range of possibilities in both speed and manoeuvrability, and Lockheed helicopters have been looped, rolled and successfully subjected to several other manoeuvres not previously accomplished by rotary wings. Some of Lockheed's earlier projects were for 300 mph airliners, but the main development in the early 1970s concerns the AH-56A Cheyenne, an extremely complex 'advanced aerial fire support system'

621

622

243

623

624

625

intended for use in limited conflicts in which difficult ground targets must be engaged and destroyed at night or in tropical rainstorms or fog. The 250 mph Cheyenne, powered by a 3,925 hp General Electric turbine, carries several tons of electronic navigation equipment, sensing devices and countermeasures, and several more tons of guns, bombs, rockets, guided weapons, powered turrets and grenade launchers. A simpler rival design is the S-67 Blackhawk by Sikorsky, whose immense contributions to helicopters include the S-61 family, of which thousands are in use in forms as diverse as amphibious anti-submarine hunter-killers and 28-seat airliners, the much bigger 8,000 hp S-65 family, and the even bigger S-64 Skycrane which has saved scores of millions of dollars in Vietnam by retrieving expensive combat aircraft that had crashed in Vietcong territory.

In France Aérospatiale have delivered more than 2,500 helicopters, most of them of the Alouette family which, when the first appeared in 1955, demolished the piston-engined opposition by being powered by a small, light and smooth gas turbine from Société Turboméca, the French firm that has done more than any other in the world to introduce the gas turbine engine in small sizes for all kinds of aircraft. British helicopters once showed promise, but a succession of mergers and cancellations left no native design of any significance until the Anglo-French Westland Lynx flew in 1971. The Lynx is a general utility machine very similar to the Bell UH-1 family. In contrast the Soviet Union, which began with designs often modelled closely upon those of Sikorsky, had by 1970 emerged as a great world leader in helicopters and convertiplanes–winged aircraft with tilting wings or propellers/rotors for VTOL–all the larger designs being bigger and more powerful than their counterparts elsewhere. Mikhail Mil, the predominant Soviet heli-copter design bureau, has produced five completely different families of helicopters all of which have been manufactured in large numbers for both military use and for Aeroflot, the Soviet civil aviation organization. Biggest of the five basic designs so far is the Mi-6, a single-rotor giant powered by two 5,500 hp Soloviev engines that first flew in 1957 and subsequently set many world records for rotary-wing aircraft for load-carrying, height and speed. Now the Mi-6 rotor system has been twinned in the gigantic V-12 already mentioned, which on 6 August 1969 smashed all helicopter load records by climbing to 7,400 ft with a useful load of 88,636 lb. For comparison, the biggest British-made helicopter (the US Sikorsky S-61) weighs 20,000 lb loaded and carries a normal maximum load of 6,000 lb.

Even the United States has nothing remotely like the V-12, although Boeing-Vertol, the world's greatest builder of tandem-rotor machines with lifting rotors at the front and rear, expect by the mid 1970s to construct the first HLH (heavy-lift helicopter) for the US Army, which will at least approach the capability of the great Soviet machine with a useful load of 45,000 lb. The problems associated with developing a very big helicopter are enormous. There is no economic short cut and many years must be spent developing big gas-turbine engines, shafts, gearboxes, transmissions and rotor systems all to an extremely high standard of engineering.

244

626

623 Soviet Mil V-12 at the Paris Salon, 1971

624 Boeing-Vertol 107 of New York Airways leaving the roof of the PanAm building, 1962

625 Augusta-Bell 204B, Italian-built version of UH-1 seen through a fish-eye lens, 1967

626 Lockheed AH-56A Cheyenne firing rockets, 1971

627 Mil Mi-10, crane version of the Mi-6, 1965

628 Aérospatiale helicopters: civil and military Frelons, the Puma, three types of Alouette and the Gazelle, 1971

Few helicopters have been made in very large numbers, the most successful designs being small utility machines by Bell, Hiller and Hughes in the United States, and the ubiquitous UH-1 series. Jet-lift machines are even rarer. Only one has made good, and this has taken 13 years to develop. The 1957 Bristol/Hawker vectored thrust idea had by 1960 resulted in the P.1127, by 1964 the Kestrel which was evaluated by a tripartite British/American/German squadron (and also in the stillborn supersonic P.1154 cancelled in 1965), and by 1968 in the definitive Harrier tactical strike fighter and reconnaissance aircraft.

The Harrier is the first aircraft ever put into production and operational use that (1) can take off vertically and land vertically (or using a very short ground run when carrying a big overload) and (2) can fly at transonic speed and manoeuvre like any other high-performance jet built to a fighter standard of strength and stiffness. These combined attributes mean that the Harrier can be hidden in a deep forest, a hillside cave or even an urban area and still be at instant readiness. The enemy never knows where it is, and cannot knock it out by destroying runways. In the Soviet Union a VTOL fighter/research aircraft in some ways similar to the Harrier flew in 1967, but it has not been seen since.

At the time of writing 90 Harriers are in RAF service, a force of 114 British-built AV-8A versions is being built up by the US Marine Corps—the only occasion that foreign military aircraft for regular use have been imported into the United States—and further sales are

627

628

245

expected. Although not truly a supersonic aircraft the Harrier is so versatile and has such unique qualities it marks a major landmark in combat aircraft design. Improvements may soon result in a supersonic version with outstanding qualities in the air-superiority role, and able to use its great engine thrust directly to help it manoeuvre. It is not likely that all combat aircraft will ever be VTOL, but many assuredly will.

629

630

629 Kamov Ka-26 utility helicopter in Soviet winter, 1966

630 Early Bell 47 inspecting pylons near Fort Worth, about 1949; many thousands of later Bell 47 versions were built

631 Westland-Aérospatiale WG.13 (Lynx) helicopter at the Hanover Show, 1972

632 BAC/Aérospatiale Concorde 001, 1969

633 Tupolev Tu-144 first prototype supersonic air-liner, escorted by Mig-21 with scaled Tu-144 wing, 1969

631

17 Through the atmosphere into space

Flight, in the sense in which the word is generally used, means aerial locomotion within the atmosphere by a vehicle supported either by its buoyancy within the air or by the dynamic lifting force gained by its moving wings. We are so used to the presence of the atmosphere that we take for granted its help in enabling us to fly. Few have the appreciation expressed by Sir George Cayley in 1816 when he called it 'an uninterrupted navigable ocean, that comes to the threshold of every man's door.' He could see how difficult flight would be if that ocean were to be removed.

Out of all the countless thousands of flying machines constructed by man to fly within the atmosphere, only one does not need the atmosphere for its operation. This is the series of rocket belts and rocket platforms developed by Bell Aerosystems in the United States. The purist might claim that these do not really 'fly' at all, any more than does a rocket projectile or artillery shell. But there is a clear distinction between these objects. Projectiles, unless they travel fast enough to go into orbit round the Earth or escape from it entirely, have a strictly limited time of flight and describe a ballistic trajectory. The rocket belt, even though it is no more than a piece of somewhat unusual apparel that is strapped on to the wearer, is indeed a flying machine. It lifts itself against gravity, can move in any direction and will continue to fly as long as the wearer wishes, or until the tank runs dry.

In most of its many public demonstrations the rocket belt has been regarded as little more than a gimmick. To watch it is invariably amusing, although its use is spiced with danger. So far nobody, including heads of armed forces, has been able to give full credence to the idea of armies using the rocket belt to hop across rivers, fortifications and other obstacles. It remains an intriguing and fully developed device that may one day find a practical application. The reason for its failure so far is the Earth's possession of an atmosphere, which enables man to fly much more economically with wings and air-breathing engines. But on the Moon and other planets the story is different. The rocket belt or rocket platform is the only possible way to fly on the Moon, because where there is no air wings are useless, and no engine but the rocket can work.

The rocket, the only heat engine that will work in a vacuum, is one of man's oldest forms of engine with a history of at least 750 years. For short-term provision of thrust even a rudimentary rocket burning black powder or cordite would have been likely to be lighter, simpler and at least as reliable as the various types of engines that the pioneer aviators actually used, but surprisingly, although a number of patents were taken

635

634 Lift-off of Atlas-Centaur with Mariner Mars spacecraft

635 Saturn V, launch vehicle of the Apollo lunar

voyages, on its transporter vehicle at Cape Kennedy. The 6,500,000 lb rocket is the heaviest and most powerful construction ever to have flown, and its

6,000,000 lb transporter is the biggest land vehicle in history

636

one of the greatest visionaries there has ever been, wrote an amazing series of treatises on rocket flight at the beginning of the present century culminating in a detailed mathematical paper on rocket space flight published in 1911. Nobody took much notice of Tsiolkovsky until almost half a century later, but by 1929 the Soviet Union had embarked on a rocket programme at Leningrad which was not long afterwards backed up by a second one in Moscow. In Germany Hermann von Oberth was the foremost in a group of eager researchers. Hardly anyone knew of Goddard, working almost alone in a remote place, and few would have understood the importance of what he was doing.

Goddard knew by 1920 that the rocket was not well suited to horizontal flight. That was, and remains to this day, the role of aircraft. The greatest ability of the rocket is its independence of the atmosphere (it actually works better in a vacuum, because there is then no back-pressure on the emerging jet of hot gas). Goddard knew the rocket would be most useful in lifting vehicles vertically to great heights. He saw no reason why the height should not be increased further and further until, at some time in the distant future, it might reach to the Moon itself. But his immediate task was to create, with his bare hands, hardware that would not come apart, rocket tanks that were structurally sound, pumps that would be light and reliable and, by 1932, a ballistic rocket equipped with control fins moved according to signals from a gyroscope that sensed any departure of the slim vehicle from a vertical path.

Goddard continued with ever more difficult rocket vehicles until the United States entered the war in 1941, when he was put in charge of US Navy rocket research. But by this time the scene had shifted to Nazi Germany, where the prospect of formidable new weapons had caused rocket development to be accorded official status and a large and growing budget. By 1942 the A-4, popularly called the V-2, had begun its flight trials. Many times bigger and more advanced than any previous rocket, it had a giant streamlined airframe occupied mainly by huge tanks of liquid oxygen and alcohol. These were fed by a turbine-driven pump, which itself was a marvel of highly rated engineering, to a double-walled combustion chamber where the two liquids mixed and burned at 3,000°C to give a thrust of 26 tons, rising to almost 30 tons after 65 seconds by which time the great rocket was many miles above the Earth and climbing steeply at some 3,000 mph. To protect the vital combustion chamber it was kept some 1,000°C cooler than the gas inside it by circulating the cold liquid oxygen through the double wall.

In 1945 the United States took to the deserts of New Mexico every A-4 rocket it could lay hands on, as well as the rocket engineers led by Wernher von Braun. Soon the Americans had created a rocket technology of their own, although ironically Dr Goddard played no part in it for he died in 1945. In 1949 an ex-German A-4 took off from the desert carrying on its nose an American rocket which at a great height separated from the first stage, lit its engine and soared to a world record altitude of 250 miles. Stage separation and vacuum ignition of a rocket engine had never been accomplished previously.

out, hardly anybody in practice did anything to build a rocket flying machine until Fritz von Opel, the German car manufacturer, fitted crude rockets to an elementary training glider in 1928.

By this time a new sort of flight was being investigated. In 1926 the American visionary and single-minded inventor Dr Robert Hutchings Goddard launched the first rocket in history to be fed with liquid propellants. Goddard knew the liquid rocket would be a long and difficult row to hoe, because it involves carrying tanks of fluid which can explode if inadvertently mixed and which for proper operation must be controlled with the utmost precision by finely engineered parts that must operate under extremely difficult conditions of acceleration, temperature and vibration. But the liquid rocket appeared to offer great advantages over the simpler motors filled with solid fuel. There were numerous mixtures of liquid propellant, many of which seemed to offer the prospect of very high performance and an exceptional specific impulse (a measure of rocket efficiency based on the rate of fuel consumption needed to generate a given thrust). Moreover, it seemed that liquid rockets could have a much greater endurance, because the propellants could be fed from a tank whose size was limited only by the ability of the rocket to lift it.

Goddard had little money and no official support, but he never gave up. He was the true scientific pioneer, for his main objective was to find out. He had no particular use for weapons of war or even for voyages to other heavenly bodies, although the Russian T. S. Tsiolkovsky,

636 Possible configuration for the NASA space shuttle, spring 1972

250

man spacecraft called the Apollo to carry men to the Moon and back. The rocket to fly the mission, the Saturn V, was in terms of weight and power many times greater than anything else ever previously designed to fly, either in the atmosphere or in space, with a lift-off weight of more than 3,000 tons, and the horsepower of its engines in the order of tens of millions. The first voyage to the Moon took place in July 1969, Astronauts Neil Armstrong and Edwin Aldrin walking on the Moon on the 20th of that month, watched in real time by a TV audience in nearly every country on Earth.

Since that historic occasion there have been several further lunar voyages, each marked by the almost flawless performance of hundreds of thousands of complicated and closely integrated components and systems. Creating a vehicle of the calibre of Saturn V and its Apollo payload modules calls for the highest quality of engineering yet undertaken by man. Each vehicle costs millions of dollars, and practically all of it is expended on its single mission. By 1965 NASA was beginning to find dollars harder to get from a Congress that needed convincing of the validity of each programme.

For many years NASA and the US Air Force had been investigating two lines of development that in reality were one. One line was the hypersonic aircraft, a sort of flattened egg-shape with a bulged underside that calculations showed could fly at immense speed through the atmosphere and then be steered down to a conventional landing on a runway. The other was the re-usable space launcher equipped with some form of aerodynamic lift and drag system – such as wings or a parachute – to allow

637

By 1955 the US government had committed itself to launch an Earth satellite in the International Geophysical year in 1957-58, and it initiated Project Vanguard for a small and slender three-stage rocket to accomplish the task. Meanwhile the awesome developments of thermonuclear weapons and the deep mathematical calculations of a Department of Defense team led by John Von Neumann had shown the possibility of a terrifying new weapon, the intercontinental ballistic missile. The ICBM would use new technology on a scale much bigger than the A-4 to carry a city-destroying warhead a distance exceeding 6,000 miles. The US Air Force contracted with Convair for the first ICBM, the giant Atlas.

By 1957 both Vanguard and Atlas were ready. Then on 4 October something happened that had no previous parallel in human history, and staggered the world. The Soviet Union launched Sputnik 1, the first man-made spacecraft, into orbit round the Earth. Among the many reactions this great accomplishment triggered off was the mighty US space programme, the creation of the National Aeronautics and Space Administration (NASA) and a vast increase in both the civil and military budgets for rocketry. These budgets were further raised when on 12 April 1961 Major Yuri Gagarin of the Soviet Air Force became the first human being to fly into space. Urgently the American Atlas missile was modified to launch the one-man Mercury capsule, and the later Titan II ICBM was likewise modified to fly the two-seat Gemini. In 1961 NASA signed a contract for a three-

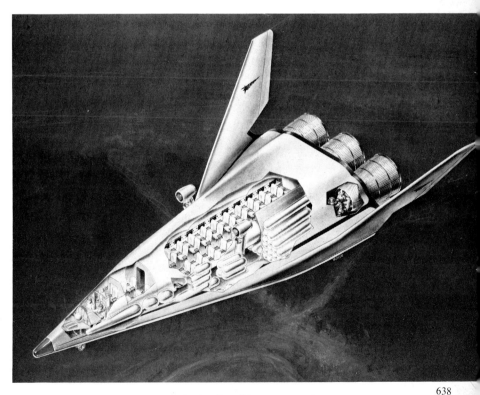

638

it to descend gently to the ocean or land and be recovered, refurbished and used again. In 1966 the two pathways began to merge into one concept: the space shuttle.

By this time the concept of an aircraft that could also fly in space—often called an 'aerospace plane'—was far from new. Indeed some of its problems had already been

637 Bell rocket belt, 1961

638 Impression of high-capacity space shuttle in atmospheric flight, suggested by Lockheed, 1969

solved by the North American X-15 research aircraft, three of which were built in 1955-58 for a research programme involving the USAF, Navy and NASA. These amazing machines, first flown in 1959, dropped from a B-52 bomber at 35,000 ft, were made of the same high-nickel alloys as are used for the hottest parts of jet engines in order to withstand the searing heat of flight at several times the speed of sound. The X-15 pilots, one of whom was astronaut Neil Armstrong, flew these aircraft to 6·18 times the speed of sound, to 4,104 mph

By 1967 several of the biggest aerospace firms in the United States were deep in studies to see how a space shuttle might best be designed. All were agreed that the basic answer was to construct a 'space aircraft' with wings of a broad ogival delta shape rather like those of the Concorde SST. Joined to it would be the booster; this would comprise two or more huge solid rockets. Both would be raised vertically until they were standing on their rocket motors with their noses pointed to the heavens. The orbiter would be joined closely above the booster

639

and to a height of 354,000 ft. In their later missions the aircraft were covered with a white paste which protected them against the heat of re-entry, while a special rocket-reaction control system controlled the trajectory until the air became thick enough for aerodynamic controls once more to 'bite'. By 1966 the X-15 had been backed up by the very successful Gemini programme using wingless two-seat spacecraft.

to form a curious kind of biplane combination. The booster would carry nothing but propellants and have no crew; the orbiter would be laden with whatever might be needed for its mission in space. The combined vehicles would lift off together and climb vertically before gradually nosing over at a height of some score of miles at a speed many times that of sound. At a height of 25 miles the orbiter would separate. The booster would

639 The loudest noise in the world: lift-off of a Saturn V seen from two miles distant

252

burn out, fall into the ocean, and be recovered and then refurbished. The orbiter would continue out to its appointed mission in space. From its capacious hold it could produce large space-station assemblies, lunar laboratories or any of many other kinds of hardware needed for space operations. Alternatively, its payload could comprise men and supplies, the return trip being the homeward journey to Earth of crews whose tour of duty on a space or lunar station had been completed.

Rocketdyne were in 1971 awarded the contract for the main engines of the space shuttle, and began producing a propulsion system to serve for a hundred space missions amounting to seven and a half hours of total operating time for each engine. Although the complete shuttle, comprising both the booster and the orbiter, was planned to cost more than a Saturn V rocket, the cost per mission would be very much less even if in practice fewer than a hundred missions were realized for each vehicle. The cost of delivering a load to the Moon or to a future space station was estimated at about one-tenth of its 1972 level. These new flying vehicles will quietly close the gap that once existed between aircraft and space rockets. Tomorrow's space vehicle will not look like a vertical tower with a pointed top but like a large aircraft of rather odd shape. When it returns to Earth it will be in all respects an atmospheric aircraft, with lift provided by a wing and steering effected by aerodynamic controls.

With the appearance of such craft proposed in the late 1970s man will have completed his initial conquest of the Earth's atmosphere and the surrounding region of the solar system. The next few decades are unlikely to bring any fundamentally new vehicles but rather to be devoted to a process of refinement. Man has demonstrated his ability to fly in abundant measure, and his flying vehicles are among those that cause him few problems. For the rest of the century his biggest transport worries will be located on Earth, and especially in his crowded cities.

Yet it would be unthinkable for man not to continue to look to the furthest horizons and to explore the solar system to the limit permitted by his technology. Until January 1972, when the programme was cancelled for lack of funds, NASA was preparing unmanned spacecraft for journeys past Jupiter, Saturn, Uranus, Neptune and Pluto – to the furthest edge of the solar system. So far all journeys into space have been cripplingly expensive because the vehicles have never been used twice. The space shuttle, with its tantalizing prospect of being used a hundred times, will undoubtedly enable men – hopefully, of many nationalities working together – to construct great space stations much nearer to Earth than the Moon and much more useful in monitoring and measuring the Earth, controlling and guiding human activity and opening up possibilities of which we can as yet gain only the dimmest understanding.

List of plates

Names of organizations frequently acknowledged below are thus abbreviated:

A	Société Nationale de Aérospatiale
AA	American Airlines
AF	Collection Air France
Ai	Alitalia
AI	Air-India
AMD	Avions Marcel Dassault
AMI	Aeronautica Militare Italiana
B-A	Breguet-Aviation
BAC	British Aircraft Corporation
BEA	British European Airways
Beech AC	Beech Aircraft Corporation
Bell	Bell Aerosystems Company
BN	Bibliothèque Nationale, Paris
Bo	The Boeing Company
BOAC	British Overseas Airways Corporation
Bu	Bundesarchiv, Koblenz
C	Cessna Aircraft Company
D	Dornier-Werke GmbH
DM	Deutsches Museum, Munich
F	*Flight International*, London
Fo	'Fokker-VFW' NV
G	Grumman Corporation
GD	General Dynamics Corporation
HS	Hawker Siddeley Group Limited
ILN	*Illustrated London News*
IWM	Imperial War Museum, London
J	Junkers-Archiv
JAL	Japan Air Lines
KLM	KLM-Royal Dutch Airlines
KP	Keystone Press Agency Limited, London
L	Lufthansa-Archiv
LC	Library of Congress, Washington
Lo	Lockheed Aircraft Corporation
MA	Musée de l'Air, Paris
MBB	Messerschmitt-Bölkow-Blohm GmbH
MD	McDonnell Douglas Corporation
MeA	Messerschmitt Archiv
MMM	Montague Motor Museum, Beaulieu
MOD	Ministry of Defence, London
N	Novosti Press Agency
NAMC	Nihon Aeroplane Manufacturing Company
NAR	North American Rockwell Corporation
No	Northrop Corporation
NPG	National Portrait Gallery, London
NYA	New York Airways
P & W	Pratt and Whitney Aircraft, Division of United Aircraft Corporation
Q	Qantas Airways Limited
RA	Ryan Aeronautical Company
RAE	Royal Aircraft Establishment, Farnborough
RAS	Royal Aeronautical Society, London
ReAC	Fairchild Republic Division
RR	Rolls-Royce Limited
S	Smithsonian Institution, Washington
Sa	Swissair
SA	Sikorsky Aircraft, Division of United Aircraft Corporation
S-A	Sud-Aviation
Saab	Saab-Scania
Sab	Sabena Belgian World Airlines
SAR	South African Railways
Sh	Short Brothers and Harland Limited
SM	Science Museum, London
SMA	Stato Maggiore Aeronautica
TWA	Trans World Airlines Inc.
UAL	United Air Lines
USAAF,NA	United States Army Air Forces, National Archives, Washington
USAF	Official United States Air Force Photo
USIA, NA	United States Information Agency, National Archives, Washington
USIAS	USIAS Service Presse, Paris
USOWI,NA	United States Office of War Information, National Archives, Washington
USN	United States Navy

Jacket: Experimental North American X-15A-2 (NA)
Title page: 1908 Wright Model A (SM)

1 Legend of King Kai Kawus; 17th-century Persian manuscript illumination (SM)
2 Francesco de Lana's proposed aerial chariot, 1670 (SM)
3 Leonardo da Vinci's design for a fixed-wing aircraft with ornithopter extension (SM)
4 'The flight of Daedalus and the fall of Icarus'; woodcut, 1493 (SM)
5 Leonardo's design for a spring-operated flying machine (SM)
6 Model of Leonardo's man-powered ornithopter (Q) Man-powered flight of Fl. Lieut. Potter, 1969 (MOD)
8 Sir George Cayley, 1773-1857 (NPG)
9 Cayley's design for a dirigible balloon, 1816 (SM)
10 Cayley's design for a vertical take-off and landing aircraft, 1843
11 Cayley's proposed flapping-wing glider
12 Cayley's sketch for a man-powered ornithopter
13 Drawings by F. W. Lanchester illustrating his vortex theory, 1907
14 Model of Langley's 'Aerodrome', 1903 (SM)
15 Ascent of an unmanned Montgolfier balloon, 1783 (SM)
16 Handkerchief bearing a representation of the balloon of MM Charles and Robert, 1783 (SM)
17 The first free-flight aerial voyage, 1783 (Private collection)
18 Second aerial voyage of MM Charles and Robert, 1783 (BN)
19 Eighteenth-century fantasy: 'Aérostat de Poste' (BN) colour
20 Return of the balloon of MM Charles and Robert, 1783 (BN) colour
21 Lunardi's balloon in London, 1784 (BN) colour
22 Place de la Concorde at Napoleon's coronation, 3 December 1804, with five balloons (BN) colour
23 St James's Park, London, decorated for the grand jubilee of 1 August 1814 (BN) colour
24 Balloon on fire, 11 July 1784 (BN) colour
25 Montgolfier's 1784 balloon, *La Flesselle* (SM)
26 Departure of Blanchard and Jeffries from Dover Castle, 1785 (SM)
27 Lunardi's ascent from the Artillery Ground, London, 1784 (SM)
28 Blanchard's twenty-eighth ascent at Nuremberg, 1787 (BN)
29 Leonardo's design for a man-powered flying machine (SM)
30 Poster advertising Cocking's parachute descent, Vauxhall Gardens, London, 24 July 1837 (SM)
31 Garnerin's balloon and parachute, 1802 (SM)
32 Three aerial travellers, 1785 (BN)
33 Battle of Fleurus, 1794 (BN)
34 The balloon *Intrepid* reconnoitring in 1862, during the American Civil War (Brailey Collection, LC)
35 Letter sent by balloon from Paris, 1870 (SM)
36 Sketch of Virginia made from *Intrepid*, 1862 (S)
37 Ascent of the *City of York* Balloon (MMM)
38 Aerial travellers (including Charles Stewart Rolls) about to make a balloon ascent in Monmouth (MMM)
39 Balloon at St Charles, Missouri, 1880 (S)
40 The Aeronautical Society's first exhibition in London, 1868 (SM)
41 Lawrence Hargrave flying a box-kite, 1894 (SM)
42 Model of Phillips's aerofoil, 1893 (SM)
43 Le Bris' second glider, 1868 (MA)

Bibliography

C. Grahame-White and H. Harper, *The Aeroplane, Past, Present and Future*, London and Philadelphia, 1911

J. E. Hodgson, *The History of Aeronautics in Great Britain*, London, 1924; New York, 1925

I. B. Hart, *The Mechanical Investigations of Leonardo da Vinci*, London, 1925; Berkeley, California, 1963

B. Laufer, *The Prehistory of Aviation*, Chicago, 1928

J. Goldstrom, *A Narrative History of Aviation*, New York and London, 1930

J. de la Cierva, *Wings of Tomorrow: the Story of the Autogiro*, New York, 1931

M. J. B. Davy, *Henson and Stringfellow*, London, 1931

F. C. Kelly, *The Wright Brothers*, New York and London, 1944

H. St G. Saunders, *Per Ardua: the Rise of British Air Power, 1911-39*, London, 1944; New York, 1945

A. Lee, *The German Air Force*, 1946

M. J. B. Davy, *Interpretive History of Flight*, 2nd ed. London, 1948

H. F. Gregory, *The Helicopter*, London, 1948

F. C. Kelly (ed.), *Miracle at Kitty Hawk: the Letters of Wilbur and Orville Wright*, New York, 1951

J. C. Hunsaker, *Aeronautics at the Mid-Century*, New Haven, Connecticut, 1952

G. A. Broomfield, *Pioneer of the Air*, Aldershot, Hampshire, 1953

C. A. Lindbergh, *The Spirit of St Louis*, London and New York, 1953

L. Morris and K. Smith, *Ceiling Unlimited: the Story of American Aviation from Kitty Hawk to Supersonics*, New York, 1953

D. Richards and H. St G. Saunders, *The Royal Air Force, 1939-1945*, 3 vols, London, 1953-4

W. A. Shrader, *Fifty Years of Flight: a Chronicle of the Aviation Industry in America, 1903-1953*, Cleveland, Ohio, 1953

Sir F. Whittle, *Jet*, London, 1953; Toronto, 1955

Orville Wright, *How we invented the Aeroplane*, ed. F. C. Kelly, New York, 1953

Marvin W. McFarland (ed.), *The Papers of Wilbur and Orville Wright*, 2 vols, New York, 1953

D. Rolfe and A. Dawydoff, *Airplanes of the World, from Pusher to Jet, 1490 to 1954*, New York, 1954

O. G. Thetford and E. J. Riding, *Aircraft of the 1914-18 War*, new ed. Marlow, 1954

R. N. Liptrot and J. D. Woods, *Rotorcraft*, London, 1955

G. G. Smith, *Gas Turbines and Jet Propulsion*, 6th ed. London and New York, 1955

G. Halle, *Otto Lilienthal*, 2nd ed. Düsseldorf, 1956

W. A. Heflin (ed.), *The United States Air Force Dictionary*, Washington, 1956

L. Beckford, *An ABC of Aeronautics*, London, 1957

Alfred Goldberg (ed.), *A History of the United States Air Force, 1907-1957*, Princeton, New Jersey, 1957

William Green and John Fricker, *The Air Forces of the World*, New York, 1958

Gabriel Voisin, *Men, Women and 10,000 Kites*, London and Toronto, 1963

P. W. Brooks, *The Modern Airliner: its Origin and Development*, London and Fallbrook, California, 1961

Sir G. de Havilland, *Sky Fever*, London and Don Mills, Ontario, 1961

Peter Wykeham, *Santos-Dumont: A Study in Obsession*, London and Toronto, 1962

F. W. Swanborough and P. M. Bowers, *United States Military Aircraft since 1909*, London and New York, 1963

E. M. Emme, *A History of Space Flight*, Washington, 1965; London, 1966

C. Dollfus, H. Beaubois and C. Rougeron, *L'Homme, l'Air, et l'Espace: Aéronautique, Astronautique*, Paris, 1965

J. L. Nayler and E. Ower, *Aviation: its Technical Development*, London and Chester Springs, 1965

A. R. Weyl, *Fokker: the Creative Years*, London, 1965

G. R. Duval, *British Flying-Boats and Amphibians, 1909-1952*, London and Fallbrook, California, 1966

C. H. Gibbs-Smith, *A Directory and Nomenclature of the First Aeroplanes, 1809 to 1909*, London, 1966

C. H. Gibbs-Smith, *The Invention of the Aeroplane, 1809-1909*, London and New York, 1966

H. F. King, *Aeromarine Origins*, London and Fallbrook, California, 1966

L. T. C. Rolt, *The Aeronauts*, London and New York, 1966

Oliver Stewart, *Aviation: the Creative Ideas*, London and New York, 1966

D. Stinton, *The Anatomy of the Aeroplane*, London and New York, 1966

J. Stroud, *European Transport Aircraft since 1910*, London and Fallbrook, California, 1966

H. J. Penrose, *British Aviation: the Pioneer Years*, London and New York, 1967

O. G. Thetford and E. J. Riding, *Aircraft of the Royal Air Force since 1918*, 4th ed. London and New York, 1968

C. H. Gibbs-Smith, *Aviation: an Historical Survey from its Origins to the End of World War II*, London and New York, 1970

Index

Compiled by Maurice Allward

References in bold figures thus: **42**, indicate an illustration

261